# Renault 6
# Owners
# Workshop
# Manual

## by J H Haynes
Member of the Guild of Motoring Writers
## and Tim Parker

**Models covered**
Renault 6 850 Saloon 845 cc
Renault 6 850L Saloon 845 cc
Renault 6 1100 Saloon 1108 cc
Renault 6 1100TL Saloon 1108 cc

ISBN 0 85696 512 X

Printed in England   *(092-6E1)*

**HAYNES PUBLISHING GROUP**
**SPARKFORD YEOVIL SOMERSET ENGLAND**
*distributed in the USA by*
**HAYNES PUBLICATIONS INC**
**861 LAWRENCE DRIVE**
**NEWBURY PARK**
**CALIFORNIA 91320**
**USA**

# Acknowledgements

Thanks are due to Renault UK Ltd for the supply of certain illustrations and technical material; Castrol Limited who provided lubrication data and the Champion Sparking Plug Company Limited who provided the colour illustrations showing the various spark plug conditions. The bodywork repair photographs used in this manual were provided by Lloyds Industries Limited who supply 'Turtle Wax', 'Dupli-Color Holts' and other Holts range products.

Lastly thanks are due to all of those people at Sparkford who assisted in the production of this manual. Particularly Brian Horsfall, Les Brazier, Ted Frenchum, Peter G Strasman, Lee Saunders and David Neilson.

# About this manual

### Its aims

The aim of this book is to help you get the best value from your car. It can do so in two ways. First, it can help you decide the work to be done, even should you choose to get it done by a garage, the routine maintenance and the diagnosis and course of action when random faults occur. But it is hoped that you will also use the second and fuller purpose by tackling the work yourself. This can give you the satisfaction of knowing that the task has been completed correctly. On the simpler jobs it may even be quicker than booking the car into a garage and going there twice, to leave and collect it. Perhaps more important, much money can be saved by avoiding the costs a garage must charge to cover labour and overheads.

The book has drawings and descriptions to show the functions of the various components so that their layout can be understood. Then the tasks are described and photographed in a step-by-step sequence so that even a novice can cope with complicated work. Such a person is the very one to buy a car needing repair yet be unable to afford garage costs.

The jobs are described assuming only normal spanners are available, and not special tools unless absolutely necessary. But a reasonable outfit of tools will be a worthwhile investment. Many special workshop tools produced by the makers merely speed the work, and in these cases guidance is given as to how to do the job without them. On a very few occasions a special tool is essential to prevent damage to components; then its use is described. Though it might be possible to borrow the tool, such work may have to be entrusted to the official agent.

To avoid labour costs a garage will often give a cheaper repair by fitting a reconditioned assembly. The home mechanic can be helped by this book to diagnose the fault and make a repair using only a minor spare part.

The manufacturer's official workshop manuals are written for their trained staff, and so assume special knowledge; therefore detail is left out. This book is written for the owner, and so goes into detail.

### Using the manual

The manual is divided into twelve Chapters. Each Chapter is divided into numbered Sections which are headed in **bold** type between horizontal lines. Each Section consists of serially numbered paragraphs.

There are two types of illustrations: (1) Figures which are numbered according to Chapter and sequence of occurrence in that Chapter. (2) Photographs which have a reference number in their caption. All photographs apply to the Chapter in which they occur, so that the reference figure pinpoints the pertinent Section and paragraph number.

Procedures, once described in the text, are not normally repeated. If it is necessary to refer to another Chapter the reference will be given in Chapter number and Section number thus: Chapter 1, Section 16. Cross-references given without use of the word 'Chapter' apply to Section and/or paragraphs in the same Chapter, eg, 'see Section 8' means also 'in this Chapter'.

When the left or right side of the car is mentioned it is as if one is seated in the driver's seat looking forward.

**Whilst every care is taken to ensure that the information in this manual is correct, no liability can be accepted by the authors or publishers for loss, damage or injury caused by errors in, or omissions from, the information given.**

# Introduction to the Renault 6

The first that was heard of the Renault 6 was in September 1968 when the 6-850 was introduced to the domestic French market. It did not appear in the United Kingdom until September of the following year. It was simply known as the 6 for there was only one engine size then available.

The 6TL or 6-1100 did not arrive until September 1970 even though it had been sold in France for some months previously. The 6 then became the 6-850 out of necessity.

The design of the 6 is easily explained by the conceived need for a more luxurious 'up market' Renault 4 on which it is based. Whilst the Renault 4 sells at a startling rate even after ten years of production the 6 fills in the gap in the Renault range, originally between the 4 and the 10 and now between the 4 and the 12. It is designed to tempt away the hesitant Renault purchaser who cannot afford the Renault 12. To some extent it succeeds.

The 6-850 and the faster smoother 6-1100 are asthetically more pleasing than the Renault 4 and provide yet another 'different' car to own. Both models are relatively expensive and it is increasingly hard to see where they fit in, now that the Renault 5 is available.

Externally there are few differences between the two models. The 6-1100 has a TL badge on the tailgate, slotted vents in the road wheels and an air intake or lower grille at the front. In the interior the 6-850 has a bench front seat (individual as an optional extra) to the 6-1100's standard individual. Otherwise there is little to pinpoint one model or another. A sunroof is a factory option on both models although a heated rear window is only available for the 6-1100.

Under the bonnet the differences are instantly recognisable. The 6-850 looks very similar to the Renault 4, nothing mechanically sophisticated, whilst the 6-1100 sports a large cross-brace, forward mounted radiator and electric fan, an alternator (from September 1971) and a larger gearbox casing. The 6-850 of course uses the Renault 4 chassis whilst the 6-1100 uses a slightly modified version incorporating some of the design of the Spanish built Fasa Renault 4.

Late 1973 saw the first styling change, a tidied up front and square headlights; mechanically little has changed except that the 6-850 is now fitted with the 6-1100 gearbox to bring it in line with all the smaller Renaults for 1974.

If one is fond of the Renault 4 then one cannot but help be fond of these models but one nevertheless might have reservations as to their place in the annals of Renault history.

This manual specifically covers the Renault 6-850 and Renault 6-1100 cars imported into the United Kingdom under the Renault type numbers R1180 (6-850) and R1181 (6-1100). It may however be of help to owners of these models exported elsewhere from France. It may cover locally produced models such as the Fasa Renault 6 (956 cc) made in Spain.

# Contents

# Buying spare parts
# and vehicle identification numbers

Spare parts are available from many sources, for example: Renault garages, other garages and accessory shops, and motor factors. Our advice regarding spare part sources is as follows:

*Officially appointed Renault garages* — This is the best source of parts which are peculiar to your car and are otherwise not generally available (eg complete cylinder heads, internal gearbox components, badges, interior trim etc). It is also the only place at which you should buy parts if your car is still under warranty — non-Renault components may invalidate the warranty. To be sure of obtaining the correct parts it will always be necessary to give the storeman your car's vehicle identification number, and if possible, to take the 'old' part along for positive identification. Remember that many parts are available on a factory exchange scheme — any parts returned should always be clean! It obviously makes good sense to go straight to the specialists on your car for this type of part as they are best equipped to supply you.

*Other garages and accessory shops* — These are often very good places to buy materials and components needed for the maintenance of your car (eg oil filters, spark plugs, bulbs, fan belts, oils and greases, touch-up paint, filler paste etc). They also sell general accessories, usually have convenient opening hours, charge lower prices and can often be found not far from home.

*Motor factors* — Good factors will stock all the more important components which wear out relatively quickly (eg clutch components, pistons, valves, exhaust systems, brake cylinders/pipes/hoses/seals/shoes and pads etc). Motor factors will often provide new or reconditioned components on a part exchange basis — this can save a considerable amount of money.

### Vehicle identification numbers

Although many individual parts, and in some cases sub-assemblies, fit a number of different models it is dangerous to assume that just because they look the same, they are the same. Differences are not always easy to detect except by serial numbers. When ordering spare parts always quote the engine and chassis number to ensure that the correct part is obtained.

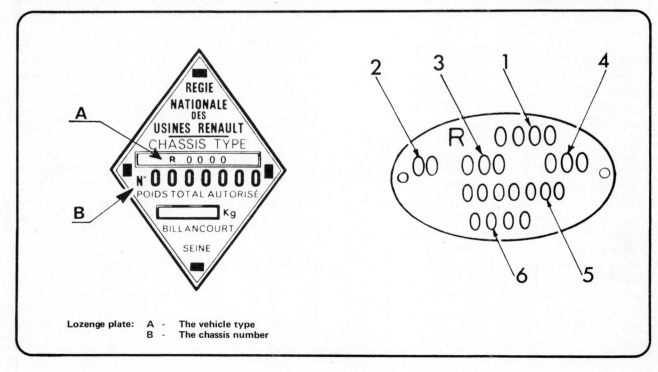

Lozenge plate:  A  -  The vehicle type
B  -  The chassis number

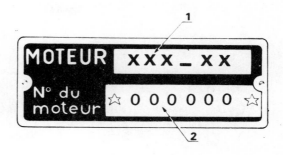

Engine number plate - 1 - The engine type
2 - The fabrication number

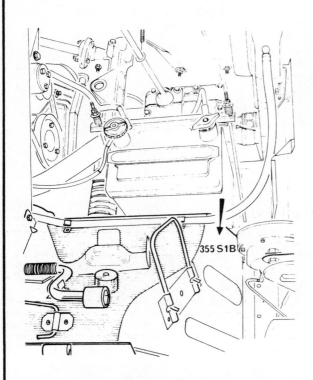

Paintwork stencil code

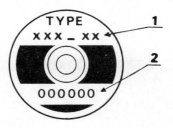

Gearbox number plate - 1 - The gearbox type
2 - The fabrication number

Oval plate: 
1 - The first 3 figures give vehicle group the fourth figure gives the engine type
2 - For 1973 models onwards only the first figure gives the gearbox type the second figures give special particulars (eg. sun roof etc)
3 - Gives the basic equipment (normal road, poor road etc.)
4 - For 1973 models onwards only additional optional equipment (heated rear window etc.)
5 - The fabrication number
6 - The model year (some models only)

Renault 6-850 1973 model

Renault 6TL 1974 model

# Tools and working facilities

### Introduction

A selection of good tools is a fundamental requirement for anyone contemplating the maintenance and repair of a motor vehicle. For the owner who does not possess any, their purchase will prove a considerable expense, offsetting some of the savings made by doing-it-yourself. However, provided that the tools purchased are of good quality, they will last for many years and prove an extremely worthwhile investment.

To help the average owner to decide which tools are needed to carry out the various tasks detailed in this manual, we have compiled three lists of tools under the following headings: *Maintenance and minor repair, Repair and overhaul,* and *Special.* The newcomer to practical mechanics should start off with the *Maintenance and minor repair* tool kit and confine himself to the simpler jobs around the vehicle. Then, as his confidence and experience grows, he can undertake more difficult tasks, buying extra tools as, and when, they are needed. In this way a *Maintenance and minor repair* tool kit can be built-up into a *Repair and overhaul* tool kit over a considerable period of time without any major cash outlays. The experienced do-it-yourselfer will have a tool kit good enough for most repair and overhaul procedures and will add tools from the *Special* category when he feels the expense is justified by the amount of use to which these tools will be put.

It is obviously not possible to cover the subject of tools fully here. For those who wish to learn more about tools and their use there is a book entitled *How to Choose and Use Car Tools* available from the publishers of this manual.

### Maintenance and minor repair tool kit

The tools given in this list should be considered as a minimum requirement if routine maintenance, servicing and minor repair operations are to be undertaken. We recommend the purchase of combination spanners (ring one end, open-ended the other); although more expensive than open-ended ones, they do give the advantages of both types of spanner.

*Combination spanners — 10, 11, 12, 13, 14 & 17 mm*
*Adjustable spanner — 9 inch*
*Engine sump/gearbox drain plug key (where applicable)*
*Spark plug spanner (with rubber insert)*
*Spark plug gap adjustment tool*
*Set of feeler gauges*
*Brake adjuster spanner (where applicable)*
*Brake bleed nipple spanner*
*Screwdriver — 4 in long x ¼ in dia (flat blade)*
*Screwdriver — 4 in long x ¼ in dia (cross blade)*
*Combination pliers — 6 inch*
*Hacksaw, junior*
*Tyre pump*
*Tyre pressure gauge*
*Grease gun (where applicable)*
*Oil can*
*Fine emery cloth (1 sheet)*
*Wire brush (small)*
*Funnel (medium size)*

### Repair and overhaul tool kit

These tools are virtually essential for anyone undertaking any major repairs to a motor vehicle, and are additional to those given in the *Maintenance and minor repair* list. Included in this list is a comprehensive set of sockets. Although these are expensive they will be found invaluable as they are so versatile - particularly if various drives are included in the set. We recommend the ½ in square-drive type, as this can be used with most proprietary torque wrenches. If you cannot afford a socket set, even bought piecemeal, then inexpensive tubular box spanners are a useful alternative.

The tools in this list will occasionally need to be supplemented by tools from the *Special* list.

*Sockets (or box spanners) to cover range in previous list*
*Reversible ratchet drive (for use with sockets)*
*Extension piece, 10 inch (for use with sockets)*
*Universal joint (for use with sockets)*
*Torque wrench (for use with sockets)*
*'Mole' wrench — 8 inch*
*Ball pein hammer*
*Soft-faced hammer, plastic or rubber*
*Screwdriver — 6 in long x 5/16 dia (flat blade)*
*Screwdriver — 2 in long x 5/16 square (flat blade)*
*Screwdriver — 1 ½ in long x ¼ in dia (cross blade)*
*Screwdriver — 3 in long x 1/8 in dia (electricians)*
*Pliers — electricians side cutters*
*Pliers — needle nosed*
*Pliers — circlip (internal and external)*
*Cold chisel — ½ inch*
*Scriber*
*Scraper*
*Centre punch*
*Pin punch*
*Hacksaw*
*Valve grinding tool*
*Steel rule/straight edge*
*Allen keys*
*Selection of files*
*Wire brush (large)*
*Axle-stands*
*Jack (strong scissor or hydraulic type)*

### Special tools

The tools in this list are those which are not used regularly, are expensive to buy, or which need to be used in accordance with their manufacturers' instructions. Unless relatively difficult mechanical jobs are undertaken frequently, it will not be economic to buy many of these tools. Where this is the case, you could consider clubbing together with friends (or a motorists' club) to make a joint purchase, or borrowing the tools against a deposit from a local garage or tool hire specialist.

The following list contains only those tools and instruments freely available to the public, and not those special tools produced by the vehicle manufacturer specifically for its dealer network. You will find occasional references to these manufacturers' special tools in the text of this manual. Generally, an alternative method of doing the job without the vehicle manufacturer's special tool is given. However, sometimes, there is no alternative to using them. Where this is the case and the relevant tool cannot be bought or borrowed you will have to entrust the work to a franchised garage.

*Valve spring compressor*
*Piston ring compressor*
*Balljoint separator*
*Universal hub/bearing puller*
*Impact screwdriver*
*Micrometer and/or vernier gauge*
*Dial gauge*
*Stroboscopic timing light*
*Dwell angle meter/tachometer*
*Universal electrical multi-meter*
*Cylinder compression gauge*
*Lifting tackle (photo)*
*Trolley jack*
*Light with extension lead*

### Buying tools

For practically all tools, a tool factor is the best source since he will have a very comprehensive range compared with the average garage or accessory shop. Having said that, accessory shops often offer excellent quality tools at discount prices, so it pays to shop around.

Remember, you don't have to buy the most expensive items on the shelf, but it is always advisable to steer clear of the very cheap tools. There are plenty of good tools around at reasonable prices, so ask the proprietor or manager of the shop for advice before making a purchase.

### Care and maintenance of tools

Having purchased a reasonable tool kit, it is necessary to keep the tools in a clean serviceable condition. After use, always wipe off any dirt, grease and metal particles using a clean, dry cloth, before putting the tools away. Never leave them lying around after they have been used. A simple tool rack on the garage or workshop wall, for items such as screwdrivers and pliers is a good idea. Store all normal spanners and sockets in a metal box. Any measuring instruments, gauges, meters, etc, must be carefully stored where they cannot be damaged or become rusty.

Take a little care when tools are used. Hammer heads inevitably become marked and screwdrivers lose the keen edge on their blades from time-to-time. A little timely attention with emery cloth or a file will soon restore items like this to a good serviceable finish.

### Working facilities

Not to be forgotten when discussing tools, is the workshop itself. If anything more than routine maintenance is to be carried out, some form of suitable working area becomes essential.

It is appreciated that many an owner mechanic is forced by circumstances to remove an engine or similar item, without the benefit of a garage or workshop. Having done this, any repairs should always be done under the cover of a roof.

Wherever possible, any dismantling should be done on a clean flat workbench or table at a suitable working height.

Any workbench needs a vice: one with a jaw opening of 4 in (100 mm) is suitable for most jobs. As mentioned previously, some clean dry storage space is also required for tools, as well as the lubricants, cleaning fluids, touch-up paints and so on which become necessary.

Another item which may be required, and which has a much more general usage, is an electric drill with a chuck capacity of at least 5/16 in (8 mm). This, together with a good range of twist drills, is virtually essential for fitting accessories such as wing mirrors and reversing lights.

Last, but not least. always keep a supply of old newspapers and clean, lint-free rags available, and try to keep any working area as clean as possible.

## SPANNER JAW GAP COMPARISON TABLE

| Jaw gap (in) | Spanner size |
|---|---|
| 0.250 | ¼ in AF |
| 0.275 | 7 mm AF |
| 0.312 | 5/16 in AF |
| 0.315 | 8 mm AF |
| 0.340 | 11/32 in AF; 1/8 in Whitworth |
| 0.354 | 9 mm AF |
| 0.375 | 3/8 in AF |
| 0.393 | 10 mm AF |
| 0.433 | 11 mm AF |
| 0.437 | 7/16 in AF |
| 0.445 | 3/16 in Whitworth; ¼ in BSF |
| 0.472 | 12 mm AF |
| 0.500 | ½ in AF |
| 0.512 | 13 mm AF |
| 0.525 | ¼ in Whitworth; 5/16 in BSF |
| 0.551 | 14 mm AF |
| 0.562 | 9/16 in AF |
| 0.590 | 15 mm |
| 0.600 | 5/16 in Whitworth; 3/8 in BSF |
| 0.625 | 5/8 in AF |
| 0.629 | 16 mm |
| 0.669 | 17 mm |
| 0.687 | 11/16 in AF |
| 0.708 | 18 mm |
| 0.710 | 3/8 in Whitworth; 7/16 in BSF |
| 0.748 | 19mm |
| 0.750 | ¾ in AF |
| 0.812 | 13/16 in AF |
| 0.820 | 7/6 in Whitworth; ½ in BSF |
| 0.866 | 22 mm |
| 0.875 | 7/8 in AF |
| 0.920 | ½ in Whitworth; 9/16 in BSF |
| 0.937 | 15/16 in AF |
| 0.944 | 24 mm |
| 1.000 | 1 in AF |
| 1.010 | 9/16 in Whitworth; 5/8 in BSF |
| 1.023 | 26 mm |
| 1.062 | 1 1/16 in AF; 27 mm |
| 1.100 | 5/8 in Whitworth; 11/16 in BSF |
| 1.125 | 1 1/8 in AF |
| 1.181 | 30 mm |
| 1.200 | 11/16 in Whitworth; ¾ in BSF |
| 1.250 | 1¼ in AF |
| 1.259 | 32 mm |
| 1.300 | ¾ in Whitworth; 7/8 in BSF |
| 1.312 | 1 5/16 in AF |
| 1.390 | 13/16 in Whitworth; 15/16 in BSF |
| 1.417 | 36 mm |
| 1.437 | 1 7/16 in AF |
| 1.480 | 7/8 in Whitworth; 1 in BSF |
| 1.500 | 1½ in AF |
| 1.574 | 40 mm; 15/16 in Whitworth |
| 1.614 | 41 mm |
| 1.625 | 1 5/8 in AF |
| 1.670 | 1 in Whitworth; 1 1/8 in BSF |
| 1.687 | 1 11/16 in AF |
| 1.811 | 46 mm |
| 1.812 | 1 13/16 in AF |
| 1.860 | 1 1/8 in Whitworth; 1¼ in BSF |
| 1.875 | 1 7/8 in AF |
| 1.968 | 50 mm |
| 2.000 | 2 in AF |
| 2.050 | 1¼ in Whitworth; 1 3/8 in BSF |
| 2.165 | 55 mm |
| 2.362 | 60 mm |

A Haltrac hoist and gantry in use during a typical engine removal sequence

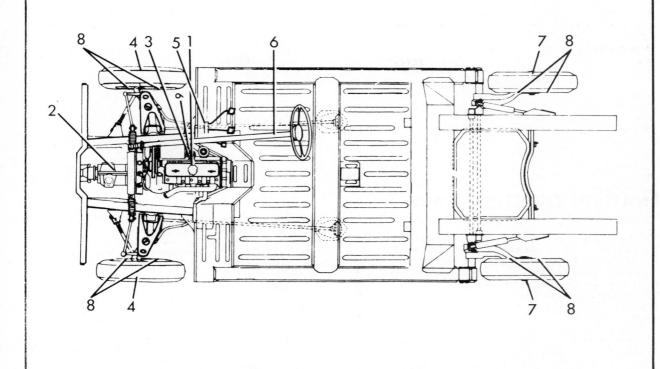

# Lubrication Chart

| COMPONENT | TYPE OF LUBRICANT OR FLUID | | | CASTROL PRODUCT |
|---|---|---|---|---|
| ENGINE SUMP (1) ... ... ... ... | Multigrade engine oil 20W/50 | ... | ... | GTX |
| TRANSMISSION (2) ... ... ... ... | SAE 80 EP ... ... ... ... ... | | | Hypoy Light |
| DISTRIBUTOR (3) AND DYNAMO BUSHES (9) | Light oil/Engine oil ... ... ... ... | | | GTX/Everyman |
| FRONT (4) AND REAR HUB (7) BEARINGS | Lithium based grease ... ... ...<br>High melting point | | | Castrol LM Grease |
| STEERING COLUMN TOP BUSH (6) ... | Multigrade engine oil 20W/50 ... ... | | | GTX |
| BRAKE MECHANISMS (ADJUSTER CAM<br>AND SHOES TO BACKPLATES) (8) ... | High melting point white grease ... ... | | | PH Grease |
| HYDRAULIC SYSTEM ... ... ... | SAE 70 R 3 ... ... ... ... ... | | | Castrol Girling Universal Brake<br>and Clutch Fluid |
| COOLANT ... ... ... ... ... | Glycol based anti-freeze ... ... ...<br>and distilled water | | | Castrol Anti-freeze |

Additionally Castrol 'Everyman' oil can be used to lubricate door, boot and bonnet
hinges, and locks, pivots (5), etc.

| | |
|---|---|
| DISTRIBUTOR CONTACT BREAKER<br>CAM AND BATTERY TERMINALS ... | Petroleum jelly |
| HYDRAULIC PISTONS ... ... ... | Rubber grease |
| INNER DRIVE SHAFT JOINTS ... ... | Specific Renault lubricant |

# Routine maintenance

Maintenance is essential for ensuring safety and desirable for the purpose of getting the best in terms of performance and economy from the car. Over the years the need for periodic lubrication - oiling and greasing - has been drastically reduced if not totally eliminated. This has unfortunately tended to lead some owners to think that because no such action is required the items either no longer exist or will last for ever. This is a serious delusion. If anything, there are now more places particularly in the steering and suspension where joints and pivots are fitted. Although you do not grease them any more you still have to look at them - and look at them just as often as you may previously have had to grease them. It follows therefore that the largest initial element of maintenance is visual examination. This may lead to repairs or renewals.

At the beginning of each chapter in the manual the routine maintenance details covering that chapter are given.

In the summary given here the 'essential for safety' items are shown in **bold type**. These **must** be attended to at the regular frequencies shown in order to avoid the possibility of accidents and loss of life. Other neglect results in unreliability, increased running costs, more rapid wear and more rapid depreciation of the vehicle in general.

---

### Every 250 miles/400 kms (or weekly, whichever comes first)

STEERING AND SUSPENSION
**Check tyre pressures - the ride and handling of this car can be severely altered by incorrect tyre pressures.**
**Examine tyres for wear or damage.**
**Is the steering smooth and accurate?**
Take note of any unusual noises when travelling and visually check the suspension and shock absorbers.

BRAKES
**Is there a fall-off of braking efficiency?**
**Try an emergency stop. Is adjustment necessary?**

LIGHTS, WIPERS AND HORNS
**Do all the bulbs work at the front, rear, interior and work well?**
**Are the headlight beams aligned properly?**
**Do both wipers and horn work fully?**

BATTERY
Check the electrolyte level and top-up if necessary.

ENGINE
Check the sump oil level and top up if required. The oil required to top up from MIN to MAX level on the dipstick is 2½ Imperial pints.
Check for visible coolant leaks (check coolant level in expansion bottle).
Check for any fluid leak puddles left under the car overnight.

---

### Every 1000 miles/1600 kms (or monthly, whichever comes first)

Check all 250 mile points and anything which you feel is not quite right.

STEERING
**Is there any free play between the steering wheel and the road wheels?**

BRAKES
**Check the fluid level in the master cylinder reservoir.**
**Top up if necessary. If significantly or regularly lower examine the system immediately for leaks.**

BODYWORK
Clean away with water any mud and road dirt from the petrol tank feed pipe inside the right hand rear wing.
Lubricate headlight adjusting screws and beam level levers.

GENERAL
Check the condition and the tension of the fan belts.
Apply glycerine (not oil) to the windscreen wiper arm spindles

---

### Every 3000 miles/5000 kms (or four monthly, whichever comes first)

Undertake all the items listed previously plus the following:

STEERING
**Examine all steering linkage, joints and bushes for signs of wear or damage.**
**Check the front and rear wheel hub bearings**
Check tightness of steering rack/radiator mounting bolts.
**Check drive shafts for wear at the outer universal joint and the rubber bellows for leaks.**

BRAKES
Adjust the brakes and lubricate the adjusters to stop them rusting solid.
**Inspect the front brake disc pads on the R1181 and renew when worn (in full sets)**

SUSPENSION
**Examine all bolts and bushes securing the suspension and shock absorbers. Tighten as necessary.**

ENGINE
Drain the sump, you will need a container of at least 5 pints, and either a 23 mm socket or a hexagonal key (10 mm) to undo the sump plug, depending on type fitted. Allow to drain when hot for five minutes. Replace sump plug and

refill with 4½ pints (6-850) or 5¼ pints (6.1100) of Castrol GTX. (20/50 engine oil - check exact capacity if fitted with cartridge filter).
Check the tension of the fan belts
Check the spark plugs.

## TRANSMISSION

Check level of oil by undoing the side filler plug with a 10 mm open ended spanner. If no oil starts to flow out top up with Castrol Hypoy Light (EP 80) using a flexible spout. The check should be made with the oil hot. Place in reverse gear to assist filling.

## BODYWORK

Lubricate all hinges including the bonnet, catches and locks with Castrol Everyman Oil. Do not forget the car's jack and 'courtesy' door plungers.

## ELECTRICS

Check proper functioning of electric cooling fan of the 6-1100 as well as the heated rear window (6-1100, if fitted).

## Every 9000 miles/15000 kms (or annually, whichever comes first)

Undertake all the checks and tasks already mentioned plus the following:

## BRAKES

Examine brake drum shoes front and rear and replace if necessary.
Check the condition of the wheel cylinder rubbers for leaks.
Check, properly, the condition of the hydraulic rigid and flexible hoses, particularly the fronts for chafing, dents and any other form of deterioration and rectify if necessary.
Lubricate the handbrake linkage, and adjust if necessary.

## SUSPENSION

Have the front wheel track checked and adjusted at your Renault garage.

## ENGINE

Change the oil filter cartridge (if fitted).
Lubricate the dynamo end 'greaser' with three drops of engine oil. (Not 6-1100).
Oil the felt pad under the rotor arm of the distributor very carefully with three drops of engine oil and grease the cam.
Fit new contact points, and adjust the gap, then the static timing.
Check static ignition timing.
Check the condition of the distributor cap and plug leads.
Fit new spark plugs set to the correct gap.
Fit new carburettor air cleaner element, and clean carburettor float chamber.
Clean the fuel pump and filter gauze for sediment.
Check the tightness of the inlet/exhaust manifold.

## TRANSMISSION

Drain the gearbox oil, when hot, into a container of at least 3 pints. You should undo both the drain plug(s) and the filler plug and place the car in reverse gear to obtain easier flow both on draining and refilling. Replace the sump plug(s). Refill with Castrol Hypoy Light (EP 80) until it just overflows from the filler plug..(On some cars fitted with special

transmission undershields you may have to remove them to do this task). Capacity 2½ Imp pints (6-850 early), 3 Imp pints (6-1100 and 6-850 late).

## CLUTCH

Adjust clearance if necessary. Visually check the condition of the carbon thrust bearing with a torch (6-850). You can see this between the radiator and the engine block in line with the flywheel.

## BODYWORK

Check and adjust if necessary the underbody height.
Check the tightness of all body parts particularly the bumpers and their mounting and all mechanical assemblies such as the gearbox mounting, and door and tailgate catches. (Check sun-roof fittings if current).
Check seat belt mounting and their fittings.
Check fixing of all rubber grommets particularly handbrake moulding.

## Every 18 months/2 years

Renew brake fluid.
Flush out the sealed cooling system and replenish.
Check underbody and wheel arches after cleaning and re-underseal if necessary.

In addition, time should be spent on the following:

## CLEANING

The best way to examine a car and know what sort of a state it is in, is to thoroughly clean it, inside and out. One of the principal results for this, which is not covered by other maintenance operations, is the finding of any traces of rust in the body panels. If rust is allowed to go unchecked it could affect some panels which may make the car unsafe and keep it off the road.

## EXHAUST SYSTEM

An exhaust system must be leakproof and keep engine noise to a reasonable level. Leaks may cause dangerous fumes to enter the interior and affect the driver and passengers - thus having an adverse effect on the driver's capabilities. Excessive noise constitutes a public nuisance. Both these faults can result in the vehicle being declared unfit for use.

**Special safety note;** Do not rely on the car jack supplied. It is not able to do anymore than just support the car for changing a wheel. For any more ambitious work, even during routine maintenance, purchase a better, stronger type.
Never fill the fuel tank to the brim - you will loose fuel at the first corner.
Never tow the car with the rope fixed to the driveshaft, bumper or tie-rod. Never tow with the bumper. In each case tow with the rope fixed around the chassis.
Most of the tasks just listed can be carried out with a small set of metric tools and feeler gauges together with a normal selection of screwdrivers and a hammer. Always prepare your ground first and make sure you have the time, the correct replacement parts and are fully in command of the tasks which you wish to start. Before undertaking more complex work read the second section of Chapter 1 for a necessary selection of tools.

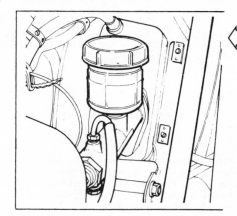

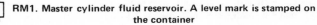

RM1. Master cylinder fluid reservoir. A level mark is stamped on the container

RM2. Grip the drive shaft and try to twist. The handbrake must be on

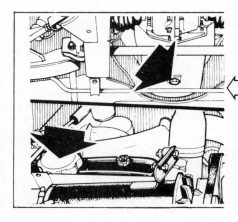

RM3. Top: Sump drain plug
Bottom: Rocker cover oil filler cap. 'Aim' the oil accurately

RM4. Left: Level/filler plug (Type 334 gearbox)
Right: Level/filler plug (Type 354 gearbox)

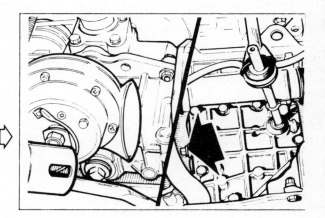

RM5. Left: R1181 carburettor air cleaner element
Right: R1180 carburettor air cleaner element

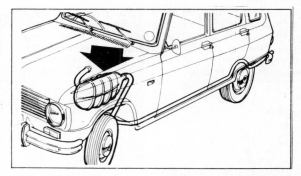

RM6. Silencer/exhaust system general layout.
See Chapter 3 for specific jointing

# Chapter 1 Engine

**Contents**

**Specifications**

### Engine - general
**R1180**

| | |
|---|---|
| Type ... ... ... ... ... ... ... ... ... | 4 cylinder, in line, ohv, pushrod operated. Cast iron block with removable cylinder liners. Aluminium cylinder head |
| Renault type number ... ... ... ... ... ... | 800—02 (Ventoux engine) |
| Cubic capacity ... ... ... ... ... ... ... | 845 cc (51.56 cu in) |

| Bore ... ... ... ... ... ... ... ... ... | 58 mm (2.284 in) |
| Stroke ... ... ... ... ... ... ... ... | 80 mm (3.150 in) |
| Compression ratio ... ... ... ... ... ... ... | 8 to 1 |
| Firing order ... ... ... ... , ... ... ... ... | 1, 3, 4, 2 |
| BHP (maximum) ... ... ... ... ... ... ... | 38 bhp at 5000 rpm |
| Torque (maximum) ... ... ... ... ... ... | 40 lb/ft at 3000 rpm |
| Engine weight (dry) ... ... ... ... ... ... | 178 lb (81 kg) |
| Normal operating temperature ... ... ... ... ... | 84°C (183°F) |

**Camshaft**

| Number of bearings ... ... ... ... ... ... | 3, running direct in block |
| End float ... ... ... ... ... ... ... ... | 0.06 mm to 0.14 mm (0.002 to 0.0055 in) |

**Connecting rods and big end bearings**

| Bearing type ... ... ... ... ... ... ... ... | Shell |
| Bearing material ... ... ... ... ... ... ... | White metal/lead indium |
| Nominal diameter ... ... ... ... ... ... ... | 38 mm (1.496 in) |

**Crankshaft and main bearings**

| Number of main bearings ... ... ... ... ... ... | 3 (No. 1 next to flywheel) |
| Bearing material ... ... ... ... ... ... ... | White metal/lead indium |
| Nominal journal diameter ... ... ... ... ... ... | 40 mm (1.575 in) |
| Regrind sizes available for all crankshaft bearings ... ... | 0.25 mm (0.010 in), 0.50 mm (0.020 in), 1 mm (0.040 in) |
| Grinding tolerances ... ... ... ... ... ... ... | 0.025 mm (0.001 in) |

**Pistons and cylinders**

| Cylinder block and liners ... ... ... ... ... ... | Cast iron, removable liners |
| Water jackets ... ... ... ... ... ... ... | Full length |
| Height of block ... ... ... ... ... ... ... | 215 mm (8.7/16 in) |
| Liner bottom locating diameter ... ... ... ... | 62.5 mm (2.15/32 in) |
| Liner protrusion ... ... ... ... ... ... ... | 0.04 to 0.012 mm (0.002 to 0.005 in) impregnated paper |
| | 0.08 to 0.015 mm (0.003 to 0.006 in) copper |
| Piston type ... ... ... ... ... ... ... ... | Aluminium alloy, 3 ring |
| Piston length ... ... ... ... ... ... ... | 64 mm |
| Overbore sizes available ... ... ... ... ... ... | 0.25 mm (0.010 in), 0.50 mm (0.020 in), 1 mm (0.040 in) |
| Gudgeon pin fitting ... ... ... ... ... ... | Press fit in connecting rod or piston |
| Direction of assembly ... ... ... ... ... ... | Arrow on piston towards the flywheel |
| Gudgeon pin length ... ... ... ... ... ... | 49 mm (1.15/16 in) |
| Gudgeon pin diameter - Press fit in small end ... ... ... | 16 mm (0.630 in) |
| Gudgeon pin diameter - Press fit in piston ... ... ... | 14 mm (0.551 in) |
| Oil pressure at 4000 rpm ... ... ... ... ... ... | 34 psi (2.4 bar) |

**Pushrods**

| Length ... ... ... ... ... ... ... ... ... | 132 mm (5 3/16 in) |
| Diameter ... ... ... ... ... ... ... ... | 5 mm (0.197 in) |

**Valves**

| Inlet - | Diameter of head ... ... ... ... ... | 28.2 mm (1.110 in) |
| | Stem diameter ... ... ... ... ... | 7 mm (0.276 in) |
| Exhaust - | Diameter of head ... ... ... ... ... | 25 mm (0.984 in) |
| | Stem diameter ... ... ... ... ... | 7 mm (0.276 in) |
| Valve guides match respective valves | | |
| | Internally ... ... ... ... ... ... | + .018 mm (0.276 in) |
| | Externally ... ... ... ... ... ... | + 4 mm, available in two oversizes: 0.10 mm, 0.25 mm |
| Valve seats - 7 mm diameter valve stem ... ... ... ... | 90° |
| Seat widths- Inlet ... ... ... ... ... ... | 1.5 mm (0.059 in) |
| | Exhaust ... ... ... ... ... ... | 1.8 mm (0.071 in) |

| | | | | | | | |
|---|---|---|---|---|---|---|---|
| Valve springs - Free length | ... | ... | ... | ... | ... | | 39 mm (1.17/32 in) |
| Wire diameter | ... | ... | ... | ... | ... | ... | 2.7 mm (0.106 in) |
| Internal diameter of coil | ... | ... | ... | ... | ... | | 16.8 mm (0.661 in) |
| Tappets - diameter | ... | ... | ... | ... | ... | | Nominal 19 mm (0.748 in) |
| | | | | | | | Oversizes available + 0.20 mm (0.008 in), 0.50 mm (0.020 in) |

| | | | | | | | |
|---|---|---|---|---|---|---|---|
| Valve lift - Inlet | ... | ... | ... | ... | ... | ... | 5.75 mm (0.226 in) |
| Exhaust | ... | ... | ... | ... | ... | ... | 6.00 mm (0.238 in) |

Valve rocker arm clearances:

| | | | | | | | |
|---|---|---|---|---|---|---|---|
| Cold engine: Inlet | ... | ... | ... | ... | ... | ... | 0.15 mm (0.006 in) |
| Exhaust | ... | ... | ... | ... | ... | ... | 0.20 mm (0.008 in) |
| Hot engine: Inlet | ... | ... | ... | ... | ... | ... | 0.18 mm (0.007 in) |
| Exhaust | ... | ... | ... | ... | ... | ... | 0.25 mm (0.010 in) |

| | | | | | | | |
|---|---|---|---|---|---|---|---|
| Cylinder head depth | ... | ... | ... | ... | ... | | 94.7 mm (3.728 in) |
| Maximum safe regrind on cylinder head | ... | ... | ... | ... | | + 0.40 mm (0.015 in) |
| Combustion chamber volume | ... | ... | ... | ... | | 27.3 cc |
| Engine oil sump capacity - maximum | ... | ... | ... | ... | | 4½ pints (2.5 litres) + ½ pt (0.25 litre) at filter change |
| - minimum | ... | ... | ... | ... | | 2½ pints (1 litre) |

**Torque wrench settings**

| | | | | | | | lbf ft | kgf m |
|---|---|---|---|---|---|---|---|---|
| Cylinder head bolts (cold) | ... | ... | ... | ... | ... | ... | 45 | 6.2 |
| Inlet/exhaust manifold nuts | ... | ... | ... | ... | ... | | 10 | 1.4 |
| Camshaft main bearing bolts | ... | ... | ... | ... | ... | | 50 | 6.9 |
| Flywheel bolts | ... | ... | ... | ... | ... | | 30 | 4.1 |
| Big-end bolts | ... | ... | ... | ... | ... | ... | 25 | 3.5 |

## R1181

**Engine - general**

| | | | | | | | | |
|---|---|---|---|---|---|---|---|---|
| Type | ... | ... | ... | ... | ... | ... | ... | 4 cylinder, in line, ohv, pushrod operated. Cast iron block with removable cylinder liners. Aluminium cylinder head |
| Renault type number | ... | ... | ... | ... | ... | | 688—10 (Sierra engine) |
| Cubic capacity | ... | ... | ... | ... | ... | ... | 1108 cc (67.6 cu in) |
| Bore | ... | ... | ... | ... | ... | ... | ... | 70 mm (2.756 in) |
| Stroke | ... | ... | ... | ... | ... | ... | ... | 72 mm (2.835 in) |
| Compression ratio | ... | ... | ... | ... | ... | | 8.3 to 1 (up to 1973) 9.5 to 1 (1973 on) |
| Firing order | ... | ... | ... | ... | ... | ... | 1, 3, 4, 2 |
| BHP (maximum) | ... | ... | ... | ... | ... | ... | 48 bhp at 5300 rpm |
| Torque (maximum) | ... | ... | ... | ... | ... | | 60 lb/ft at 3000 rpm |
| Engine weight (dry) | ... | ... | ... | ... | ... | | 200 lbs (approx) |
| Normal operating temperature | ... | ... | ... | ... | | 78° |

**Camshaft**

| | | | | | | | |
|---|---|---|---|---|---|---|---|
| Number of bearings | ... | ... | ... | ... | ... | | 4, running direct in block (one sleeved) |
| End float | ... | ... | ... | ... | ... | ... | 0.06 to 0.11 mm (0.002 to 0.005 in) |

**Connecting rods and big end bearings**

| | | | | | | | |
|---|---|---|---|---|---|---|---|
| Bearing type | ... | ... | ... | ... | ... | ... | Shell |
| Bearing material | ... | ... | ... | ... | ... | | White metal/lead indium |
| Nominal diameter | ... | ... | ... | ... | ... | | 43.98 mm (1.731 in) |

### Crankshaft and main bearings

| | |
|---|---|
| Number of main bearings ... ... ... ... ... ... | 5 (No. 1 next to flywheel) |
| Bearing material ... ... ... ... ... ... | White metal/lead indium |
| Nominal diameter ... ... ... ... ... ... ... | 46 mm (1.811 in) |
| Regrind sizes available for all crankshaft bearings ... ... | 0.25 mm (0.010 in), 0.50 mm (0.020 in), 1 mm (0.040 in) |
| Grinding tolerances ... ... ... ... ... ... ... | 0.020 mm (0.001 in) |

### Pistons and cylinders

| | |
|---|---|
| Cylinder block and liners ... ... ... ... ... ... | Cast iron, removable liners |
| Water jackets ... ... ... ... ... ... ... | Full length |
| Height of block ... ... ... ... ... ... | |
| Liner bottom locating diameter ... ... ... ... | 75.5 mm (2.972 in) |
| Liner protrusion ... ... ... ... ... ... | 0.05 to 0.12 mm (0.002 to 0.005 in) (paper) |
| Piston type ... ... ... ... ... ... ... | Aluminium alloy, 3 ring |
| Piston length ... ... ... ... ... ... ... | |
| Overbore sizes available ... ... ... ... ... ... | 0.25 mm (0.010 in), 0.50 mm (0.020 in), 1 mm (0.040 in) |
| Gudgeon pin fitting ... ... ... ... ... ... | Press fit in connecting rod |
| Direction of assembly ... ... ... ... ... ... | Arrow on piston towards flywheel |
| Gudgeon pin length ... ... ... ... ... ... | 59 mm (2.5/16 in) |
| Gudgeon pin diameter ... ... ... ... ... ... | 18 mm (0.709 in) |
| Oil pressure at 4000 rpm ... ... ... ... ... ... | 55 psi (4.0 bar) |

### Pushrods

| | |
|---|---|
| Length ... ... ... ... ... ... ... ... | 173 mm (6 13/16 in) |
| Diameter ... ... ... ... ... ... ... ... | 5 mm (0.197 in) |

### Valves

| | | |
|---|---|---|
| Inlet - | Diameter of head ... ... ... ... ... | 33.5 mm (1.319 in) |
| | Stem diameter ... ... ... ... ... | 7 mm (0.276 in) |
| Exhaust - | Diameter of head ... ... ... ... ... | 30.3 mm (1.193 in) |
| | Stem diameter ... ... ... ... ... | 7 mm (0.276 in) |
| Valve guides match respective valves | | |
| | Internally ... ... ... ... ... ... | 7 mm + 0.018 mm (0.276 in) |
| | Externally ... ... ... ... ... ... | 11 mm + 0.4 mm, available in two oversizes: 0.10 mm and 0.25 mm |
| Valve seats ... ... ... ... ... ... ... | | 90° |
| Seat widths - Inlet ... ... ... ... ... ... | | 1.1 to 1.4 mm (0.043 to 0.055 in) |
| Exhaust ... ... ... ... ... ... | | 1.4 to 1.7 mm (0.055 to 0.067 in) |
| Valve spring free length ... ... ... ... ... | | 42 mm (1.21/32 in) |
| Wire diameter... ... ... ... ... ... ... | | 3.4 mm (0.134 in) |
| Internal diameter of coil ... ... ... ... ... | | 21.6 mm (0.850 in) |
| Valve rocker arm clearances: | | |
| Cold engine: | Inlet ... ... ... ... ... ... | 0.15 mm (0.006 in) |
| | Exhaust ... ... ... ... ... ... | 0.20 mm (0.008 in) |
| Hot engine: | Inlet ... ... ... ... ... ... | 0.18 mm (0.007 in) |
| | Exhaust ... ... ... ... ... ... | 0.25 mm (0.010 in) |

| | | | | | | | |
|---|---|---|---|---|---|---|---|
| Cylinder head depth | ... | ... | ... | ... | ... | ... | 72 mm (2.835 in) per 8.3:1 c/r |
| | | | | | | | 70.15 mm (2.762 in) per 9.5:1 c/r |
| Maximum safe regrind on cylinder head | ... | ... | ... | ... | 0.50 mm (0.020 in) |
| | | | | | | | |
| Engine oil sump capacity - maximum | ... | ... | ... | ... | 5.25 pints (3 litres) + ½ pt (0.25 litre) at filter change |
| - minimum | ... | ... | ... | ... | 2.5 pints (1.5 litres) |

**Torque wrench settings**

| | | | | | | lbf ft | kgf m |
|---|---|---|---|---|---|---|---|
| Cylinder head bolts (cold) - first stage | ... | ... | ... | ... | 20 | 2.8 |
| - final stage | ... | ... | ... | ... | 45 | 6.2 |
| Inlet/exhaust manifold nuts | ... | ... | ... | ... | 10 | 1.4 |
| Rocker shaft pedestal nuts and bolts | ... | ... | ... | ... | 15 | 2.1 |
| Camshaft pulley hub bolts | ... | ... | ... | ... | 45 | 6.2 |
| Big-end bolts ... | ... | ... | ... | ... | 25 | 3.5 |
| Crankshaft main bearing bolts | ... | ... | ... | ... | 50 | 6.9 |
| Camshaft sprocket bolt | | | | | | |
| 20 mm long with washer and lockplate | ... | ... | ... | 15 | 2.1 |
| 30 mm long with washer and no lockplate | ... | ... | ... | 20 | 2.8 |

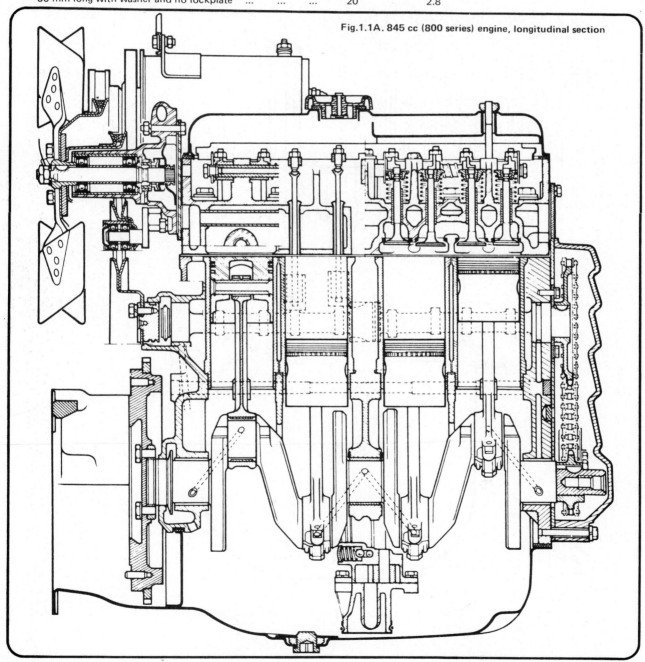

Fig.1.1A. 845 cc (800 series) engine, longitudinal section

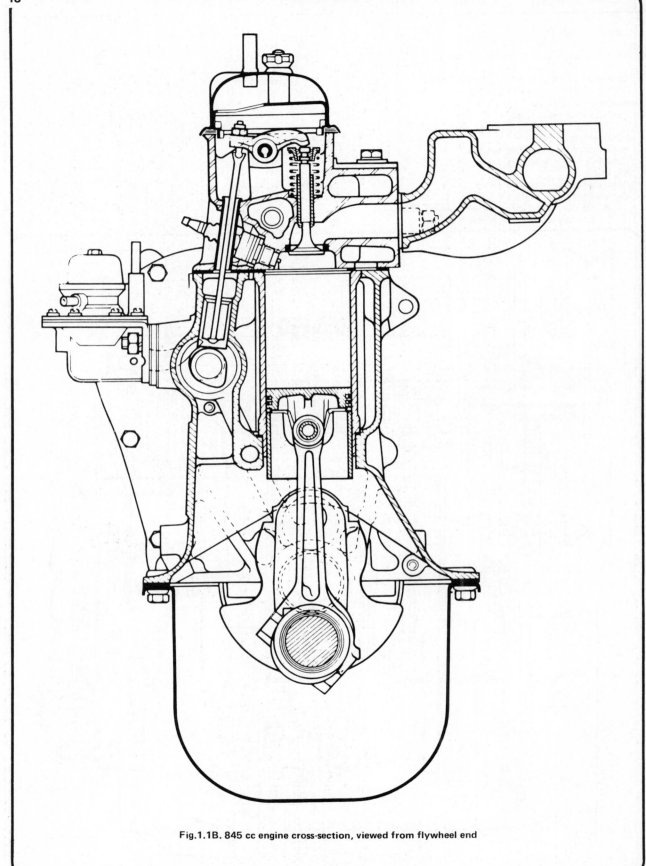

Fig.1.1B. 845 cc engine cross-section, viewed from flywheel end

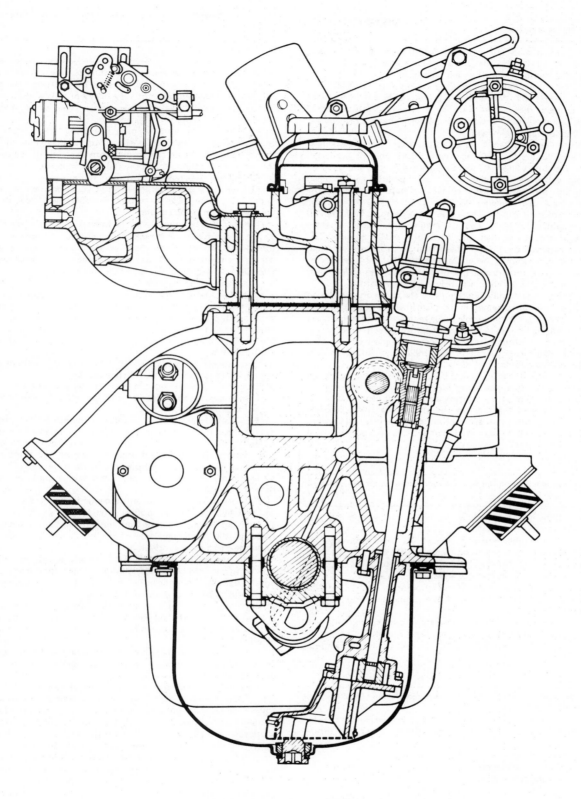

Fig.1.1C. 845 cc engine cross-section, viewed from timing end

## 1  General description

The Renault 6-850 (from now referred to as the R1180) and the Renault 6-1100 (R1181) have different engines. The R1180 has the old Ventoux three-bearing crankshaft engine of 845 cc. The Sierra engine with five bearing crankshafts of 1180 cc is fitted to the R1181. Whilst they are quite different in terms of the parts used, they are very similar in design. Consequently it must be assumed that methods are similar in the sections following, unless special note is made.

Both the engines have a longer stroke than bore, the smallest having very long stroke characteristics. Both engines are fitted with aluminium cylinder heads. Engines are four cylinder, fitted with two valves per cylinder, which are operated by overhead rockers and pushrods from a single camshaft mounted in the right hand side of the engine block.

The crankshaft runs in three/five main bearings and the end float is controlled by a pair of semi-circular thrust washers located in the upper half of the centre main bearing. The camshaft is driven by a single chain from a sprocket on the rear end of the crankshaft. The chain is controlled by a tensioner. The camshaft in turn drives the oil pump through a skew gear and the oil pump drive shaft also drives the distributor.

The pistons are a fully floating fit to the connecting rods and the gudgeon pins are retained in the piston with circlips. The con rod small end bush is renewable to be reamed to fit the gudgeon pin. The lubrication system is of the forced-feed type to the crankshaft main bearings, connecting rod, big end bearings, camshaft and valve rocker gear. The oil pump is fully submerged and is of the twin gear type.

The engine is flexibly mounted in the car at three points on the chassis: one either side of the block onto the chassis rails and the third at the end of the gearbox on the front crossmember. It will be appreciated that neither the engine nor the gearbox is fully supported when any one mounting is removed. All versions of the engines covered here are fitted with a single downdraught fixed jet carburettor.

## 2  Major operations which may be carried out with the engine in place

The following work may be conveniently carried out with the engine in place:
1  Removal and replacement of the cylinder head assembly.
2  Removal and replacement of the clutch assembly.
3  Removal and replacement of the engine mountings.
4  Removal and replacement of the sump.
5  Removal and replacement of the oil pump.
6  Removal and replacement of the connecting rod big end bearings.
7  Removal and replacement of pistons and connecting rods (after the removal of the cylinder head and sump).
8  Removal and replacement of the flywheel (after removing the gearbox and clutch).

## 3  Major operations which entail the engine being removed from the vehicle

1  Removal and replacement of the timing cover and timing gear.
2  Removal and replacement of the camshaft.
3  Removal and replacement of the crankshaft main bearings.
4  Removal and replacement of the crankshaft.

## 4  Method of engine removal

There is only one method of engine removal for this car and that is a straight up and out lift together with the gearbox. It is NOT possible to take the engine out without the gearbox.

## 5  Engine removal - 850 cc

1  Throughout this description it must be understood that the engine is being removed together with the gearbox. The engine and gearbox together are not very heavy or bulky and it is quite within the capabilities of two people. The whole operation should not take more than 1½ hours.
2  Position the car with its nose just under the centre of the beam or tripod to be used as the lifting support. This will mean that the engine can be swung out from the front of the car once the car is made immobile. Apply the handbrake.
3  Disconnect the battery and then remove it to a safe place. The battery tray is a good place to put your tools whilst working under the bonnet. Tie these battery cables well clear of other obstructions onto the engine.
4  Remove the bonnet. Undo the bonnet check and earth strap.
5  Undo the two bonnet hinge fixing bolts at the bottom end of the hinges. Do not undo them on the bonnet. Have a second person lift the bonnet off the car and place on its side somewhere safe. Do not place near the car on its largest surface.
6  Drain the cooling system See Chapter 2.
7  Then disconnect the hoses between the radiator and the water pump and the heater and the water pump. Retain the securing clips if of the worm screw thread type, discard and get replacements if of the split pin type. Undo the overflow pipe at the radiator and strap the pipe to the inner wing near to the expansion bottle.
8  Disconnect the leads to the dynamo and tie them to the bulkhead. They can only be refitted one way.
9  Disconnect the LT input lead at the coil and tie back.
10  Disconnect the fuel pipe at the fuel pump inlet and bend gently back.
11  Remove the air cleaner by undoing the nut in its centre and lift off. Plug the air inlet of the carburettor to stop dirt getting in, with a piece of non-fluffy rag. Disconnect the middle exhaust pipe between the manifold and the silencer and remove. The silencer will hang safely unsupported beneath the wing.
12  Disconnect the throttle cable and choke cable at the carburettor and tie back.
13  Pull off the water temperature gauge lead at the sender unit and tie back, then starter motor connections.
14  Remove the oil pressure warning light lead at the sender unit fitted in the right hand side of the block and tie back. Then undo the earth strap on the block.
15  Drain the engine sump of its oil. A container of not less than 5 pints is required. After five minutes replace the sump plug and lightly tighten. Do not throw the old oil down the drain. Ask your local garage to dispose of it for you.
16  Jack up the car so that both front wheels are just off the ground and place the vehicle on axle stands just to the rear of the tubular front crossmember under the sump, on the side members.
17  Remove the gearbox and outer undertrays and then drain the gearbox into a container having two pints capacity. When drained, replace the drain plugs.
18  Remove the gearshift linkage. Unhook the gearshift lever return spring and undo the two mounting bracket nuts on the top of the radiator unhook the tie rod at the top only. Pull the gearshift lever upwards through the shift rod end eye releasing the lever from the gearbox. Pull out the lever from the rod's eye firstly having removed the pin from its top. Remove the spring from the anti-rattle washer on the shift rod and then undo both nuts from the centre bolts connecting the two halves of the shift rod. Split the rod - the bulkhead end will push through into the car (do not loose sight of the anti-rattle washer) and remove. The radiator end will lift off the radiator together with the mounting bracket. Some vehicles have a gearbox earth strap. Remove that too.
19  Remove the radiator tie rods completely by undoing the one bolt through the front crossmember and the two bolts on

5.7a The thermostat sits in the hose itself

5.7b R1180 return heater hose at the water pump with proper hose clip

5.7c Feeder heater hose with non-usable hose clip. Renew it

5.8 Dynamo connections cannot be muddled for they are different sizes

5.9 Again the connections need not be muddled. The coil here is very dirty.

5.11 This is the best exhaust clamp to use in this place

5.12a The throttle cable has a soldered end and is ...

5.12b ... sprung by a captive spring on the rocker cover

5.12c The choke cable is a stiff cable. Treat carefully; do not over bend

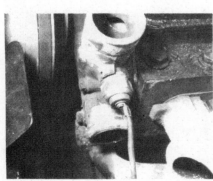

5.13 Water temperature sender unit in the water pump housing

5.14 Oil pressure sender unit. (The engine is removed here to show location)

5.18 Undo the gearshift mechanism here. Both screws

the side member.

20 Undo the two holding bolts which locate the radiator to the steering rack and remove the bolts with the radiator. Unbolt the steering rack, marking and retaining any mounting shims. This is best done from below with the help of a 14 mm tubular spanner. Care must be taken with the radiator not to allow it to be damaged on the blades of the fan.

21 Undo the clutch idle lever rod and remove. Then remove the clutch cable from the car by releasing it from the swivel at one end and the clutch pedal at the other. This is obvious when looking at it.

22 Disconnect the steering column at the flexible coupling, only two of the bolts need be removed completely.

23 Disconnect the speedometer drive at the gearbox. This is located with a press-in-fit and is held there by an abutting bolt which must be unscrewed first. Tie the cable back onto the inner wing.

24 Disconnect the drive shafts from the transmission unit with the aid of a special pin punch when type 334 gearbox is fitted. See Chapter 7.

25 Retain drive shafts safely. See Chapter 7.

26 Remove the front wheels.

27 Disconnect the upper ball joints on the outer ends of the upper wishbones, at the stub axle carriers. A ball joint remover should be borrowed for this (most good garages will hire out this piece of equipment at weekends or overnight for a substantial deposit) although the joints can be separated with two wedges. Do not use a cold chisel.

28 Hold the stub axle carriers, hubs and brakes with a piece of string so that they do not pull on the brake pipe and the drive shafts should be well free of the gearbox. The type 354 drive shafts require a slightly longer 'pull' than those of the type 334. Watch the oil seals in the differential adjusting ring nuts.

29 The steering rack will now be free to lift out, first one side then the other, up and out, having undone the bolts connecting each end of the rack to the steering arms.

30 Place a stout rope under the sump in a vertical line just to the rear of the dynamo around the engine. Knot the rope so that it is single loop and place the hook of the hoist under the loop as close to the rocker cover as possible. Pull on the hoist until it is just short of taking any weight.

31 Get under the car and undo the nuts on both the engine side mounts. Remove and put in a safe place.

32 Now undo the gearbox mounting. Remove all four bolts. The gearbox will not slip down yet.

33 Check finally that there is nothing still connected to the engine and gearbox by passing your hand around both. The unit is ready to lift out.

34 One person should take the strain on the hoist whilst another lifts the gearbox with his hands tilting it upwards and the engine back nearly touching the bulkhead. Take more strain on the hoist and lift the unit up and away from the car still with the second person holding the gearbox at the required tilt and steadying it away from the car. Be careful not to bash anything, particularly the control box. If you have positioned the by-now-immobile car in the correct place relevant to the lifting beam the unit will come up easily. Once well above the crossmember at the front of the car, lower the unit very gently whilst the person steadying the gearbox pulls it further away from the car onto the ground. If done properly neither person is unduly strained nor in any danger.

35 The engine and gearbox will sit upright on a flat surface. It is a little unsteady though and should be placed on a soft surface whilst still resting on its sump and propped under the engine mountings. An old blanket or coat is the ideal surface. The engine is now ready to be split from the gearbox. See Chapter 6. Replace the engine mountings and gearbox mounting nuts and bolts onto their respective units.

5.19 This must be undone before the radiator brace can be disconnected

5.20a Watch the radiator matrix on the fan blades

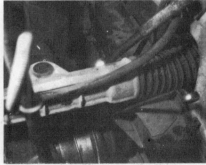

5.20b The two spanners locate the second fixing bolts under the steering rack

5.21 This stop on the gearbox locates the end of the outer clutch cable

5.22 Remove only two captive bolts

5.23 The outer cable stop is just above the entry of the cable into the gearbox

5.24a Early R1180 only have roll pins which need punching out from below here

5.24b Only early 850 cc have these drive shafts

5.29a Clean the steering arms first before using any spanners

5.29b The steering rack must be removed

5.30 The gearbox has already been removed. Note the location of the rope

5.32a Loosen the gearbox mounting from inside first

5.32b Remove the mounting complete if possible

**6 Engine removal - 1100 cc**

1 As can be seen from the accompanying illustrations the R1181 engine and gearbox removal sequence looks as if it ought to be very similar to that of the R1180, except for the radiator and centre cross brace. This is in fact the case; consequently the description following will be a list of tasks, except where greater detail is necessary, which should be read in conjunction with Section 5. Therefore read Section 5 now but alter the sequence where shown next.

2 Once again the engine and gearbox is no bulkier, quite suitable for two people to tackle. 1½ hours should be allowed for removal. No special tools are needed.
3 Disconnect the battery and remove.
4 Remove the bonnet.
5 Undo the hinges in the same way.
6 Drain the cooling system. See Chapter 2.
7 Disconnect the two main radiator hoses at the radiator. Disconnect the overflow pipe and remove the expansion bottle from the centre cross brace.
8 Disconnect the leads to the alternator and tie-back.
9 Disconnect the LT and HT connections to the coil and tie appropriately.
10 Disconnect the inlet pipe at the fuel pump (mechanical).
11 Remove the carburettor air cleaner. Remove the inlet pipe from its bracket on the inner wing. Disconnect the fuel pipe at the carburettor (electric fuel pump only) and tie-up.
12 Disconnect the throttle and choke cables at the carburettor. Remove the middle exhaust pipe between the manifold and the front silencer.
13 Pull off the water temperature gauge lead at the sender unit and tie back, then the starter motor connections.
14 Remove the oil pressure warning light lead from the engine block and tie back. Undo the engine earth strap.
15 Drain the engine oil sump. A container of 5 pints is necessary.
16 Jack up the car so that both front wheels are off the ground.
17 Remove the gearbox and outer undertrays, and then drain the gearbox oil.
18 Remove the gearchange linkage. Undo the centre connecting split pin. Remove the front 'eye' link and push the rear end through the bulkhead.
19 Remove the centre cross brace held at each end to the

6.1a(1) Fuel feed pipe disconnection 1100 cc. (2) Steering coupling

6.1b(1) Cross brace centre brace 1100 cc. (2) Alternator connections (3) Expansion bottle

6.1c(1) Gearshift connection 1100 cc. (2) Top hose (3) Coil connections (4) Expansion bottle hose

6.1d(1) Battery terminal connections 1100cc. (2) Air cleaner and hose

inner wings by two setscrews at each end. There is a centre brace which must be removed. Thread the radiator hose through the brace. Then remove the hoses from the water pump at the same time disconnecting the two heater hoses bring them back to the inner wings. If the cooling fan relay be fitted to the cross brace remove it and tie it back. Remove the car jack.

20 Undo the two bolts which hold the steering rack to the chassis frame.

21 Undo the clutch cable at the release lever/rod. See Chapter 5.

22 Disconnect the steering column at the flexible coupling.

23 Disconnect the speedometer drive cable at the gearbox.

24 Retain the drive shafts with the proper drive shaft retaining clips. See Chapter 7.

25 Remove the front wheels.

26 Remove the front brake calipers from their mounting points and tie back with string in front stretching the brake hoses.

27 Disconnect the upper ball joint with a ball joint remover.

28 Pull the drive shafts out of the differential carrier. Watch the oil seals in the differential adjusting ring nut.

29 Undo the steering arms at each end of the steering rack and remove the steering rack.

30 Place a rope under the sump at each end and get ready to haul the engine/gearbox out.

31 Disconnect the engine from the engine side mountings.

32 Undo the gearbox mounting pad and take the weight of the engine/gearbox unit.

33 Make your final checks.

34 Haul the unit out. Watch the clearance, it's very tight.

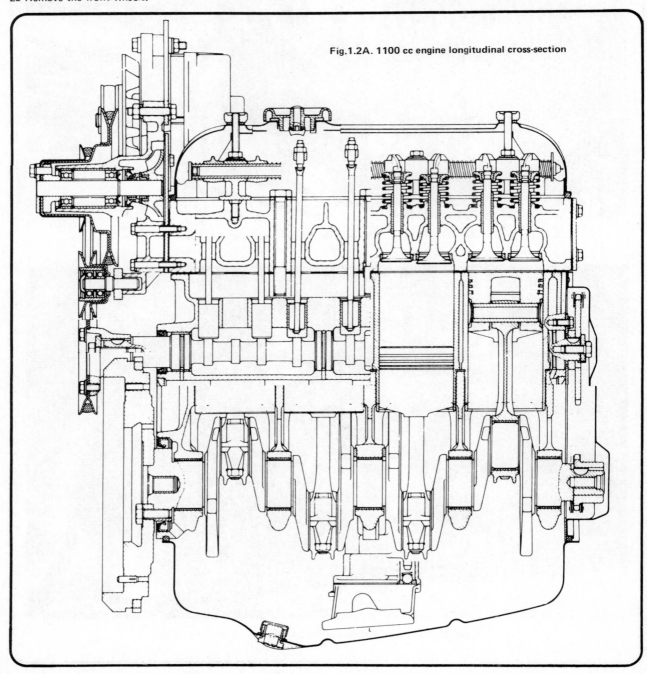

Fig.1.2A. 1100 cc engine longitudinal cross-section

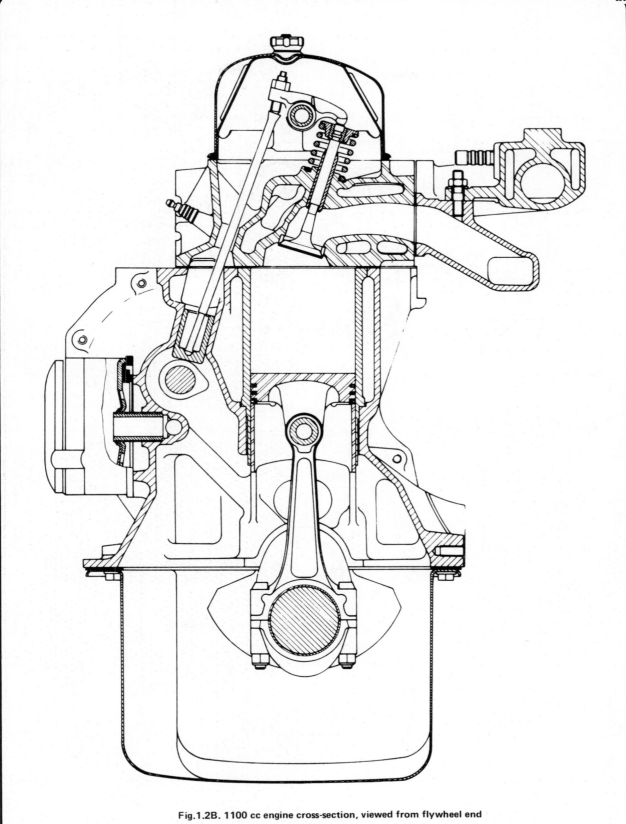

Fig.1.2B. 1100 cc engine cross-section, viewed from flywheel end

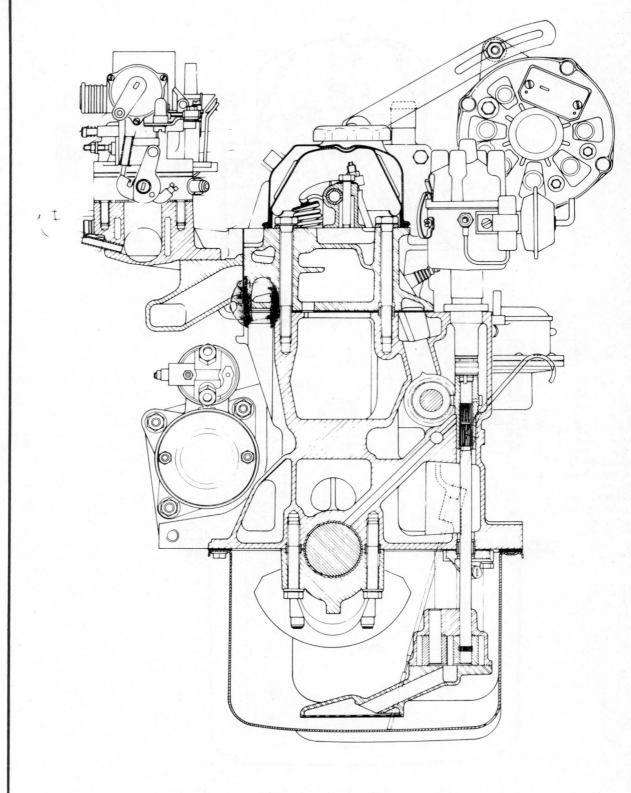

Fig.1.2C. 1100 cc engine cross-section, viewed from timing end

## 7 Engine dismantling - general

1  Owners who have dismantled engines will know the need for a strong work bench and many tools and pieces of equipment, which make their life much easier when going through the process of dismantling an engine. For those who are doing a dismantling job for the first time, there are a few 'musts' in the way of preparation which, if not acquired, will only cause frustration and long delays in the job in the long run. It is essential to have sufficient space in which to work. Dismantling and reassembly is not going to be completed all in one go and it is therefore absolutely essential that you have sufficient area to leave things as they are when necessary. A strong work bench is also necessary together with a good engineer's vice. If you have no alternative other than to work at ground level, make sure that the floor is at least level and covered with a suitable wooden or wood composition material on which to work. If dirt and grit are allowed to get into any of the component parts all work which you carry out may be completely wasted. Before actually placing the engine wherever it is that you may be carrying out the dismantling, make sure that the exterior is now completely and thoroughly cleaned.

2  Once dismantling begins it is advisable to clean the parts as they are removed. A small bath of paraffin is about the best thing to use for this, but do not let parts which have oilways in them become immersed in paraffin otherwise there may be a residue which could cause harmful effects later on. If paraffin does get into oilways every effort should be made to blow it out. For this may be necessary to carry the particular part to a garage fitted with a high pressure air hose. Short oilways such as there are in the crankshaft can be cleared easily with wire.

3  Always obtain a complete set of gaskets when the engine is being dismantled - no gaskets on an engine are re-usable and any attempt to do so is quite unjustified in view of the relatively small cost involved. Before throwing any gaskets away, however, make sure that you have the replacement to hand. If, for example, a particular gasket cannot be obtained it may be necessary to make one, and the pattern of the old one is useful in such cases.

4  Generally speaking, it is best to start dismantling the engine from the top downwards. In any case, make sure it is firmly supported at all times so that it does not topple over whilst you are undoing the very tight nuts and bolts which will be encountered. Always replace nuts and bolts into their locations once the particular part has been removed, if possible. Otherwise keep them in convenient tins or pots in their groups, so that when the time comes to reassemble there is the minimum of confusion.

## 8 Engine dismantling - ancillaries

1  A word of warning at this stage is that you should always be sure that it is more economic to dismantle and overhaul a worn engine rather than simply to exchange it on the Renault Factory scheme.

2  If you are intending to obtain an exchange engine complete, it will be necessary first of all to remove all those parts of the engine which are not included in the exchange. If you are stripping the engine completely yourself with the likelihood of some outside work being done by specialists, all these items will be taken off anyway.

3  Short engines are not available from Renault Limited. It is as well to check with whoever may be supplying the replacement exchange unit what it is necessary to remove, but as a general guide the following items will have to be taken off. Reference is given to the appropriate Chapter for details of removal of each of these items:

Dynamo - Chapter 10
Distributor - Chapter 4
Thermostat - Chapter 2
Carburettor - Chapter 3
Inlet/exhaust manifold - Chapter 1
Fuel pump - Chapter 3
Engine mounting brackets - Chapter 1
Distributor/oil pump drive - Chapter 4
Gearbox - Chapter 6
Ignition coil - Chapter 4
Static timing pointer - Chapter 1
Belt tensioner - Chapter 2
Dipstick
Fan and its pulley - Chapter 2
Starter motor - Chapter 10
Always clean the engine before exchanging.

## 9 Inlet/exhaust manifold - removal

1  If the engine is being completely dismantled or if the cylinder head is being removed, it is not necessary to detach either the inlet/exhaust manifold, prior to carrying out this work.

2  The only occasions when one would expect to have to remove the manifold would be to renew a suspected leaking gasket or, of course, a cracked or damaged manifold.

3  Both manifolds have to be removed together as they are one unit and are mounted to the engine on a common gasket.

4  First of all disconnect all the carburettor controls and fuel pipe connection to the carburettor and remove the carburettor together with its air cleaner from the inlet manifold flange. Details are given in Chapter 3. Next disconnect the exhaust pipe from the flange on the manifold by undoing the clamp removing it completely. The exhaust pipe to the silencer will then hang down with the silencer. It supports itself quite safely. Undo and remove with a tubular spanner the four nuts which hold the whole manifold to the head. (On some models there is a bracing piece between the inlet manifold carburettor studs and two cylinder head bolts. It is essential to remove these two cylinder head studs to remove the bracing piece and then the manifold. A 14 mm socket or ring spanner will undo these. Even if the cylinder head is not going to be removed these bolts must be undone. It should not disturb the cylinder head gasket if done carefully, and the bolts replaced correctly). Note the position of the heat shield between the starter motor and exhaust manifold on the 1100 cc engines, this is detached when the retaining manifold nuts and washers are removed.

## 10 Valve rocker gear - removal

1  It is not necessary to remove the valve rocker gear from the cylinder head in order to remove the cylinder head from the engine, either in or out of the car. In fact the valve rocker gear can only be removed under the following conditions:
a) The cylinder head is removed from the engine with the engine still in the car.
b) The engine is removed from the car with the cylinder head still attached to the engine.
c) The water pump must be removed from the cylinder head under ALL CONDITIONS.

2  Remove the rocker cover by undoing the two retaining nuts and lift off. Lift off the rocker cover gasket.

3  Breather pipes etc will differ from model to model and should be extracted with care. All lift off easily.

4  We assume that the water pump is off the cylinder head. Remove the cylinder head end plate.

5  Extract the little rubber grommet from the end of the cylinder head away from the water pump. Prise it outwards with a screwdriver (photo).

6  Undo the two locking nuts located on the centre pedestals, having prised the locking plate flat with a screwdriver. These nuts, 8 mm, locate the split rocker shaft in the pedestals. Remove together with the locking washers (photo).

7  Unscrew the shaft end plugs and remove the four clips, two end springs and the two shaft end plug setscrews (photo).

8  If the cylinder head is still on the engine but it is out of the car, slacken off all the valve rocker arms using a ring spanner.

Unscrew the eight adjusting pins about two turns.

9  The easiest method of extracting the rocker arm shafts is
with Renault Special Tool Number Mot 31. It is recommended
that if you are going to do this job that you purchase this cheap
tool - it is a lot easier, especially when replacing. A shaft
extractor can be made by using a bolt of 11 mm diameter about
two inches long, threaded for about an inch. Unscrew the end
bolts and screw in this bolt through the end of the cylinder head
into the rocker shaft until it is fairly tight. Then lever the bolt
out of the hole again as straight as you can, having removed the
locking springs. With luck the shaft will follow it and the rocker
arms will fall off the shaft together with their floating springs.
Retrieve the rocker arms noting their position, with the springs.
Repeat for the other end. Be careful, it is not too easy without
the real tool - the head is made of aluminium and does not take
kindly to bashing around. (It is this form of shaft extraction
which does not allow the removal in the car). Photos A and B.

## 11  Cylinder head - removal

1  The cylinder head may be removed with the engine either in
or out of the car.
2  If the engine is to remain in the car, the following must be
done first:
a) Drain the cooling system.
b) Remove the air cleaner from the carburettor and preferably
   remove the carburettor also as a safety precaution.
c) Remove both top and bottom radiator hoses completely.
d) Disconnect all the leads from the spark plugs.
e) Disconnect the heater water pipes from the water pump
   housing at the front of the cylinder head.
f) Disconnect and remove the fuel feed pipe from the fuel
   pump which goes to the carburettor.
g) Undo the exhaust manifold to exhaust pipe clamp and allow
   pipe to hang.
h) Pull away the throttle cable (R.H.D. cars only) and tie to
   right hand side inner wing.
i) Undo and position gear shift rod and radiator tie rod.
j) Remove electrical lead to water temperature sender unit in
   water pump casting.
k) Remove the outer fan belt which runs round the fan pulley
   and the dynamo, then the other drivebelt (see Chapter 2) and
   the dynamo. The primary drivebelt jockey pulley should also
   be removed.
Note: The water pump should remain on the head for ease of
movement but this is not essential. It is however easier to remove
the water pump with the head out of the car.
3  With the foregoing completed removal of the cylinder head is
now the same whether the engine is in or out of the car. Remove
the two nuts which locate the rocker cover, remove the rocker
cover with the gasket.
4  If the engine is still in the car make absolutely sure at this
stage that it is OUT OF GEAR and the handbrake is on. Leaving
the valve rocker gear in place undo the 12 cylinder head bolts
(10 bolts for R1181 models) in the reverse sequence of the
tightening order which is shown in Figs 1.3A and B.
IT IS ESSENTIAL THAT YOU HAVE THE CORRECT
SOCKET WITH WHICH TO UNDO THESE BOLTS.
5  On the R1180 engine, a special socket will be required to
undo the cylinder head bolts. This is Renault Part Number Mot
23-12 384, it is a special 14 mm socket with a 3/8 inch drive
which has been machined very finely on its outside. You will
need a 3/8 inch-converter-to-½ inch-drive if you have the normal
type of socket set drive in current use. Purchase this socket and
special extension at the outset - there is no other way - you will
break something, if only yourself, if you attempt this task
without these tools. On R1181 engines a conventional 17 mm
socket spanner will unscrew the 10 bolts.
6  The cylinder head may now be free enough to lift clear. If
however it is reluctant to move, loosen it sideways so that it
swivels slightly. This action ensures that the cylinder liners aren't
stuck to the head. Tap the head very lightly on the spark plug

side to achieve this if necessary but take great care - remember
that the head is manufactured in aluminum. On removal, place
the head out of the way on a flat surface.
7  Do not turn the engine over to remove the head because you
will disturb the removable cylinder liners. Once these and their
base seals are disturbed the pistons have to be removed etc and if
it was only your intention to replace the cylinder head gasket
you have created a lot of unnecessary work. When the head is
removed the pushrods will be left floating in the tappet chest.
Remove these and place them through a piece of cardboard in
their correct order for replacement. Be careful that the cam
followers do not become dislodged at this stage.
8  Remove the old cylinder head gasket and retain for
inspection.
9  Once the head is removed and you do not wish to dismantle
the pistons, liners and their seals, place retaining clamps on the
liners. On the 1180 engine these can be made from large washers
about 1½ inches in diameter, and some metal tubing, galvanised
pipe used on building sites is ideal, about 2 inches long. You will
need four of each. Replace the four head bolts which go between
cylinders one and two and three and four with the washers flat on
the block and the tube over them. Once the bolts are fairly tight
the liners will not shift. On the 1181 engines the liner retainers
are similar to above but only three lengths of tube are necessary

10.2 If the rocker cover sticks tap it gently

10.4 The gasket will stick. Be patient

10.5 Try to renew these plugs, they perish and leak

10.6 Use the correct spanner for they easily strip their threads

10.7 Only these clips pull right off

10.9a Mole grips will work if the proper tool is not available

10.9b Record how these springs locate, for ease of replacement

11.6 Do not hit the cylinder head with a steel faced hammer

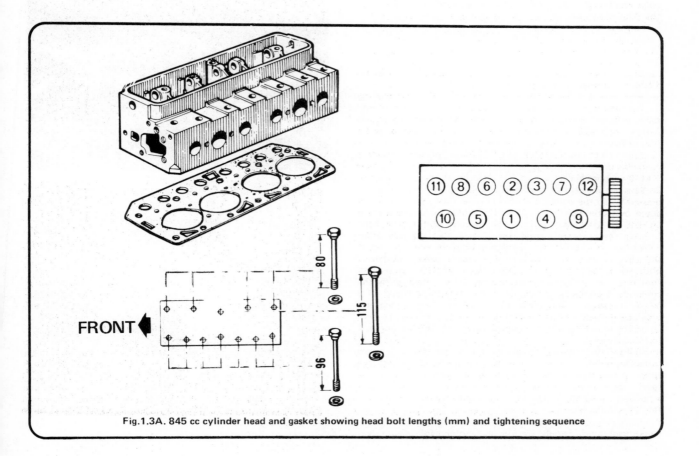

Fig.1.3A. 845 cc cylinder head and gasket showing head bolt lengths (mm) and tightening sequence

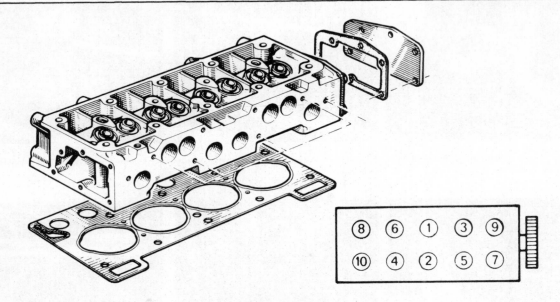

Fig.1.3B. 1100 cc cylinder head and gasket showing head bolt tightening sequence

and should be about 3 inches long. Referring to Fig. 1.3B retain using bolt numbers 1, 4 and 5.

Special Note: Apart from the removal of the valve rocker gear, the valves and the valve springs. all dealt with in this Chapter, there is one further task to be carried out on the cylinder head: checking and replacing the internal water distribution tube, its cover plate and gasket. This will be dealt with in Chapter 2 on the Cooling System.

## 12 Valve removal

1  With the valve rocker gear removed and with the water pump taken off, see Chapter 2, the valves are relatively easy to remove with the cylinder head on the bench. On the R1181 engine a proprietary valve spring compressor should be used in this operation, but the R1180 head is quite different and the following procedure should be taken.

**R1180 cylinder head**

2  Start at one end of the head by placing some highly compressed rag in the combustion chamber and then placing it face down onto the bench. This effectively holds the valves in place on that cylinder, when you remove the valve spring and collets.

3  With the aid of a second person to extract the two collet halves from the top of the valve stem, press down on the top of the valve spring washer/cap with two equally sized screwdrivers both with blades of about 3/8 inch across. The spring will compress with its cap and because the valve is held up by the compressed rag the collets will fall outwards to be collected. This is not dangerous - the valve springs are not very strong and provided the motions are undertaken precisely and are unrushed, all will be well. Retain the collets in order - they differ from inlet to exhaust valve.

4  Release the pressure on the valve cap once the collets are expected, remove the cap (sometimes known as spring seat), the spring (single springs only are used on all valves, but be sure to record those from the inlet valves and those from the exhaust separately - they differ in strength) and the lower washers.

**R1181 cylinder head**

5  Place the cylinder head on the 'spark plug' side and fit the compressor. Work should start at one end and follow on down

13.1 Record the original location of each pushrod

the head.

6  Tighten the compressor so that the 'foot' is in the centre of the valve being released. The 'claw' should sit on the top of the valve spring cap. Continue to compress the spring until the collets are loose.

7  Release the pressure on the valve cap once the collets are extracted, remove the cap (sometimes known as spring seat), the spring (single springs only are used on all valves but be sure to record those from the inlet valves and those from the exhaust separately - they differ in strength) and lower the washers.

8  Do one combustion chamber at a time before extracting the valves themselves. Repeat the process for each chamber and record the order in which the valves are removed. Place them through a piece of cardboard in order, as you would the pushrods, for further inspection.

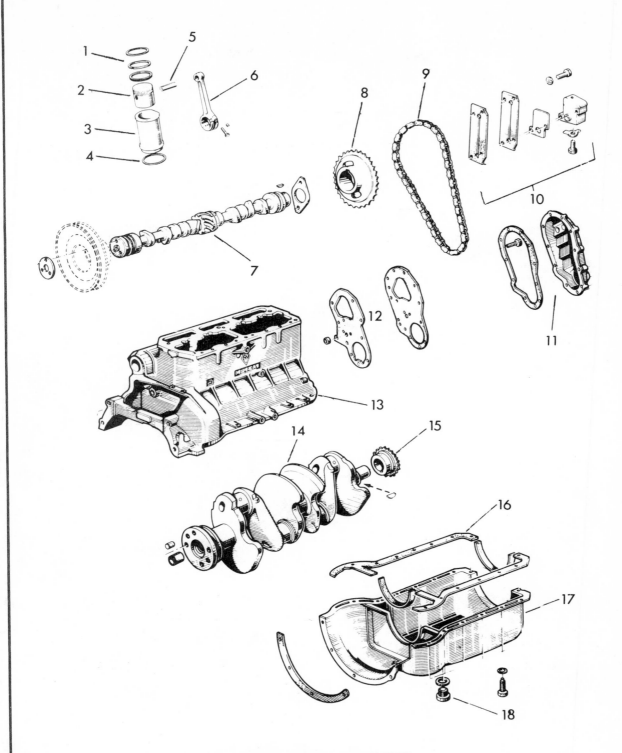

**Fig.1.4A. 845 cc ENGINE COMPONENTS**

| | | | |
|---|---|---|---|
| 1 Piston rings | 6 Connecting rod | 11 Timing cover/gasket | 16 Sump gasket |
| 2 Piston | 7 Camshaft | 12 Backplates | 17 Sump |
| 3 Liner | 8 Camshaft sprocket | 13 Block | 18 Sump plug |
| 4 Liner seal | 9 Timing chain | 14 Crankshaft | |
| 5 Gudgeon pin | 10 Chain tensioner | 15 Crankshaft sprocket | |

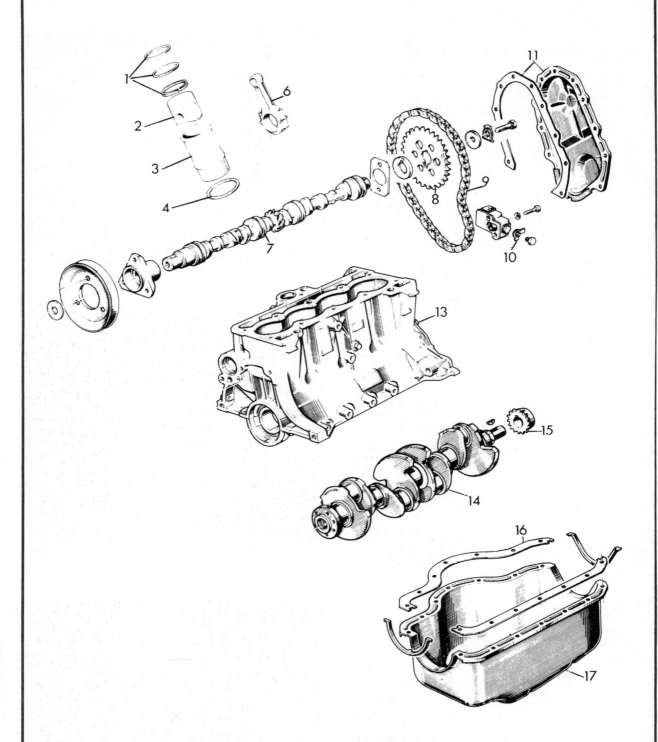

**Fig.1.4B. 1100 cc ENGINE COMPONENTS**

| 1 | Piston rings | 6 | Connecting rod | 10 | Chain tensioner | 15 | Crankshaft sprocket |
| 2 | Piston | 7 | Camshaft | 11 | Timing cover/gasket | 16 | Sump gasket |
| 3 | Liner | 8 | Camshaft sprocket | 13 | Block | 17 | Sump |
| 4 | Liner seal | 9 | Timing chain | 14 | Crankshaft | | |

## 13 Tappet removal

1 With the cylinder head and the pushrods removed the tappets can be extracted.
2 Each one can be removed by pushing one's index finger right into the tappet, pushing out the oil and then pulling it upwards. A technique will soon be developed to raise them up in this way.
3 Place the tappets in their correct order for imspection and possible correct replacement.

## 14 Timing cover, gears and chain - removal

1 The timing cover is located at the rear end of the engine, nearest to the bulkhead, and can only be removed with the engine out of the car because of its close proximity with the bulkhead. (It has been removed with the engine in the car albeit with great difficulty but it was found to be pointless because nothing else could be done to the timing gear without the engine out.) It is located by eleven setscrews, some direct into the block, some tightened with nuts.
2 Remove the timing cover and its gasket by undoing the screws. The cover is quite heavy and has some sharp machined edges. Remove the camshaft belt pulley from the other end (845).
3 Remove the chain tensioner by unlocking and unscrewing the retaining cylinder bolt. Insert a 3mm Allen key into the retaining cylinder, turn the key in a clockwise direction until the pad carrier assembly is no longer under tension and the tensioner and its thrust plate should be free.
4 845 cc: To remove the timing chain and sprockets a two legged puller is necessary. Do not attempt to take off either of the sprockets without drawing them both away together with the camshaft.
5 Remove the two camshaft flange fixing bolts through the camshaft sprocket. Then draw off the crankshaft sprocket. Make sure the tappets and the distributor drive is away; Also the fuel pump.
6 Once the crankshaft sprocket is clear the chain can be fitted away. The camshaft is now full.
7 1100 cc: The principle for this engine is the same except that the camshaft sprocket is located to the camshaft with a setscrew through its centre, a location tab and a locking tab. Once this sprocket is loosened it should pull off enabling the chain to be removed. The crankshaft sprocket does not need pulling off.
8 The backplate can now be removed.

## 15 Camshaft - removal

The camshaft runs directly in the block without shell bearings. Unlike more conventionally designed cars, the camshaft drives pulleys or sprockets at both ends which means that it can only be removed once the engine is out of the car. The cylinder head must also be removed as must the tappets or cam followers, so must the distributor, its drive pinion and drive gear (see Chapter 4) and so must the fuel pump (see Chapter 3).
2 Remove the pulley at the end of the camshaft nearest the flywheel. It is held by three setscrews and spring washers. It should fall off as it is only a face to face fit.
3 The 845 cc camshaft removal was described in the previous section as its removal is necessary to facilitate timing gear and chain removal.
4 The 1100 cc camshaft is removed in the same way as that of the 845 cc once the sprocket has been removed.
5 Do not damage the lobes.

14.2 Camshaft pulley is very similar for both models

14.5 Once on properly it pulled the crankshaft sprocket easily 845 cc

14.6 The sprocket and camshaft come away together with the timing chain

## 16 Sump - removal

1   The sump may be removed with the engine and gearbox in the car and, of course, with it out, provided the engine has been separated from the gearbox and is lying on its side. With the engine still in the car it is really arm aching work if you are lying on the ground under the car, it is not much better with the car on a ramp or over a pit.

2   Drain the sump of its oil. A 5 pint container is necessary. Replace the sump plug after five minutes.

3   Remove the anti-roll bar. Chapter 10, Section 3.

4   Undo the four bolts which hold the tubular crossmember between the chassis rails and the suspension mounting brackets. Then remove the crossmember altogether.

5   Undo the four bolts which locate its front edge to the gearbox if still fitted in the car. These are clearly visible.

6   With a long screwdriver undo the two setscrews which have cuts in their heads first. These are located at the rear of the sump and must be got at by passing the screwdriver through the two holes in the floor of the car close to the edge. This will not apply with the engine out of the car.

7   Undo and remove all the sump setscrews which remain. (Two at the front end will be nuts on locating studs). Catch the square star washers. Lower the sump and remove the gasket which should come away in four parts.

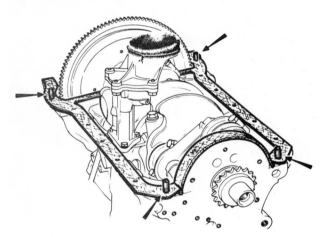

Fig. 1.5A. 845 cc Sump gasket positioning
(Note exact position of cork end piece)

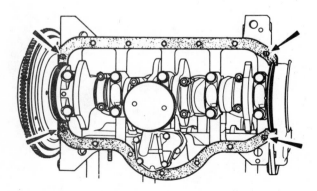

Fig.1.5B 1100 cc Sump gasket positioning
(Note positioning of plastic end pieces)

## 17 Oil pump - removal

1   The oil pump may be removed from the engine whilst the engine is still in the car, It is necessary first of all to remove the sump. As the oil pump drive spindle also drives the distributor, care must be taken to ensure that the ignition timing is not lost when the oil pump is removed and eventually replaced. It is, therefore, necessary also to remove the distributor cap and turn the engine until the rotor is in line with the number one plug high tension lead contact. The timing marker on the crankshaft pulley wheel must then also be against the top dead centre position. For full details of engine timing refer to Chapter 4.

2   Once the crankshaft has been set to the correct position the distributors should be removed. By looking down into the distributor mounting opening it will be possible to see the top of the oil pump spindle and the position of the offset slot. Take a careful note of this position.

3   The pump may be removed by undoing the three 10 mm setscrews. The inner of the three is difficult to get at with a spanner and much patience should be exercised with this screw. The pump should pull out together with its spacer face gasket.

## 18 Big end bearings, pistons, connecting rods and liners - removal

1   It is possible to remove the big end bearings, pistons, connecting rods and liners from the engine with the engine still in the car, provided that the sump has been removed in all cases and the cylinder head, the pistons, connecting rods and liners. With the engine removed from the car, the task is much easier and generally cleaner, but, of course, it is understood that if a quick emergency repair job is to be done and speed is of the essence, then it would be in order to do any work with the engine still in the car. The pistons and their connecting rods must be removed from the top of the engine once their connecting rod end caps have been removed (845cc models only. Pistons and connecting rods must be renewed together with liners in 1108cc engines). It will not be possible to do this with the improvised cylinder liner retainers in position. It must therefore be assumed that if a piston or pistons is removed that the liners will be disturbed and have to be replaced. It is possible to buy from Renault Limited under part numbers Mot 12 some special liner retainers quite cheaply which will retain the liners and allow pistons to be removed. It is a good idea if you are going to the extent of replacing the pistons to relocate and reseal the liners anyway at the same time cleaning the sludge away from their outside. But if speed is the essence - buy the proper liner retainers.

2   With the sump removed and the crankshaft exposed, each of the big end bearing caps can be detached after removing the two bolts and their locking washers (bend back the locking washers with a pair of pliers) which hold each cap to the connecting rod stud. Rotate the engine to bring each connecting rod cap into position for unscrewing the nuts.

3   With the nuts removed, each big end bearing cam can be pulled off. It must be noted that the connecting rods and big end caps are marked with a small punch mark on the end of the connecting rod and cap, which matches up on each one. If the same connecting rods and caps are to be re-used, they must be replaced exactly as they came out. The same applies to the big end bearing shells which will be released as soon as the connecting rods are detached from the crankshaft. It is inadvisable to re-use these shells anyway, but if they are not renewed they must be put back in exactly the same location from which they came.

4   If any difficulty is experienced in removing the big end bearing caps from the studs of the connecting rods, it will help if the crankshaft is revolved in order to dislodge them. If this is done, however, care must be taken to ensure that nothing gets jammed when the connecting rod comes away from the crank-

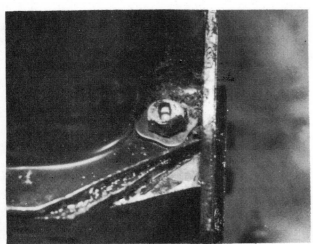

16.6 One of the special sump bolts and square washers

17.2 Check the distributor drive setting before removing

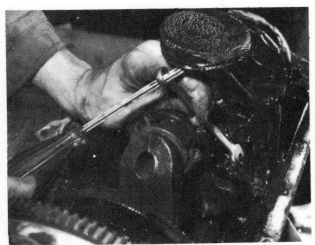

17.3 A satisfactory way of undoing the inner oil, pump screw

shaft on the top of its stroke. Once released, connecting rods and pistons can be pushed up through the cylinder bores and out of the top of the block on 845cc engines. For 1108cc engines it will be necessary to remove the piston connecting rod and liner at the same time, and then to withdraw the piston connecting rod through the bore of each liner. Once the pistons are removed, ensure that they are kept in such a way that they can be individually identified and replaced in the same bore if necessary.

5   845cc engines: If you have had to leave the liner retainers off, you should now remove the liners. If they are still fitted and you wish to remove the liners for reboring or replacement, now remove the retainers.

6   To remove the liners, or liners and pistons/connecting rods, tap the bottom of the liners from beneath with a piece of wood which will not tend to split. If you hit them with steel of any kind they will crack without fail and will be instant scrap.

7   Tap all four loose before you remove one. Lift them upwards and note where they were fitted and which way round. Provided you have drained the cooling system well, little liquid sediment will be left although there will almost certainly be a lot of rust particles there. If the crankshaft is to remain in the block, cover it as well as you can from below with non-fluffy rag to stop the likelihood of liquid or sediment falling on the journal surfaces - it will not actually do them any harm but it is difficult to remove when you are ready to reassemble. Only now remove the metal 'figure of 8' rings which seal the liners to the block. These can be either of copper or composition and vary in thickness.

### 19 Gudgeon pins - removal

The gudgeon pins will be removed if it is desired to fit new pistons to the existing connecting rods or vice versa. The gudgeon pins are held in position by a circlip in each side of the piston and after this is removed with circlip pliers only, any carbon should be cleaned away. Warm the piston and connecting rod assemblies, preferably in warm oil, when the gudgeon pin can be pushed out with the finger. If the piston is cold and the gudgeon pin is tight, it should not be forced out.

### 20 Flywheel - removal

1   The flywheel may be removed with the engine in the car provided that the gearbox and clutch assemblies sump are removed first. The flywheel would normally be removed in these circumstances for purposes of renewing the starter ring, which may have damaged teeth, or because of a badly scored face due to a badly worn clutch friction disc.

2   With the gearbox and clutch removed as described in Chapter 6 and 5 respectively, the four bolt heads which secure the flywheel to the crankshaft flange will come into view. These bolts are locked into position by tab washers. Knock back the tabs and then undo and remove the four securing bolts. It may be necessary to lock the flywheel to obtain leverage on the securing bolts. Use a screwdriver on the starter ring and lock it onto the block. It is obvious where to do this. As there are two positions to locate the dowel pin in the crankshaft flange it is necessary to mark the exact locating position of the flywheel. Note the position of the dowel pin relative to the machined timing cut on the edge of the flywheel. The flywheel is located to the crankshaft flange on a register and is positioned by a dowel pin. It will be necessary to use a little leverage in order to draw the flywheel off and great care should be taken that it does not come off with a sudden jerk and fall down. One way of preventing this is by putting a stud, another, longer bolt with the head sawn off, into one of the bolt holes so that when the flywheel comes free, the end of the stud will support it. Should the locating dowel come out, replace it in the crankshaft immediately - in the correct position!

## 21 Crankshaft and main bearing removal

1   It is only possible to inspect and replace some of the main bearing shells with the engine still in the car (not the front or rear ones) at least for all practical purposes. For this reason if you want to be really sure of an adequate inspection and replacement of these bearings, they must only be looked at as a total operation: i.e., the main bearings together, and this can only be done with the engine out of the car and the timing cover removed. Main bearings seldom need replacing by themselves, it is more than likely that further overhaul is necessary and therefore the engine is likely to be out of the car.

2   With the engine removed from the car it is necessary for the sump, oil pump, timing cover and gear (but not crankshaft sprocket) to be removed, together with the flywheel. It is also desirable that the cylinder head should have been removed so that the engine may be stood inverted. If the liners are to be retained the engine should be placed on its side.

3   The connecting rod bearing caps should all have been removed and, of course, this will have been done if the pistons are being removed from the engine as well.

4   Using a good quality socket spanner remove the two bolts from each of the three main bearing caps. Then lift off each of the caps.

5   With the main bearing caps removed the crankshaft may be carefully lifted out of the block and it should then be placed somewhere safe where it cannot fall or be damaged. The upper half main bearing shells may then be removed from the crankcase, together with the semi-circular thrust washers fitted at the centre main bearing.

20.2 Mark the flywheel for exact replacement

## 22 Lubrication system - description

The engine has a very basic but effective oil flow system. Oil from the sump is pumped by the submerged oil pump up to the centre main bearing and then up to the main oil gallery under pressure. From there it is distributed through drillings to the other main bearings, the big end bearing, the camshaft bearing surfaces, the rocker shafts and arms, the timing gear and the cylinder bores. A film of oil should be maintained on all these surfaces by this method. There are normally adequate gaskets to keep the oil inside the block at the sump, rocker cover and timing cover and aluminium plugs at each end of the oil gallery. Two types of oil seal thrower stop the oil leaking at the ends of the crankshaft. Oil drips back into the sump to be recirculated. There is no removable oil filter on early models, a gauze filter is, however, fitted to the oil pump inlet to keep the worst sludge at bay.

## 23 Engine mountings - removal

1   The engine mountings (those fixed to the engine block) are basically rubber blocks which connect and hold the engine onto the chassis rails. They are mounted either side, half way along the block and are not interchangeable. They can be replaced individually with the engine in the car provided the engine is supported suitably.

2   The right hand side mounting is a simple metal fabrication which is stuck to the hard rubber block. This has to be replaced as a unit and is held to the engine block by three setscrews. Undo the nut which locates the rubber block to the chassis rail then, with the engine suitably supported (if still in the car), unscrew the three setscrews, one will have to be located from underneath the car. The mounting block will then come away as will the coil mounting bracket, but separately. The chassis rail mount can be removed by undoing four bolts which pass through the chassis and be lifted away.

3   The left hand side mounting is constructed with two metal fabrications, one acting as a brace to the other on which is stuck the hard rubber block. However three setscrews can be undone after the one nut locating the block to the chassis rail has been undone, and the two fabrications will come away together (one is bolted at right angles to the other). Only the one fabrication attached to the rubber block need be replaced. The chassis rail mount can be removed in the same way as the one on the right hand side.

### PART 2 – EXAMINATION AND RENOVATION

## 24 Engine - examination

1   Examination of an engine runs in two phases. The first is a visual and aural examination when it is running and in the car, and the second is when it is out of the car, having decided that something is wrong and needs repairing. It is a matter to decide when to take the car off the road, and do something about putting right whatever faults may be. In general, if the oil and fuel consumption are perfectly reasonable, the performance is satisfactory, and it is not suffering from overheating, under-heating, or any other fault which causes aggravation and irritation on the road to a large degree, it is best left alone. Provided the regular maintenance requirements are carried out there is no need to take it to pieces.

2   The first indications of an engine becoming worn (if one has not been able to get the exact mileage that the engine has travelled) are an increase in oil consumption and possibly a corresponding increase in fuel consumption. This may also be accompanied by a falling off in performance. On any car it is not always easy to detect a falling off in performance and it is quite a good idea to drive another car of the same type which is known to be in very good condition, to make a comparison. If the signs are that the engine is performing poorly, using too much petrol and beginning to burn oil, then one of the first things to do is to test the compression in each cylinder with a proper compression testing gauge. This will indicate whether the pistons are leaking in the cylinders or the valves are leaking in the head. Depending on the results, the cylinder head may be removed and further examination carried out to the bores and head as described in subsequent Sections. Early action at this stage could well restore the engine to a satisfactory condition. Furthermore, such action would not call for a great deal of either money or time. If the condition is left, however, it will get progressively worse until such a time as the simple repairs which would have been needed earlier have reached the stage where more major operations are necessary. This will be proportionately much more expensive and time consuming.

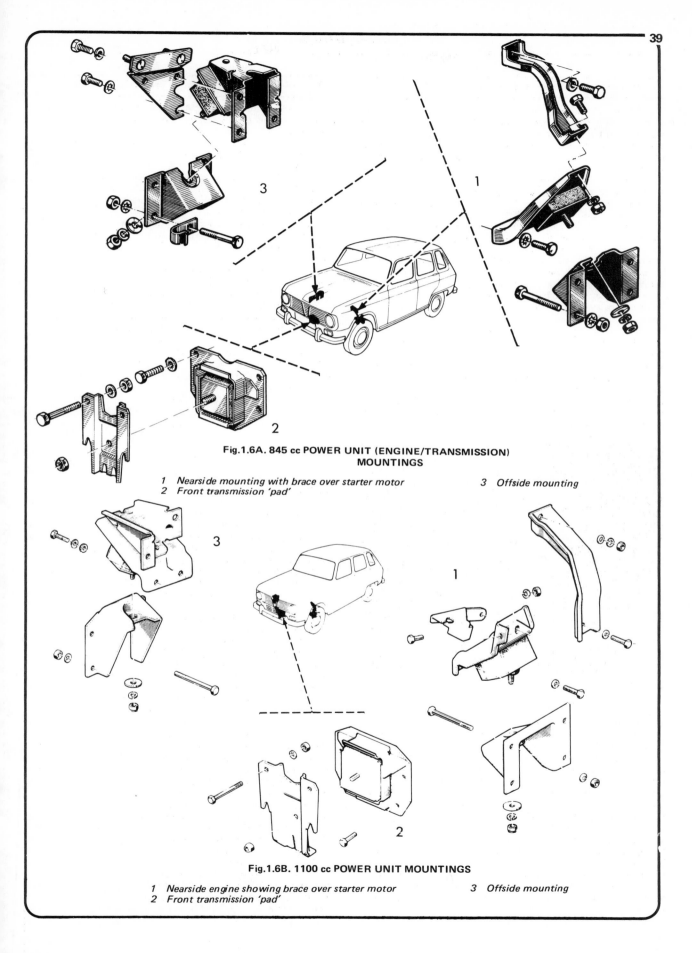

**Fig.1.6A. 845 cc POWER UNIT (ENGINE/TRANSMISSION) MOUNTINGS**

1  Nearside mounting with brace over starter motor
2  Front transmission 'pad'

3  Offside mounting

**Fig.1.6B. 1100 cc POWER UNIT MOUNTINGS**

1  Nearside engine showing brace over starter motor
2  Front transmission 'pad'

3  Offside mounting

## 25 Crankshaft and main bearings - examination and renovation

1  With the crankshaft removed examine all the crankpins and main bearing journals for signs of scoring or scratches. If all the surfaces of the bearing journals are obviously undamaged, check next that all the journals are round. This can be done with a micrometer or caliper gauge, taking readings across the diameter of each journal at six or seven points. If you do not own a micrometer or know how to use one, you should have little difficulty at any garage that has good mechanics to get someone to measure it for you.

2  If the crankshaft has ridges or severe score marks in it, it must be reground. The manufacturers of the Renault go further and say that a crankshaft in this condition should be renewed but as this can be a very expensive procedure, it is felt that regrinding should suffice in all but the most extrodinary situation. If there are no signs of ridging or severe scoring of the journals, it may be that the measurements indicate that the journals are not round. If the amount of ovality exceeds 0,002 inch it is possible that regrinding may be necessary. Certainly if it is more than this figure it is necessary. Here again it is best to get the advice of someone who is experienced and familiar with crankshafts and regrinding them to give an opinion.

3  The main bearing shells themselves are normally a matt grey in colour all over and should have no signs of pitting or ridging or discolouration as this usually indicates that the surface bearing metal has worn away and the backing material is showing through. It is worthwhile renewing the main bearing shells anyway if you have gone to the trouble of removing the crankshaft, but they must, of course, be renewed if there is any sign of damage to them or if the crankshaft has been reground. When the crankshaft is reground the diameter is reduced and consequently one must obtain the proper undersized bearing shells to fit. These will normally be supplied by the firm which has reground the crankshaft. Regrinding is normally done in multiples of 0.010 inch as necessary and bearing shells are obtainable to suit these standard regrinding sizes. If the crankshaft is not being reground, yet bearing shells are being renewed, make sure that you check whether or not the crankshaft has been reground once before. This will be indicated by looking at the back of the bearing shell and this will indicate whether or not it is minus 0.010 inch or more. The same type of shell bearing must be used when they are renewed.

## 26 Big end bearings - examination and renovation

The connecting rod, or big end bearings, are subject to wear at a greater rate than those for crankshaft. Signs that one or more big end bearings is getting badly worn are a pronounced knocking noise from the engine, accompanied by a significant drop in oil pressure due to the increased clearance between the bearing and the journal permitting oil to flow more freely through the resultantly larger space. If this should happen quite suddenly and action is taken immediately, and by immediately is meant within a few miles, then it is possible that the bearing shell may be replaced without any further work needing to be done. If this happens in an engine which has been neglected and oil changes and oil filter changes (on those models so fitted) have not been carried out as they should have been, it is most likely that the rest of the engine is in a pretty terrible state anyway. If it occurs in an engine which has been recently overhauled, then it is almost certainly due to a piece of grit or swarf which has got into the oil circulation system and finally come to rest in the bearing shell and scored it. It is in these instances where a replacement of the shell alone accompanied by a thorough flush out of the lubrication system may be all that is required.

## 27 Cylinder liner bores - examination and renovation

1  The liner bores may be examined for wear either in or out of the engine block; the cylinder head must, of course, be removed in each case. If the liners are still in the block and it is hoped that they will not need renovation the liner retainers must be left in place so that relocation does not have to take place. However, if you have got to the stage where the pistons are out it is better to remove the liners for inspection even if they do not require renovation. Relocation itself does not take much time, skill or money. Each bore may be examined in turn with the piston at the bottom of its stroke. A perfect cylinder is, as its name implies, perfectly cylindrical in shape. That is, the sides are parallel and a cross section is perfectly circular.

2  First of all examine the top of the cylinder about a quarter of an inch below the top of the liner and with the finger feel if there is any ridge running round the circumference of the bore. In a worn cylinder bore a ridge will develop at the point where the top ring on the piston comes to the uppermost limit of its stroke. An excessive ridge indicates that the bore below the ridge is worn. If there is no ridge, it is reasonable to assume that the cylinder is not badly worn. Measurement of the diameter of the cylinder bore both in line with the piston gudgeon pin and at right angles to it, at the top and bottom of the cylinder, is also another check to be made. A cylinder is expected to wear at the sides where the thrust of the piston presses against it. In time this causes the cylinder to assume an oval shape. Furthermore, the top of the cylinder is likely to wear more than the bottom of the cylinder. It will be necessary to use a proper bore measuring instrument in order to measure the differences in bore diameter across the cylinder and variations between the top and bottom ends of the cylinder. As a general guide it may be assumed that any variations more than 0.010 inch indicates that the liners need renewing. Provided all variations are less than 0.010 inch it is probable that the fitting of new piston rings will cure the problems of piston to cylinder bore clearances. Once again it is difficult to give a firm ruling on this as so much depends on the amount of time and effort which the individual owner is prepared or wishes tp spend on the task. Certainly, if the cylinder bores are obviously deeply grooved or scored, they must be renewed regardless of any measurement differences in the cylinder diameter. If the engine has been removed from the car for overhaul anyway, any cylinder bore wear in excess of 0.005 inch certainly qualifies it for new liners, to do otherwise would be a waste of time and effort. However, one must bear in mind again the fact that new liners will require the fitment of new pistons and the expense of this once again could affect the owner's decision.

Cylinder liners and pistons are available as matching sets.

## 28 Connecting rods, pistons and piston rings - examination and renovation

1  Pistons and rings are normally examined in relation to the cylinder bores. With the cylinder head removed it is possible to check the amount of movement between the piston and the wall, both visually and with the aid of a feeler gauge. Liner retainers must be fitted. If the condition of the bores seems to be satisfactory, any excessive clearances between piston and bore (0.010 inch and upwards) could be due to wear of the piston itself. Piston ring wear is almost certain to have taken place also if this is the case, and will necessitate removal of the pistons for further examination. First of all, look for signs of damage to the piston ring grooves, and to the sides of the piston where scoring may be apparent. Any deep scoring or any obvious breakage between the piston ring grooves and the top of the piston will, of course, call

for a new piston. If the pistons do not appear worn or damaged, next check the clearance between the piston rings and the piston ring grooves. This can be done with a feeler gauge and if it is in excess of the specified clearances the pistons should be renewed. Excessive clearance between the rings and the grooves allows the rings to chatter and they will break very easily. Unfortunately, the wear usually occurs on the piston rather than on the piston rings, although new rings should be used as a check before condemning the pistons.

2  To check the condition of the rings it will be necessary to remove them from the piston. Only the top ring on each piston need be checked and, in fact, if one of these piston rings is bad it is reasonable to assume that the others will be similar and the whole lot should be renewed. Remove the top piston ring by spreading the ends apart sufficiently to enable it to be pulled out of the groove and over the top of the piston. Care must be taken not to twist the ring or draw it off unevenly, otherwise it could easily break. The ring should then be placed inside the cylinder bore from which it came pressed down approximately two inches. It should lie perfectly horizontal across the bore and this can be achieved by using a piston from which all the rings have been removed to press it down square. Then the gap between the ends of the piston rings should be measured with a feeler gauge; if the piston ring gap exceeds that specified then the piston ring is worn out and should be replaced. If the top ring is worn it is reasonable to assume that the other two are worn on the same pistons as well. Rings are normally only obtainable in sets anyway so any thoughts of economy by renewing one or two rings on a set of four pistons are really not worthwhile.

3  Provided the engine has not seized up or had some other calamitous damage caused to it, it is most unlikely that the connecting rods are in need of renewal at any time. In cases of seizure one or more could have become bent and to check this they will need setting up on a special jig. This is normally only within the competence of a specialist engineering organisation.

4  See Section 18 of this Chapter for details of the removal and refitting of new pistons, gudgeon pins and small end bushes.

## 29 Valve rocker gear - examination and renovation

Each rocker should move freely on the rocker shaft without any signs of looseness or slackness. If any slackness is apparent it will be necessary to dismantle the assembly. If either the rocker bushes in the rocker arms and/or pedestals or the rocker shaft are obviously scored and worn at those points where the rockers are pivoting then they shuold be renewed. The rockers themselves should also be examined on the faces where they bear onto the top of the valve stems and if signs of wear are excessive they should also be renewed.

## 30 Cylinder head, valves, valve springs and guides - examination and renovation

1  Once the cylinder head has been removed, it should be placed upon a work bench so that a thorough examination can be carried out.

2  First of all, all the valves should be removed.

3  The valves should be examined for signs of pitting or burning, particularly around their egdes and where they seat into the cylinder head. If the valves are very much contaminated with carbon, this should first of all be removed with a wire brush. Very hard spots of carbon may need chipping off with the edge of a very hard blade or tool. Be very careful, it is an aluminium head! Exhaust valves are the ones most likely to suffer from burning and if this is apparently quite severe, then the valves should be discarded. Next replace each valve into its own guide, after thoroughly cleaning the guide and valve stem, and check to see that there is no sideways movement of the valve in the guide. A very small amount of play is permissible but if it is very considerable, then it means that oil and exhaust gases can all make their way past the stem of the valve and this is not

conductive to good performance. If the guides are obviously badly worn, then it will be necessary to have new ones fitted, together with new valves. The fitting of valve guides on this engine is a specialist task as they have to be reamed out to give a very close tolerance after fitting. If it is thought that the wear is on the valve stem rather than in the guide, the best way to check is to obtain a new valve and try it in position.

4  If the valves are apparently in good general condition the next thing to do is to examine the valve seats themselves in the cylinder head. Here again, there should be no signs of pitting or burning. The valve seats should also be checked to make sure there are no cracks. If there are signs of damage to the seat in any way, then the head itself may need fitting with a new valve seat inserts. Possibly, the existing valve seats may be recut. Give this job to a specialist. Provided the valves and seats are in good condition, then it is possible to reseat them by grinding in position using a carborundum paste. This grinding-in process should also be carried out when a new valve is being fitted.

5  The carborundum paste used for this job is normally supplied in a double ended tin with coarse paste at one end and fine paste at the other. In addition, a suction tool for holding the valve head so that it may be rotated is also required. To grind in a valve, first smear a trace of the coarse paste onto the seat face and fit the suction grinder to the valve head. Then with a semi-rotary motion grind the valve head into its seat, lifting the valve occasionally to redistribute the grinding paste. When a dull matt continuous line is produced on both the valve seat and the valve then the paste can be wiped off. Apply a little fine paste and finish off the grinding process. If a light spring is placed over the valve stem behind the head this can often be of assistance in raising the valve from time to time against the pressure of the grinding tool so as to redistribute the paste evenly round the job. The width of the line which is produced after grinding should not be more than 1.8 mm. If, after a moderate amount of grinding, it is apparent that the seating line is much wider than this then it means that the seat has already probably been cut back once or more times previously, or else the valve has been ground several times. Here again, specialist advice is best sought on occasions such as this.

6  After each valve has been ground in, the traces of carborundum paste which will remain in the area of the seat and inlet port must be thoroughly flushed away with paraffin. If possible, a high pressure air line should be used to blow away the final traces. Obviously particles of carborundum grit are not wanted anywhere inside the engine.

7  Before the valves are finally replaced, all traces of carbon should be cleaned from them and also from the cylinder head itself. A wire cup brush and an electric drill are very useful in doing this work in the head. The face of the cylinder head should also be scraped perfectly clean and free from accumulations of carbon which may be upon it. Do not use any abrasive paper for cleaning but rather a flat bladed scraper. Make sure that no odd particles of gasket or carbon fall into the orifices in the casting. If they should, get them blown out.

8  Examine all the valve springs to make sure that they are of the correct length according to the specifications. It will have been noticed when they were being removed whether any were broken, and if they are then they should be renewed. It is a good idea to renew all the valve springs anyway. If you have reached this stage it is false economy not to do so. They are relatively cheap.

9  It is a good idea to renew the valve spring seating washers which sit directly on the cylinder head. These wear reasonably quickly.

10  Before reassembling the valves and springs to the cylinder head make a final check that everything is thoroughly clean and free from grit and then lightly smear all the valve stems with engine oil prior to reassembly.

## 31 Timing chain and sprockets - examination and renovation

Examine the teeth of both sprockets for wear. Each tooth on

the sprocket is in the shape of an inverted V and if the side of the tooth is concave in shape it is an indication that the tooth is worn badly and the sprocket should therefore be renewed. If the sprockets are worn and have to be renewed then the chains should also be renewed. If the sprockets are satisfactory, examine the chain to make sure there is no play between the links and if the chain is held out it should not bend when held horizontal. In view of the relative cheapness of these items it is worthwhile putting on a new chain anyway. Examine the tensioner pivot for signs of excessive wear which could cause rattling and also the tensioner itself. If the chain has gouged a deep groove into the tensioner renew it.

## 32 Camshaft and tappets - examination and renovation

1   The camshaft lobes should be examined for signs of flats or scoring or any other form of wear and damage. At the same time the tappets should also be examined, particularly on the faces where they bear against the camshaft, for signs of wear. If the case hardened surfaces of the cam lobes or tappet faces have been penetrated it will be quite obvious as there will be a darker, rougher pitted appearance to the surface in question. In such cases, the tappet of the camshaft will need renewal. Where the camshaft or tappet surface is still bright and clean and showing slight signs of wear it is best left alone. Any attempt to reface either will only result in the case hardened surface being reduced in thickness with the possibilty of extreme and rapid wear later on.

2   The skew gear in the camshaft which drives the oil pump shaft and indirectly the distributor also should be examined for signs of extreme wear on the teeth. Here again if the skew gear teeth are badly worn and ridged, it will mean renewal of the complete camshaft. This is quite probable on 'tired' engines. Examine also in conjunction with this the teeth on the driven gear.

3   The camshaft bearing journals should be perfectly smooth and show no signs of pitting or scoring as they are relatively free from stress. If the bearing surfaces are scored or discoloured it would suggest that the camshaft is not 'running true'. This will certainly mean camshaft renewal - if very bad have your local engineering works or Renault agent check the alignment of the block and the camshaft as the camshaft runs directly in the block. Proprietary camshafts replacement bearings are not available. Fortunately, it is rare for the camshaft journals and bearings to wear out at anything like the same rate as the rest of the engine. Having ascertained that the faces of the tappets are satisfactory, check also that the tappets are not a loose fit in their respective bores. It is not likely that they are loosely fitting, but if so they should be renewed.

## 33 Flywheel - examination and renovation

1   There are two areas in which the flywheel may have been worn or damaged. Firstly, is on the driving face where the clutch friction plate bears against it. Should the clutch plate have been permitted to wear down beyond the level of the rivets, it is possible that the flywheel has been scored. If this scoring is severe it may be necessary to have it refaced or even renewed.

2   The other part to examine is the teeth of the starter ring gear around the periphery of the flywheel. If several of the teeth are broken or missing, or the front edges of all teeth are obviously very badly chewed up, then it would be advisable to fit a new ring gear.

3   The old ring gear can be removed by cutting a slot with a hacksaw down between two of the teeth as far as possible, without cutting into the flywheel itself. Once the cut is made a chisel will split the ring gear which can then be drawn off. To fit a new ring gear requires it to be heated first to a temperature of 220°C, no more. This is best done in a bath of oil or an oven, but not, preferable, with a naked flame. It is much more difficult to spread and heat evenly and control it to the required

temperature with a naked flame. Once the ring gear has attained the correct temperature it can be placed onto the flywheel making sure that it beds down properly onto the register. It should then be allowed to cool down naturally. If by mischance, the ring gear is overheated, it should not be used. The temper will have been lost, therefore softening it, and it will wear out in a very short space of time.

4   Although it is not actually fitted into the flywheel itself, there is a bush in the centre of the crankshaft flange onto which the flywheel fits. Although this bush is more correctly associated with the gearbox or clutch it is mentioned here as well as it would be a pity to ignore it whilst carrying out work on the flywheel. If it shows signs of wear it should be renewed. If suitable extractors are not available to get it out another method is to fill the recess with grease and then drive in a piece of close fitting steel bar. This should force the bush out. A new bush may be pressed in.

## 34 Oil pump - examination and renovation

1   Only work on the oil pump with it removed from the block.

2   Unscrew the four setscrews which hold the cover face and filter to the main body.

3   Take care with the ball seating boss, the ball bearing and the pressure relief spring which will come away when the cover face is removed.

4   Take out the driven gear and then the drive gear and the shaft.

5   Clean all the parts with petrol or paraffin and check the condition of the splines on the drive shaft. They should be unchewed and straight.

6   Check the condition of the ball bearing and its seating. There should be no irregularity nor ridges in either. The ball should be replaced anyway if you have reached this stage.

7   Check the spring. If possible replace it anyway at this stage. Obtain the correct replacement without fail.

8   Check the clearance between the pump gears and their body. If over 0.20 mm replace the gears. Also check the cover joint face for marks and irregularities. Replace if scored.

9   It may be found that if two or more parts need replacing that it is more economic and quicker to replace the whole pump. There is no exchange scheme.

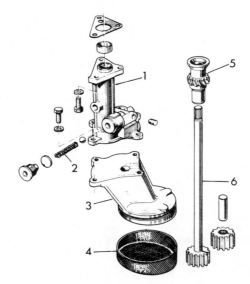

### Fig. 1.7A. 845 cc OIL PUMP COMPONENTS

| | |
|---|---|
| 1   Top body | 4   Gauze filter |
| 2   Relief valve mechanism | 5   Distributor /camshaft drive |
| 3   Lower body | 6   Shaft and pump rotors |

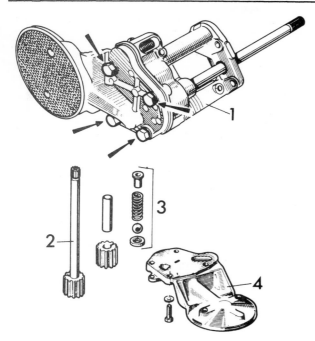

Fig. 1.7B. 1100 cc OIL PUMP COMPONENTS

1   *Arrows show two halves fixings*
2   *Shaft and pump rotors*
3   *Relief valve mechanism*
4   *Lower body*

## 35 Inlet/exhaust manifold - inspection

Exhaust and inlet manifolds should be examined for signs of cracks or other breakages, particularly on the mounting lugs. The mating faces of both manifolds where they join the cylinder head should be examined to make sure that they are completely flat and free from pitting or burrs of any sort. Use a straight edge to check the faces of the manifold for distortion. If there is any distortion or signs of severe pitting or burning the manifold should be renewed. Provided the manifolds are sound, accumulations of carbon within the ports may be removed with a wire brush or scraper.

## 36 Decarbonisation

1   Modern engines, together with modern fuels and lubricants have virtually nullified the need for the engine to have a 'decoke' which was common enough only a few years ago. Carbon deposits are formed mostly on the modern engine only when it has to do a great deal of slow speed, stop/start running, for example, in busy traffic conditions. If carbon deposit symptoms are apparent, such as pinking or pre-ignition and running on after the engine has been switched off, then a good high speed run on a motorway or straight stretch of road is usually sufficient to clear these deposits out. It is beneficial to any motor car to give it a good high speed run from time to time.
2   There will always be some carbon deposits, of course, so if the occasion demands the removal of the cylinder head for some reason or another, it is a good idea to remove the carbon deposits when the opportunity presents itself. Carbon deposits in the combustion chambers of the cylinder head can be dealt with as described under the section head 'Cylinder head - inspection and renovation'. The other carbon deposits which have to be dealt with are those on the crowns of the pistons. This work can easily be carried out with the engine in the car, but great care must be taken to ensure that no particles of dislodged carbon fall

either into the cylinder bores and down past the piston rings or into the water jacket orifices in the cylinder block. Liner retainers must be fitted.
3   Bring the first piston to be cleaned to the top of its stroke and then using a sheet of strong paper and some self adhesive tape, mask off the other three cylinders and surrounding block to prevent any particles falling into the open orifice in the block. To prevent small particles of dislodged carbon from finding their way down the side of the piston which is actually being decarbonised press grease into the gap between the piston and the cylinder wall. Carbon deposits should then be scraped away carefully with a flat blade from the top of the crown of the piston and the surrounding top edge of the cylinder. Great care must be taken to ensure that the scraper does not gouge away into the soft aluminium surface of the piston crown.
4   A wire brush, either operated by hand or a power drill, should not be used if decarbonising is being done with the engine still in the car. It is virtually impossible to prevent carbon particles being distributed over a large area and the time saved by this method is very little.
5   After each piston has been attended to clean out the grease and carbon particles from the gap where it has been pressed in. As the engine is revolved to bring the next piston to the top of its stroke for attention, check the bore of the cylinder which has just been decarbonised and make sure that no traces of carbon or grease are adhering to the inside of the bore.

## PART 3 – REASSEMBLY AND REPLACEMENT

## 37 Engine reassembly - general

It is during the process of engine reassembly that the job is either made a success or a failure. From the very word go there are three basic rules which it is folly to ignore, namely:
1   Absolute cleanliness. The working area, the components of the engine and the hands of those working on the engine must be completely free of grime and grit. One small piece of carborundum dust or swarf can ruin a big end in no time, and nulify all the time and effort you have spent. No matter what the pundits say this engine and its other components can be reconditioned and rebuilt very successfully and continue working efficiently. It is necessary to rebuild this engine in operating theatre conditions - warmth, light and space.
2   ALWAYS, no matter what the circumstances may be, use new gaskets, locking tabs, seals, nyloc nuts and any other parts mentioned in the Sections in this Chapter. It is pointless to dismantle an engine, spend considerable money and time on it and then to waste all this for the sake of something as small as a failed oil seal. Delay the rebuilding if necessary.
3   Don't rush it. The most skilled and experienced mechanic can easily make a mistake if he is rushed.
4   Check that all nuts and bolts are clean and in good condition and ideally renew all spring washers, lockwasher and tab washers as a matter of course. A supply of clean engine oil and clean cloths (to wipe excessive clean oil off your hands only!) and a torque spanner are the only things which should be required in addition to all the tools used in dismantling the engine.

## 38 Engine block preparation

1   Assuming that the engine has been completely stripped for reconditioning and that the block is now bare, before any reassembly takes place it must be thoroughly cleaned both inside and out.
2   The ideal situation is to dip the block in a garage's cleaning tank usually filled with a mixture of paraffin and cleaning fluid, and then to leave it submerged for an hour or so. Then get to work on it with a wire brush and screwdriver. Clean out all the crevices, do not scratch any machined surfaces, and scrub both the inside and out. The tappet chest is prone to hide sludge. A great deal of sediment often collects around the liner seatings.

Chip this away if necessary.

3   Hose down the block with a garden hose and if possible dry it off with an air jet. Dry and thoroughly clean out the block with non-fluffy rag until it is spotless. The water will not make it go rusty provided you dry it off well.

4   Clean out all the oilways with a test tube/bottle brush and finally dry these. You should now not need to worry if you had to eat your lunch from the side of the block!

5   Check the two oil gallery aluminium plugs at each end of the block and the two screw-in camshaft bearing plugs on the top of the block. These should be solidly intact and show no signs of being weepy. If they do, drill a hole in their centre and cork-screw them out. Tap and peen in new ones very gently. These are supplied with the gasket sets necessary for the rest of the overhaul. (If you reluctant to do this job ask your engineering works to do it for you - it is, however, quite easy).

## 39 Crankshaft and main bearing - reassembly

1   Stand the cylinder block inverted on the bench and gather together the bearing caps, new bearing shells and have the crankshaft without the flywheel fitted alongside line up in the way in wich it will eventually be placed into the cylinder block. Make sure that the oilways in the crankshaft are all quite clear.

2   Make sure that the bearing housings in the cylinder block are perfectly clean and smooth in preparation for the fitting of the top halves of the main bearing shells. Each bearing shell has an oil hole in it, some have two, and this must line up with the corres-ponding hole in the cylinder block. Each shell is notched, and this notch also must line up with the corresponding notch in the cylinder block. Carefilly fit each shell into its proper position, taking care not to bend, distort or scratch it in any way. When they are in position lubricate the shells with a liberal quantity if clean engine oil.

3   Making sure that the crankshaft is the right way round, next pick up and very carefully lower it square and straight into position on the shell bearings in the crankcase. (photo)

4   Again, make sure that the bearing caps are perfectly clean and fit the shells so that the notches in their ends line up and fit snugly into the grooves in the bearing caps. There are no oilways in the bearing caps so that the holes in the end bearing shells will not line up with anything. (photo)

5   The crankshaft end float is controlled by two semi-circular thrust washers which fit at the sides of the centre main bearing journal. Place these in position and slide them round into the gap between the bearing housing and the flange of the crankshaft, making sure that the white metal/grooved face abut onto the crankshaft. Once these are in position the end float can be checked by pushing the crankshaft as far as it will go in one direction and measuring the gap between the face of the thrust washer and the machined surface of the flange with a feeler blade. End float should be between 0.05 and 0.23 mm. (Adjusting flanges of differing sizes are available - the correct ones should have been supplied with the new bearing by your machinists).

6   Next arrange all the bearing caps complete with their shells so that you know precisely where each one should go. They are easily identifiable by their particular shape. As there is the possibility of a seepage of oil through the end main bearing cap mating faces it is permissible to put a very thin smear of non-setting jointing compound onto the outside edge of the vertical face where the bearing cap locates into the crankcase. Lubricate the main journals of the crankshaft liberally with clean engine oil and place all the bearing caps in position and fit the bolts. The front main bearing cap has a machined front face and this must line up with the rear surface of the cylinder block. Make sure that this is done with a straight edge before finally tightening down the bolts.

7   When all the caps are settled correctly in position, tighten the bolts down evenly, starting at No 1, at the flywheel end and working to the opposite end, using a torque spanner, to the correct torque as given under the specifications. When this has

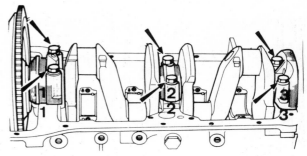

Fig. 1.8A. 845 cc crankshaft, 3 main bearings
(No. 1 next to flywheel)

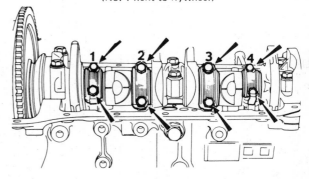

Fig. 1.8B. 845 cc crankshaft, big end bearing numbering
(No. 1 next to flywheel)

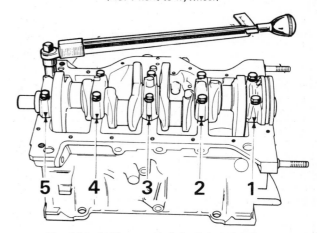

Fig. 1.8C. 1100 cc crankshaft, 5 main bearings
(No. 1 next to flywheel)

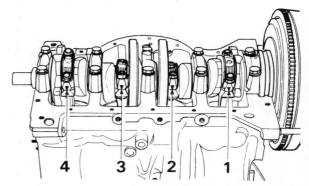

Fig. 1.8D. 1100 cc crankshaft, big end bearing numbering
(No. 1 next to flywheel)

39.2a This main bearing shell should locate like this (845 cc)

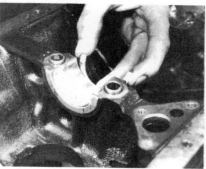

39.2b The thrust washers are being fitted

39.3 Lower the crankshaft very gently

39.4 The main bearing caps have no oil feed holes

39.6 All the main bearing caps are quite different from each other

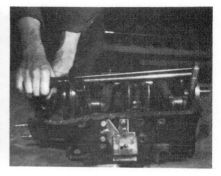

39.7 Exact torque settings are important so as not to strain the bolts

been done revolve the crankshaft to make sure that there are no intermittent tight spots. When viewed from the front of the car, the 845 cc crankshaft rotates in a clockwise direction while the 1100 cc crankshaft rotates in an anti-clockwise direction. Any sign that something is binding whilst the crankshaft is being revolved indicates that something is wrong and there may be a high spot on the bearings or on the crankshaft itself. This must be investigated or a damaged bearing could result.

8   Now fit the front main bearing oil seal. This is a circular oil seal, which has a very fragile inner lip. Always fit a new one. Oil it well with engine oil, and press it by hand into the correct position. Tap it gently fully home with a piece of wooden dowel until its fully in. There should be a slight recess between it and the outer edge of the block/bearing cap.

### 40 Pistons, gudgeon pins and connecting rods - reassembly

If new pistons are being fitted to the existing connecting rods, it is assumed that the fit of the new gudgeon pins which will be supplied with the pistons is correct in the small end bush of the connecting rod. There is a hole in the piston skirt, below the gudgeon pin, approximately 3.5 mm in diameter. This is to face towards the timing gear (rear) end of the block and the inclined face of the big end must face towards the right when seen from the same side as the hole in the piston. Make sure the piston is sufficiently warm to enable the gudgeon pin to slide easily through the bosses and then place the gudgeon pin halfway into the piston, insert the connecting rod the correct way round, and push the gudgeon pin completely home into position. Warm the piston in very hot water. Fit the circlips into the grooves on each end of the piston with circlip pliers to locate the gudgeon pin in position.

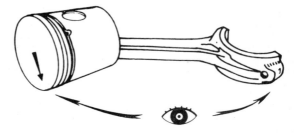

Fig. 1.9A. 845 cc - position of piston on connecting rod

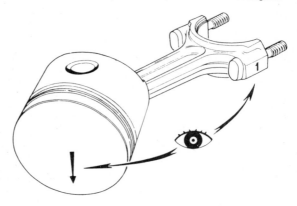

Fig. 1.9B. 1100 cc - position of piston on connecting rod

## 41 Piston rings - replacement on pistons

1   Before fitting new piston rings to the old pistons, make sure
the ring grooves in the piston are completely clean and free of
carbon deposits. A piece of old, broken piston ring is a useful
tool for doing this, but make sure that the sharp edge is not
permitted to gouge out any pieces of metal. Check also that the
specified gap between the edge of the new piston ring and the
groove is correct.

2   All rings must be fitted from the top of the piston. To get the
new rings into position involves spreading them sufficiently to
clear the diameter of the piston itself and then moving them
down over the existing grooves into their appropriate positions.
Care must be taken to avoid straining them to a point where
they could break. A piece of thin shim steel or an old feeler
gauge blade is a very useful means of guiding the ends of the
rings over the grooves to prevent them inadvertently dropping in,
rather than passing over each groove.

3   Before fitting the rings to the piston it is important to check
that the end gap matches the cylinder bore into which they will
eventually be fitted. Push the rings down the bores using the
piston until they are about 2½ inches below the top surface of
the top of the liner. Then measure the gap. If the gap is too large
you have either got the wrong piston rings or the cylinder bores
are worn more than you had anticipated. If the gap is too small
then it will be necessary to remove a piece of material from the
end of the ring. The gap may be increased to the correct specification by clamping the end of the ring in a vice so that a very
small portion of the end projects above the top of the vice. Then
use a fine file to take off the material in very small quantities at
a time. Do not clamp the ring so that the end being filed projects
too far above the vice jaws or it may easily be snapped off while
the filing is being done.

4   When every ring has been checked and the gaps made correct
the rings should be assembled to the piston to prevent them
being mixed up with other rings which will be fitted to other
bores. Fit the bottom scraper ring first placing it over the top of
the piston and spreading the ends. Move it down the piston a
little at a time, taking care to prevent it from snagging in the
grooves over which it will pass. The next ring to be fitted is the
lower compression ring and this only goes on one way up. The
top edge of the ring will be marked 'top' and this, of course,
should go uppermost. Don't be misled into thinking that this
means that the ring is the top one on the piston. The top
compression ring, which is the last one to go on the can be fitted
either way up on the piston. When all the rings are in position in
their grooves, try and arrange the gaps to be equally spaced
around the piston. Place the gap of the oil control ring over an
undrilled portion of the groove. Obviously, if the gaps of all the
rings are in a straight line there will be a much greater tendency
for compression loss at that point.

41.4 Place the ring gaps at 120 degree intervals round the piston

## 42 Liner fitment check

1   If the liners have been removed to be checked, renewed and
relocated or just to be reseated they should be located after the
crankshaft has been fitted - to ease the fitting of the crankshaft,
but it in fact matters little. In the majority of cases the crankshaft is in the block and the procedure for fitting is the same
whether the engine is in or out of the car.

2   If new liners are purchased with new pistons as a set you must
keep the piston with its liner. This means that if you have
already fitted the pistons to the rods that you must be careful as
to the order in which the liners go into the block, ie, that No 1
rod with its piston still goes into its respective liner in the No 1
position.

3   When fitting liners into the block you must first do so
without the pistons fitted in the liners, but this is only a trial
run. It is in fact a good idea to make this trial run without
committing yourself to placing any piston and its liner to any
position, place your liner before you fit the piston to any
particular connecting rod. Once the liners are placed in their
easiest position you can then match the position of the liner to
the piston to the connecting rod. All liners are interchangeable in
the block.

4   Check that the liners are in good, clean condition without
any cracks, even hairline ones, on the outside. Make sure you
have a selection of base seals of different thicknesses. These
seals are available in 0.007 mm marked with a blue spot, 0.10
mm marked with a red spot and 0.14 mm marked with a green
spot. Buy the latest type. They are usually copper or aluminium
coated with a plastic which softens and seals, but sometimes
paper.

5   Lightly oil the holes in the block into which the liners must
fit and hold the block upright on the bench by supporting the
sump face of the blocks of wood. (It is easier to do this with the
block held in position in the car!)

6   Hold a liner on the bench and slide the thinnest of the seals
over the end. With the seal fully home place the liner carefully
into the block until it sits firmly in. Do not place the seal in the
block and then slide in the liner; it does not work!

7   Repeat this with the other three liners using the same
thickness of seal. Tap all four liners very gently with a rubber
faced hammer to make sure they are fully home.

8   Using a metric feeler gauge measure the projection of the top
of each liner in turn above the surface of the block. This is done
by placing the blade or blades on the block face and running
your finger across (you should have clean hands anyway) from
the feeler gauge to the liner top. The projection should be
between 0.04 and 0.011 mm. The nearer 0.011 mm the better. If
you are some way out remove the liners and then replace them
using a different thickness of seal. Go through the permutations
until you have it right. Provided you have all four liners with the
same projection it matters little that one liner has used one
thickness of seal and the other another.

9   Now that you have found out which seals to use, you cannot
know without doing this, you should remove the liners,
recording their order and the seals used, to fit them with their
pistons and connecting rods outside the engine. If the liners have
been removed, never fit the liners to the block and then fit the
pistons, always install the complete liner/piston assembly.

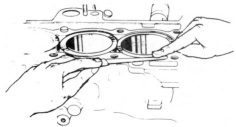

Fig. 1.10. Liner fitment check with a feeler blade

### 43 Pistons, connecting rods and big end bearings - reassembly into liners

1  Do not fit the pistons to the liners with the liners in the block, whether the engine is in or out of the car. Remove the liners and fit them on a bench.

2  If new piston rings, on either new pistons or the old pistons, are going into the original cylinder bores it is important that the piston ring gaps should be checked before fitting the piston assemblies. This will mean removing the rings from a new piston in order to check them. In order to assist the bedding in of the new piston rings to the original cylinder bore, it is a good idea to remove the oil glaze which builds up on a bore as an engine becomes more used. This can be done with very fine glass paper, wrapped round a wooden plug of suitable diameter. Careful and thorough cleaning out afterwards will also be necessary, so unless you are perfectly sure that you can do this job safely, it is best not to do it at all.

3  Place the liners in their order of fitment, positioned with their flats mating with each other.

4  Oil the piston. Tap the piston and connecting rod assembly into the top of the liner making sure the arrow on the crown of the piston faces towards the flywheel and that the number stamped on the big end faces away from the camshaft (once all is assembled in the block). Fit a suitable clamp around all of the piston rings to compress them into the grooves of the piston. It is possible to improvise a ring compressor out of a suitably sized hose clip, but great care should be exercised if this is done as it is not possible to get it to lie dead flat due to the adjusting screw housing projecting beyond the edge of the clip. This can permit the edge of a piston ring to escape its control and then be trapped against the cylinder block face and consequently break. If a strip of sheet metal is cut from an old tin and used in conjunction with a hose clip this is less likely to happen. With the rings suitably clamped, the piston may then be gently tapped into the bore.

5  Fit a new shell bearing into the connecting rod half of the big end, making sure that the notch in the end of the shell lines up with the notch in the connecting rod. (photo).

6  Repeat for each piston and then place the liners and piston assemblies into the block, as has been described in the previous Section.

7  Lubricate the big end journal on the crankshaft with clean engine oil and pull the connecting rod down onto the journal. Fit a new shell bearing into the cap, lining up the notch accordingly. Oil the shell and replace it onto the big end studs. With the big end bearing caps marked there should be no difficulty in making sure that the same cap goes onto the same connecting rod the right way round. Refit the nuts and tighten them down to the correct torque. It is a good idea to purchase a set of new big end nuts each time this job is done. These nuts do sometimes stretch and weaken. Locitite is a good additional safety measure.

8  With the pistons and liners assembled in the block recheck the liner projection with a feeler gauge as previously described. If now outside the tolerance you must disassemble and start again.

9  Do not now turn the engine over until the liner retainers are installed or the cylinder head is replaced.

### 44 Flywheel - replacement

1  Before replacing the flywheel to the crankshaft flange, the mating faces must be examined carefully for any signs of dents or burrs and be cleaned up as necessary. All traces of oil and grit must also be removed, and the locating dowel peg should be in position on the crankshaft flange. Offer up the flywheel to the flange squarely and locate it carefully into position without damaging the edges of the mating faces (photo).

2  Once the flywheel is securely mounted the set bolts should be fitted with new tab washers and progressively tightened up to the specified torque. If possible, it is a good idea to check the flywheel run-out at the outer edge of the clutch facing. If this exceeds a total of 0.08 mm then it means that the flywheel is

43.4 Always use a piston ring clamp, it's easy to break rings without

43.5 You can put your bearing shells in now before the liners are located

43.6a Do not grease these paper liner seals. They will sit in place without

43.6b Make doubly sure the pistons are in the right way.

43.7a No. 4 end cap with No. 4 connecting rod

43.7b Once again the correct torque is essential

not fitted square with the crankshaft and serious vibration problems could result when the engine is running. A dial gauge will be needed to check this run-out (photos A and B).

## 45 Oil pump - replacement

1   Wipe clean the mating surfaces of the oil pump and the cylinder block.
2   With a new paper gasket offer up the pump and screw up the three holding setscrews. Do not forget their spring washers. Tighten hard, it is not possible to use a torque wrench. You do not have to worry about engine timing at this stage (photos A and B).

## 46 Sump - replacement

1   Replacing the sump gasket is quite one of the most difficult jobs to do on the Renault 6 engine with the engine out of the car - with the engine in the car it is worse! With the engine on the bench it is only the flywheel which gets in the way, with the engine in the car and you are underneath everything gets in the way!
2   With the engine on the bench make sure that it is the cylinderhead down resting on wooden blocks. The flywheel must be fitted and torqued down. Before replacing the sump make quite sure that all big end bearing cap nuts are tight, all main bearing cap bolts are tight, and that the oil pump has been replaced and securely tightened down. Clean the block and sump mating surfaces until they are quite clean and dry. Allow the two front and rear cork sections of the gasket to soak in warm water for about ten minutes.
3   Fit four studs one at each end of the cylinder block, two on each side, into the sump bolt holes. Smear the rear main bearing cap sealing face with gasket cement and mould over its appropriate section of cork gasket (photo).
4   Fit the two long side pieces of cork gasket over the four locating studs. The tips of these two sections will just overlap the ends of the rear main bearing cap section. Place some gasket cement on these joints. With luck the three sections now fitted will stay in place.
5   This is the difficult piece to fit. Smear some gasket cement in the front main bearing cap sealing groove and place it into the last piece of cork gasket. Its ends should overlap the two long sections this time. Wait a few moments to make sure that it does not move.
6   Carefully place over the sump on the four locating studs. Once in position do not move it. Quickly but carefully screw in the sump bolts until they are all in, half done up. Quickly check that the rear and side cork sections have not disappeared inside the sump. You cannot see the front main bearing cap section.
7   Tighten the securing bolts in a diagonal manner, taking care not to move the sump pan. Place nuts on the four studs and tighten. You should now have a good seal. (photo)
8   The procedure for refitting the sump pan when the engine is in the car is the same as just described up until paragraph 3, except that you must only fit locating studs to the front of the block, not to the rear. This time smear all the mating edges of the block with gasket cement. Press up the rear main bearing cap cork section, then the two long side members - the gasket cement and the locating studs should keep them in place for a short time.
9   Press into place the front main bearing cap cork section - this too should hold itself in place because of the gasket cement, the grip of the groove and because it has lost most of its springiness by being soaked in warm water.
10   Again quickly but carefully offer up the sump to the block. Offer up the rear end first tilting it so that the end of the sump hits the rear main bearing cap first, and rests on the lip of the floor section. Holding the sump pan very steady with one hand, fir two securing bolts at the rear end and tighten just a fraction.

Offer up the other end now onto the front main bearing cap and the two locating studs. Hold steady with one hand and secure those two studs with nuts, tightening just a fraction.
11   Before tightening any more replace all the other sump bolts and then tighten them all, including the four nuts in a diagonal manner. Again with luck and a steady hand you should have a good seal. (Remember to use the two screw top bolts at the very rear end. You will have to balance them on the top of a screwdriver and push it through the two holes in the floor).
12   If the engine is in the car you should now replace the bolts which mate the front end of the sump to the gearbox. This is a straight reversal of the disassembly. Some sumps are fitted with a bracing piece. Also you should replace the anti-roll bar and relocate the crossmember (photo).

## 47 Camshaft and tappets - replacement into cylinder block

1   The engine must be out of the car for the camshaft to have been removed. With the camshaft removed the tappets must first have been removed. Also the cylinder head should have been removed. Refitting the camshaft and tappets is virtually the reversal of their removal. Never refit the tappets before the camshaft; it does not matter however whether the oil pump is fitted. The distributor and the skew gear drive must be removed.
2   Clean all old gasket cement from the timing cover end of the block. Fit the chain tensioner gauze filter. Fit the timing gear-to-block end plate and its gasket, smearing it with gasket cement. Fit its two holding set screws.
3   Have the engine resting on its sump on some soft material. Lubricate the lobes and bearing surfaces of the camshaft well.
4   845 cc: Always refit the camshaft with its sprocket attached. Have a Renault Agency align it for you if a new sprocket is to be fitted. Now reverse the removal procedure but tap on the crankshaft sprocket over its Woodruff key with a hide headed hammer. Insert the camshaft in straight and gently.
5   1100 cc: Replace the camshaft as a direct reversal of the removal.
6   In each case read Section 49 before going further.
7   Refit the oil pump drive skew gear. Then fit the distributor drive offset slotted key. See Chapter 4.
8   Replace the tappets into their respective chambers once well oiled, if you are in the least bit doubtful as to their condition. Once fitted do not turn the block on its side without the cylinder head in place otherwise they may fall out.

44.1 Relocate the flywheel in its same position

44.2a Never leave out the locking tabs

44.2b You will not hold the flywheel with your hand. Hold the crankshaft with a piece of wood.

45.2a 1100 cc oil pumps do not have paper seals under them!

45.2b This is an 845 cc oil pump

46.3 The sump gasket surfaces must be spotless

46.6 This is a tricky location even with the engine on the bench

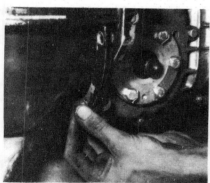

46.12 The bracing piece next to the gearbox

47.2a Make sure this filter is clear

47.2b Check the gasket does not cover any oil ways

47.2c The end plate. Two fixing screws to go

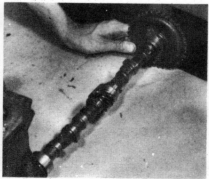

47.4 The camshaft (845 cc) can be inserted but only so far

47.8 Replace the tappets in their original position

**48 Engine mountings - replacement**

1   Engine mounting replacement is the exact reversal of their removal, see Section 22.

2   If the engine is out of the car and you have assembled it in the ordered sequence here, it is now a good time to replace them for they will allow you much greater manoeuvrability. You can

just about lift the whole engine by them and they will afford good propping points.

3   Engine mountings on this car should be renewed with reasonable frequency, for they weaken quite soon. If you are rebuilding your engine, then renew them. Weak engine mountings allow too much movement back and forth of the engine on acceleration, and the exhaust pipe will hit the inner wing through which it passes.

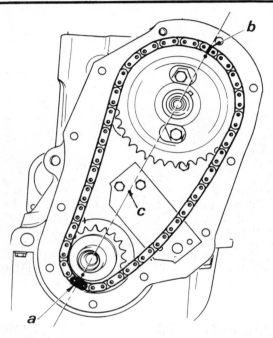

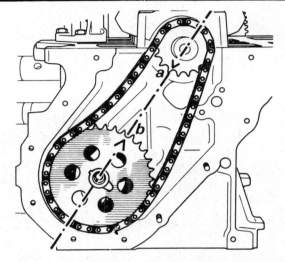

**FIG. 1.11B. 1100 cc TIMING CHAIN ALIGNMENT**

*a*   Crankshaft sprocket mark to oppose 'b'
*b*   Camshaft sprocket mark to oppose 'a' upon shortest line

**FIG. 1.11A. 845 cc TIMING CHAIN ALIGNMENT**

*a*   Yellow link of chain to meet dot on crankshaft sprocket, outer
*b*   Scribed mark on chain to meet dot on camshaft sprocket, outer
*c*   Points 'a' and 'b' to align with dot 'c', 'a' and 'b' to be on outer edges of sprockets

**Fig. 1.12A. 845 cc Distributor drive shaft alignment with No.1 cylinder in firing position**
(Note: Drive shaft slot set at 60° to longitudinal line of engine. Also, largest offset of drive towards No.1 cylinder - flywheel end)

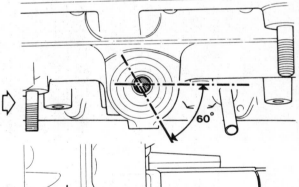

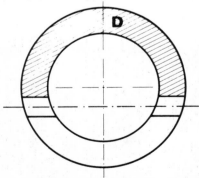

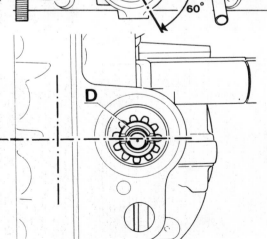

**Fig. 1.12B. 1100 cc Distributor drive shaft alignment with No.1 cylinder in firing position**
(Note: Drive shaft slot set at 90° to longitudinal line of engine. Also, largest offset 'D' of drive towards No. 1 cylinder - flywheel end)

## 49 Timing gear and cover - replacement - engine timing

1 845 cc: Because the camshaft has to be replaced with its sprocket fitted the timing chain must be replaced with the camshaft/sprocket and the crankshaft sprocket as one assembly.

2 Heat the crankshaft sprocket in hot water. Put the timing chain on it and the camshaft sprocket as shown in Fig 1.11A. Push in the camshaft and the crankshaft sprocket. Once fully home check the timing with the figure.

3 Tighten the camshaft flange through the holes in the camshaft sprocket. Replace the chain tensioner, see Paragraph 6.

4 Check once again all is well, with the chain tensioner adjusted and replace the cover using a new gasket.

5 1100 cc: The 1100 cc timing gear is replaced in a very similar way except that Figure 1.11B should be looked at. As the crankshaft timing sprocket did not have to be removed at dismantling and the camshaft sprocket was withdrawn prior to removing the camshaft it will now only be necessary to loop the timing chain round both sprockets and bolt the camshaft sprocket to the camshaft. Adjust the positions of the crankshaft and camshaft to achieve the correct timing mark alignment as shown.

6 The chain tensioner is easily replaced and adjusted.

7 Refit the chain tensioner together with its thrust plate.

8 Insert the 3mm Allen key into the retaining cylinder and turn in a clockwise direction until the pad carrier presses against the chain, with tension. Do not overtighten, you will wear out the pad.

9 Tighten the retaining cylinder bolt and lock it. Then tighten the timing gear-to-block plate and the oil feed plate. Replace the timing cover.

10 Timing the engine is now important although it is not necessary to fit the distributor yet. Study the two figures 1.12A and 1.12B for the two engines and then fit the distributor drive/oil pump skew key. It must be accurate.

49.3a This photo shows the two flange holes behind the camshaft sprocket

49.3b Use a socket wrench for their fixing

49.4a Double check now that the timing is correct

49.4b Always use a new gasket

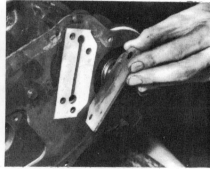
49.7a The timing chain has been removed for clarity

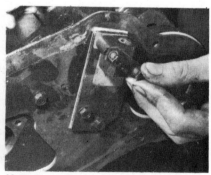
49.7b The adjuster block on its plate

49.7c Note the two long bolts at the top of the photo

49.8 Do not over adjust

49.10a First the skew gear ...

49.10b ... then the distributor drive segment

50.1b New valve springs are very cheap and worth renewing

### 50 Valve and springs - reassembly to cylinder head

1   With the head perfectly clean and having carried out all the necessary renewals and renovations as required, lightly lubricate the valve stem for the first valve to be replaced and fit it in its guide. If the same valves are being used again they should have been kept in order so that they may go back in the same place.
2   Use the same process with the compressed rag and two equal screwdrivers as used on the disassembly 11/3. Have a second person pop in the collets when the spring is compressed, release the pressure and go onto the next valve in that combustion chamber. Remember that not only are the inlet valves and their springs different from the exhaust but so are the collets. The inlet collets have one ridge, and the exhaust has two ridges in its centre.

50.2a Another method uses an open ended spanner to compress the valves

50.1a Never mix old valves into new seats

50.2b Inlet collet - 1 ridge. Exhaust collet - 2 ridges

## 51 Valve rocker gear - reassembly

1 If the engine is in the car you must refit the rocker gear to the cylinder head before you replace the cylinder head. If the engine is out of the car it does not matter whether you fit it before you replace the head or not. Basically it cannot be replaced once the cylinder head is fitted to the engine in the car. However, the water pump and its end plate must not be fitted.

2 Replacing the valve rocker gear is a direct reversal of its removal without exception. You should however always oil all the parts upon refitting. Always replace the rubber end plug with new every time the rocker gear is dismantled. A further point to remember - do not overtighten the rocker shaft pedestal locking bolts, they may strip their threads! Relock the tab washers.

## 52 Inlet/exhaust manifold - replacement

1 In all situations it is preferable to refit the manifold to the cylinder head before fitting the head to the block. This will then not make it necessary to undo any head studs to mount the manifold bracing piece, after the head has been refitted, and it is considerably easier to tighten the securing nuts.

2 Always use new manifold gaskets, slip these over the four studs. They look like two sections of three rings with the two mounting holes between the rings. It does not matter which way they face. Place on the manifold over the studs and using new nuts and spring washers, bolt up the manifold. Tighten hard but do not overtighten, making sure that the studs do not strip out of the head. Should they do so you will have to dismantle and refit new studs having had helicoils fitted by your Renault agent. (If you have removed the cylinder head studs make absolutely sure you remount them the right way round, they have different length threads at each end and it matters!)

3 On R1181 engines don't forget to relocate the heat shield between the manifold and the starter motor, and retain with the manifold nuts and washers.

## 53 Water pump - refitting

Under any circumstances it makes little difference whether you refit the water pump before refitting the cylinder head to the block. Fitting is a reversal of the removal, exactly.

## 54 Cylinder head and pushrod - refitting to the cylinder block

1 Again the procedure for refitting the head is similar whether the engine is in or out of the car.

2 Make sure that the new cylinder head gasket is the correct one. Clean the top of the blcok of all dust and make sure that it and the head surfaces are prefectly flat.

3 Remove the cylinder liner retaining clamps.

4 Fit the gasket in position on the block, crimped edges towards the block. Do not use any gasket cement or grease.

5 Position the cylinder head on the gasket and fit the bolts and their washers. Make sure that the right length bolts go in the right place - this does matter. (Do not forget to fit the manifold bracing piece before fitting the centre left hand bolt). The pushrods will have to be guided in. Refit the pushrods into the respective tappets, cup end up. You should, of course, make sure that the rocker clearances are very wide. It is a good idea to use new washers.

6 Tighten the bolts in the correct sequence progressively. First to 20 lb ft and then finally to 45 lb ft. You must, of course, use the correct socket and drive together with a torque spanner.

7 After the first 300 miles of running with a new cylinder head gasket wait until the engine is cold then undo all the cylinder head bolts ¼ of a turn and retorque them in the correct sequence to 45 lb ft.

51.2a Tap in the rocker shaft half

51.2b Now the rockers ...

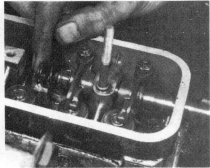
51.2c and the coil springs ...

51.2d another rocker arm ...

51.2e and yet another rocker after the pedestal ...

51.2f and another shorter spring

51.2g Make sure the thread is clean before tightening

51.2h The end nut is difficult to start

51.2j Do not tighten too hard

51.2k A new end plug has been fitted. Do not omit

51.2l Make sure the rocker cover gasket does not bow

52.2a Use new gaskets here every time

52.2b Do not omit the carburettor support brace

52.2c This last bolt can be left until this point of assembly

53.1 Again always use a new gasket for the water pump

54.2 'Haut' or top, visible

54.5a Make sure both mating surfaces are clean

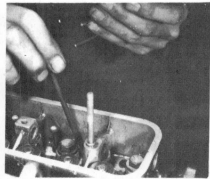

54.5b Replace the pushrods in their original positions

54.6 Never tighten the cylinder head down without a torque wrench

55.2 Use metric feeler blades for accurate setting

## 55 Valve rocker clearances - checking and adjustment

1   The valve rocker clearances are important as they control the amount of valve opens and when it opens and thus can affect the efficiency of the engine.

2   The clearances should be measured and set by using a feeler blade between the rocker arm and the end of each valve stem. This is done when the valve is closed and the tappet is resting on the lowest point of the cam. Use only metric feeler blades (photo).

3   To enable each valve to be in the correct position for checking with the minimum amount of engine turning the procedure and order of checking should follow the sequence given in the following tables. In the table the valves are numbered 1 to 8, starting from the front of the cylinder head. A valve is fully open when the rocker arm has pushed the valve down to its lowest point.

| Open Valve | Adjust clearance (cold) |
|------------|------------------------|
| No 8 (ex)  | No 1 (ex  0.20 mm)     |
| No 6 (in)  | No 3 (in  0.15 mm)     |
| No 4 (ex)  | No 5 (ex  0.20 mm)     |
| No 7 (in)  | No 2 (in  0.15 mm)     |
| No 1 (ex)  | No 8 (ex  0.20 mm)     |
| No 3 (in)  | No 6 (in  0.15 mm)     |
| No 5 (ex)  | No 4 (ex  0.20 mm)     |
| No 2 (in)  | No 7 (in  0.15 mm)     |

4   Using two spanners, first slacken the locknut on the adjusting stud and then put the feeler blade, of appropriate thickness, between the rocker arm and valve stem of the valve being adjusted. Slacken the stud adjuster if the gap is too small to accept the blade.

5   Turn the adjusting screw until the feeler blade can be felt to drag lightly when it is drawn out of the gap.

6   Hold the adjuster with a screwdriver and tighten the locknut. Check the gap once more to make sure it has not altered as a result of locking the stud.

7   If the engine is being assembled on the bench, or after the head has been taken off, the gaps should be set 0.2 mm more than specification in the first instance.

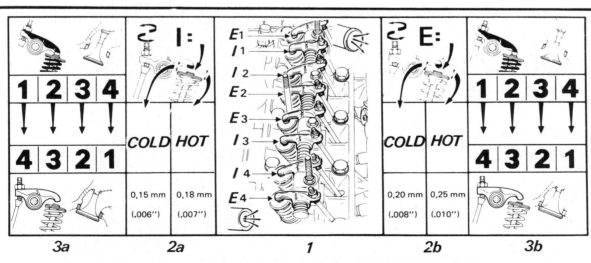

**FIG. 1.13. VALVE CLEARANCE ADJUSTMENT (BOTH MODELS)**

1   Shows inlet (1) and exhaust (e) valve numbering
2a  Shows clearances for inlet valves in hot or cold state
2b  Shows clearances for exhaust valves in hot or cold state
3a  Shows which inlet valve is closed when a given inlet valve is open
3b  Shows which exhaust valve is closed when a given exhaust valve is open

## 56 Engine reassembly - final stages

1 Before replacing an engine into the car, all those ancillary parts which are removed before the engine was stripped should be replaced. These items were listed in Section 7. One possible exception is the carburettor which projects in a somewhat vulnerable way and could be damaged expensively if any mishap occurred on replacing the engine.

2 Refit the rocker gear cover, even though it has to be taken off again, as this will protect the rocker gear from damage and dust. Leave the new gasket to be fitted later.

## 57 Engine replacement in car

Generally speaking, the replacement of the engine is a reversal of the removal procedure but the following points should be borne in mind.

1 The engine and gearbox have been removed together, they should be reassembled and replaced together. This takes care of the possible difficulties one may encounter fitting the gearbox input shaft into the clutch.

2 When lowering the engine into the car make sure first that it is suspended at the correct attitude. It is difficult and possibly dangerous to have to alter the angle of tilt whilst it is suspended.

3 Always lower the engine very slowly and watch it all round all the way. It is easy to wrench out wire and pipes due to being in too much of a hurry and not noticing these things when they flip back in the way - as they always seem to do.

4 If the engine will not go where it should, look and find out why. Do not try and force anything.

5 Always fit a new oil filter (if fitted), air cleaner element, spark plugs and contact points, and fill with fresh oil and coolant.

6 Replace all the suspension and steering parts as well as the drive shafts before attempting to start the engine. Always lower the car to the ground and use the following check list, as well as reading the relevent parts in the rest of this book concerning those components which you have had to touch to remove the engine but which are not actually engine components, before attempting to start the car.

7 Once the engine has started and all is well you must have the car retracked at the front wheels before undertaking any regular use.

8 The following check list should ensure that the engine starts safely and with little or no delay and that the car is ready to move:

a) Fuel pipes to fuel pump and carburettor connected and tight.
b) Coolant hoses to radiator and heater connected and tight.
c) Radiator and block coolant drain plugs shut and tight.
d) Cooling system filled and bled.
e) Sump drain plug screwed and tight.
f) Oil filter cartridge tight (if fitted).
g) Oil in sump and dipstick replaced.
h) Oil in transmission unit and plugs tight.
i) LT wires connected to the distributor.
j) Spark plugs clean and tight.
k) Valve rocker clearance set.
i) HT leads all connected and secure.
m) Distributor rotor arm fitted.
n) Choke and accelerator cable fitted and working through their total range.
o) Earthing cable from engine block to battery and battery to inner wing secure.
p) Starter motor cable to battery connected and secure.
q) Dynamo leads connected.
r) Oil pressure warning and coolant temperature sender unit cables connected.
s) Battery charged and secure in position.
t) All loose tools removed from the engine compartment.
u) Clutch cable refitted and adjusted.
v) Gear change linkage replaced.
w) Steering rack replaced and all ball joints secure and tight.
x) Steering column reconnected.
y) Drive shafts refitted to transmission unit and roll pins replaced and greased, and speedometer cable replaced. See Chapter 7.
z) Handbrake cables, linkage and engine mountings secure.

Leave the bonnet off and the lights unconnected for the initial start but replace before venturing on to the road!

9 As soon as the engine starts, run it steadily at a fast tick-over for several minutes and look all round for signs of leaks and loose or unclipped pipes and wires. Watch the instrument and warning lights and stop the engine at the first indications of anything nasty!

## Fault finding

| Symptom | Reason/s | Remedy |
| --- | --- | --- |
| Engine will not turn over when starter switch is operated | Flat battery<br>Bad battery connections<br>Bad connections at solenoid switch and/or starter motor | Check that the battery is fully charged and that all connections are clean and tight. |
| | Starter motor jammed | With a pre-engaged starter fitted, rock the car back and forth with a gear engaged. If this does not free pinion remove starter. |
| | Defective solenoid | Bridge the main terminals of the solenoid switch with a piece of heavy duty cable in order to operate the starter. |
| | Starter motor defective | Remove and overhaul starter motor. |
| Engine turns over normally but fails to fire and run | No spark at plugs | Check ignition system according to procedures given in Chapter 4. |
| | No fuel reaching engine | Check fuel system according to procedures given in Chapter 3. |
| | Too much fuel reaching the engine (flooding) | Check the fuel system as above. |
| Engine starts but runs unevenly and misfires | Ignition and/or fuel system faults | Check the ignition and fuel systems as though the engine had failed to start. |

| Symptom | Reason/s | Remedy |
| --- | --- | --- |
|  | Incorrect valve clearances | Check and reset clearances. |
|  | Burnt out valves | Remove cylinder head and examine and |
|  | Blown cylinder head gasket, dropped | overhaul as neccessary. |
|  | liners |  |
|  | Worn out piston rings | Remove cylinder head and examine |
|  | Worn cylinder bores | pistons and cylinder bores. Overhaul as |
|  |  | necessary. |
| Lack of power | Ignition and/or fuel system faults | Check the ignition and fuel systems for |
|  |  | correct ignition timing and carburettor |
|  |  | settings. |
|  | Incorrect valve clearances | Check and reset the clearances. |
|  | Burnt out valves | Remove cylinder head and examine |
|  | Blown cylinder head gasket | and overhaul as necessary. |
|  | Worn out piston rings | Remove cylinder head and examine |
|  | Worn cylinder bores | pistons and cylinder bores. Overhaul as |
|  |  | necessary. |
| Excessive oil consumption | Oil leaks from crankshaft front oil seal, | Identify source of leak and renew seal |
|  | timing cover gasket and oil seal, rocker | as appropriate. |
|  | cover gasket, sump gasket, sump plug |  |
|  | washer |  |
|  | Worn piston rings or cylinder bores | Fit new rings or rebore cylinders and |
|  | resulting in oil being burnt by engine | fit new pistons, depending on degree of |
|  | Smoky exhaust is an indication | wear. |
|  | Worn valve guides and/or defective | Remove cylinder heads and recondition |
|  | valve stem seals | valve stem bores and valves and seals as |
|  |  | necessary. |
| Excessive mechanical noise from engine | Wrong valve to rocker clearances | Adjust valve clearances |
|  | Worn crankshaft bearings | Inspect and overhaul where necessary. |
|  | Worn cylinders (piston slap) |  |
|  | Slack or worn timing chain and sprockets, | Adjust chain and/or inspect all timing |
|  |  | mechanism. |
| Unusual vibration | Fan blade broken off | Break off another fan blade to balance |
|  |  | fan until renewal is possible. |
|  | Broken engine/gearbox mounting | Renew mounting |
|  | Misfiring on one or more cylinders | Check ignition system |

NOTE: When investigating starting and uneven running faults do not be tempted into a snap diagnosis. Start from the beginning of the check procedure and follow it through. It will take less time in the long run. Poor performance from an engine in terms of power and economy is not normally diagnosed quickly. In any event the ignition and fuel systems must be checked first before assuming any further investigation needs to be made.

# Chapter 2  Cooling system

**Contents**

**Specifications**

| | |
|---|---|
| Type of system ... ... ... ... ... ... ... | Pressurised with centrifugal circulation pump, fan and thermostat Sealed system |
| Coolant capacity ... ... ... ... ... ... ... | R1180: 9¾ pints (5.6 litres) * <br> R1181: 11 pints (6.2 litres) <br> Both to include heater and expansion chamber |
| Coolant ... ... ... ... ... ... ... | Mixture of equal proportions of antifreeze (glycol) and distilled water |
| Expansion chamber ... ... ... ... ... ... ... | Glass bottle adjacent to radiator |
| Radiator ... ... ... ... ... ... ... | Gilled tube type cooled by fan |
| Fan ... ... ... ... ... ... ... ... | R1180: Conventional belt driven 6 bladed fan <br> R1181: Electric, thermostatically controlled fan mounted remote from the engine |
| Water pump ... ... ... ... ... ... ... | Centrifugal-driven by belt from camshaft pulley |
| Fan belt tension ... ... ... ... ... ... ... | R1180: ¼ in, at longest run <br> R1181: ½ in, at longest run |
| Thermostat opening temperature ... ... ... ... ... | 84°C (183°F) normal |
| R1181 electric fan cut-in temperature ... ... ... ... | 92°C (198°F) |
| Cut-out temperature ... ... ... ... ... ... | 82°C (180°F) |

For heater - See Chapter 11

*1973 on models may have 8¾ pints (5.1 litres) capacity

## 1  General description

The engine cooling liquid is circulated round the system on the thermosyphon principle, assisted by a belt driven impeller type pump.

The system is pressurised and sealed so that boiling will only occur at abnormally high temperatures and that there is no loss of coolant. As the coolant heats up it expands and flows into the expansion chamber, which is fitted with a blow-off valve should the pressure and therefore the temperature get too great. No coolant should be lost as air pressure and not water pressure is ever lost because the expansion chamber is never more than about 1/3 filled with coolant. As the coolant becomes cool it

will flow back into the radiator under the vacuum principle.

The circuit also incorporates a thermostatically controlled valve which restricts the amount of water passing through the radiator until the correct engine operating temperature is reached. This assists rapid warming up and keeps the engine at a constant running temperature regardless of ambient conditions.

The principle of operation is as follows. The water heated by the engine rises out of the cylinder head towards the thermostat which, if cold, is closed. It then diverts via the heater (or heater by-pass pipe if the heater valve is shut) straight to the pump and thence back to the engine.

When the engine warms up a proportion of the warm water will pass via the thermostat valve to the top of the radiator down through which it will pass and cool. The pump will then draw the cold water from the bottom of the radiator and pass it back to the engine (the pump has two inlets). If the engine temperature should rise excessively the thermostat valve will close off the by-pass outlet thus directing all water through the radiator.

It is important that the system is always sealed properly and that it is filled with the correct coolant which ideally is 50% antifreeze (glycol) and 50% distilled water. To maintain correct antifreeze properties and to safeguard against internal damage to the aluminium cylinder head this mixture should be adhered to at all times. Because of the sealed system this mixture is safe during the whole year in any climate.

The R1180 utilises a belt driven cooling fan whilst the R1181 has a thermostatically contolled electric fan. The R1180 has a centrally mounted radiator over the transmission unit whilst the R1181 radiator is bolted to the front body cross panel.

## 2  Cooling system - draining

1  Stand the car on level ground and if hot allow to cool for at least 15 minutes. Remove the expansion chamber safety valve cap. The safety valve is undone by unscrewing the large knurled plastic cap. If very stiff use a rag over the top and undo carefully with a pair of adjustable grips.
2  Undo the radiator drain plug located at the bottom left hand side of the radiator. Use the correct spanner - it is a brass plate and does not like pliers. To save the coolant is pointless - most of it will drain under the car at various points and you would need a recepticle the size of a bath to claim it all. However it is a good idea to lay newspaper underneath the car to soak up the worst of it. The coolant will trickle out at first. Wait until it begins to gush before unsealing the radiator cap. This indicates that the expansion chamber is empty; you cannot see, the bottles are usually pretty dirty.
3  Make sure at this stage that the heater is in the on position and then open the bleed plug for the heating system which is located on the bulkhead on the left-hand side (R1180) and right-hand side (R1181). There is a second one on the R1181 close to the water pump. Open this too. Undo it fully but do not remove.
4  Now drain the cylinder block but removing the plug located at the rear of the engine block on the right hand side, about halfway down. This is quite fiddly.
5  Allow the car to stand for another five minutes before tackling anything else so that the last drip can fall.
6  It is possible to drain these parts mentioned separately so that you need not drain the blcok for example, simply because you wish to change a radiator top hose. It is a simple enough system to understand and functions in a conventional manner.
7  If sediment blocks the drain holes poke them gently with some wire to free.

2.4 Cylinder block drain plug. Note end of starter motor

## 3  Cooling system - flushing

1  Every so often it is a good practice to flush out the system to remove any loose sediment, and scale which may have accumulated. The time to do this is when the coolant is being drained. With the sealed system, however, the need for topping up should be very infrequent so that the deposits of lime and so on, from regular additions of new water, are negligible. The need for flushing, therefore, is usually only caused by some other factor - such as a leak which allows air to enter the system and cause oxidisation or the use of an antifreeze of a type which may cause corrosion.
2  To check the need for flushing open the radiator drain tap and if the liquid coming out is obviously very dirty, although it can be a deep colour, and full of solid particles let it run out. If it clears as more runs out and the outflow is in no way restricted then there is no great problem. If, however, constant poking with a piece of wire is needed and the liquid continues very dirty then obviously a flush is needed.
3  To flush out, simply leave the radiator and block drain taps open and after removing the radiator cap, run a hose through the system for about 15 minutes (ordinary water is quite safe). If the taps show signs of blockage keep poking them out. If the blocking is persistent remove the tap completely so that a larger orifice may permit the obstruction to clear itself. In some bad cases a reverse flush may help and this is easily done by removing the radiator and running the hose into the bottom tank so that it flows out of the filler neck.
4  If the radiator flow is restricted by something other than loose sediment then no amount of flushing will shift it and it is then that a proprietary chemical, suitable for aluminium heads, is needed. Use this according to the directions and make sure that the residue is fully out afterwards. If leaks develop after using a chemical cleaner, a proprietary radiator sealer may cure them but the signs are that the radiator has suffered considerable chemical corrosion and that the metal is obviously getting very thin in places.

## 4  Cooling system - refilling and bleeding

1  Always flush out before refilling if the old coolant was particularly dirty. (Clean out the glass expansion chamber too).
2  Screw up both block and radiator drain plugs. Make sure that a copper washer is fitted to the radiator plug. Make sure all the hose clips are tight and that the hoses are in good condition.
3  Mix 50% distilled water and 50% antifreeze in a clean gallon can. Mix a further pint of the coolant. It is essential to use a glycol based antifreeze, such as Castrol antifreeze, so that it cannot damage the cylinder head. Ideally distilled water should be used to ensure long life of the system as it is by definition very pure, however, it is possible to use clean soft water, if distilled water is not available.
4  Pour 1¼ pints of the liquid through a funnel (a flexitop bottle is ideal) into the glass bottle, to 30 mm (1.3/16″) above maximum mark, and replace the safety valve. (Check the bottle sealing rings).
5  Fill the rest of the cooling system through the radiator top, leaving the heater in the on position and bleed screws still undone.
6  Once the radiator is full, on the R1180 clamp the hose from the bleed screw as near to the water pump as is possible. On the R1181 use two clamps as near to the water pump as possible on the two hoses feeding the two bleed screws.
7  Start the engine and run at a fast tickover (1500 rpm) keep filling the radiator with more coolant.
8  When continuous coolant flows out of the bleed screw(s) without a trace of air, close them. Do not now touch them.
9  Remove the clamp(s). Top up the radiator and replace the cap.
10 Stop the engine, allow to cool and then recheck the level and check for leaks.

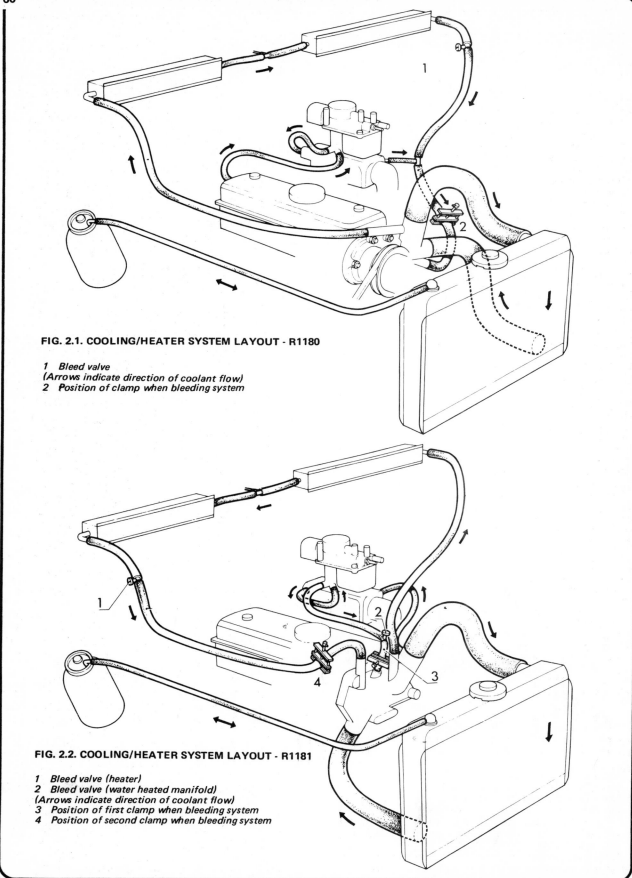

**FIG. 2.1. COOLING/HEATER SYSTEM LAYOUT - R1180**

1  Bleed valve
(Arrows indicate direction of coolant flow)
2  Position of clamp when bleeding system

**FIG. 2.2. COOLING/HEATER SYSTEM LAYOUT - R1181**

1  Bleed valve (heater)
2  Bleed valve (water heated manifold)
(Arrows indicate direction of coolant flow)
3  Position of first clamp when bleeding system
4  Position of second clamp when bleeding system

## 5  R1180 Radiator - removal, inspection, cleaning and replacement

1    Drain the cooling system as described earlier in Section 2.
2    Slacken the clip and remove the top radiator hose where it connects to the radiator. Slacken also the clip securing the bottom hose to the radiator and pull off the hose.
3    The radiator is held onto a special bracket which is itself held by two studs to the steering rack. There is also a tie rod from the front crossmember to the top of the radiator which is held there by one more stud which, with another, also locates the gear shift rod front bush.
4    Remove the tie rod and then the radiator itself as described in Chapter 1.
5    Thoroughly clean the exterior of the radiator. It has presumably been removed in order to repair a leak or for further examination of a suspected blockage (except, of course, as part of a procedure to get access to something else).
6    Some radiators are made of steel and brass, some of all brass. If the steel has rusted through, little short of replacement can take place but all brass parts can be repaired with solder where exterior leaks are accessible. The technique of soldering is not discussed here but suffice it to say that the surfaces to be joined must be thoroughly cleaned, then tinned and the solder able to 'run' in the repair. It is fruitless merely depositing blobs of solder about the place. It would be better to use a resin filler paste which in fact can be used for such repairs in limited applications. Care must also be taken when soldering to localise any heat used. Otherwise the radiator may start to disintegrate where you least want it to. A leak in the internal parts of the honeycomb, if not severe, can be cured with one of the specialist sealers added to the cooling liquid. If severe, professional attention will be needed. Another way for emergencies only, is to block the whole of the honeycomb in the suspect area with resin filler paste. Old fashioned remedies such as mustard, egg whites and porridge oats added to water, are not recommended as they have been known to have sinister effects on water pumps and thermostats. There is much less liquid in modern systems and these foodstuffs cannot be digested so readily!
7    Replacement of the radiator is a direct reversal of removal. Make sure the bottom mounting rubber bushes are in good condition between the bracket and the radiator. Also be sure that the two bolts which locate this bracket and the steering rack are really tight.

## 6  R1181 Radiator - removal, inspection, cleaning and replacement

1    The fixing of the R1181 radiator is nearer the front of the car, on the cross panel. It is held by two horizontal studs and nuts and two rubber channels on the front cross panel. An electric fan is attached to it.
2    Removal and replacement of this radiator is much simpler than that of R1180. Disconnect the electrical connections to the fan and to its thermostat. Disconnect the top and bottom hoses and the top expansion chamber feed. Remove the two stud nuts and washers and lift the radiator away.
3    Read the previous section for radiator cleaning. Replacement is a reverse procedure. See the subsequent sections for fan its and thermostat removal.

## 7  Expansion bottle - removal and replacement

1    Removal of the glass expansion bottle is very easy. Unscrew the two screws which locate its wire strap to the inner wing (R1180) or centre cross brace (R1181) and lift out.
2    Replacement is again a reversal of its removal. It can be cleaned with hot water and soap and should be well rinsed.

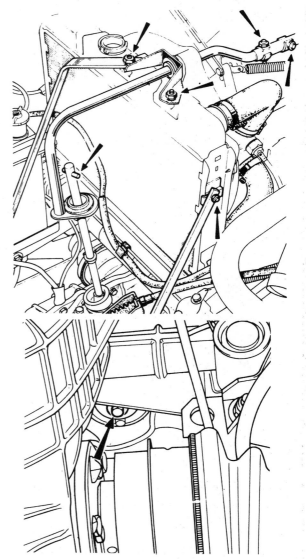

**Fig. 2.3. Radiator fixing points (R1180)**

*Top       points visible under bonnet*
*Lower     fixing point behind steering rack seen*
*from underneath car*

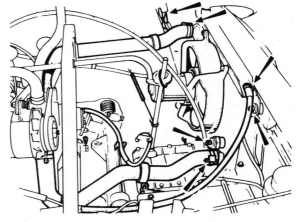

**Fig. 2.4. Radiator fixing connection points (R1181)**

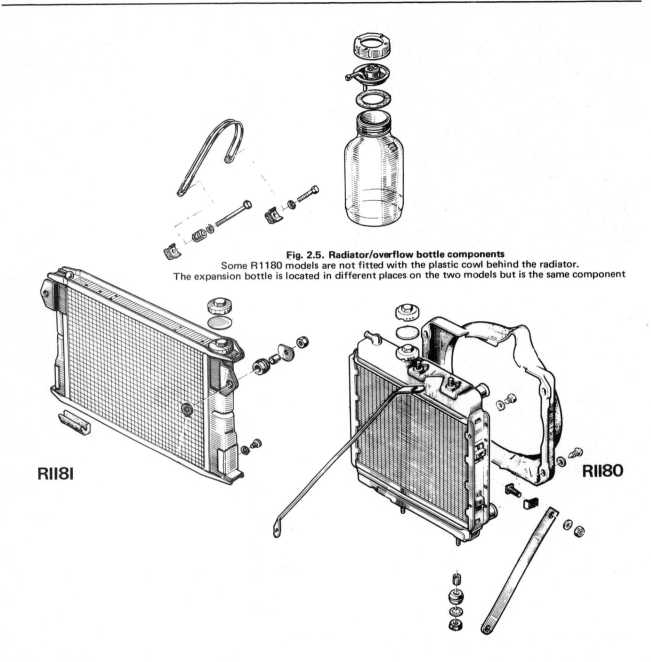

**Fig. 2.5. Radiator/overflow bottle components**
Some R1180 models are not fitted with the plastic cowl behind the radiator.
The expansion bottle is located in different places on the two models but is the same component

R1181

R1180

## 8   Thermostat - removal, testing and replacement

1   If the engine gets too hot or stays too cool, then the thermostat is probably to blame.

2   Drain out sufficient coolant to lower the level about 4 inches
(say a quart) so that no more will be lost when the top radiator
hose is next detached from the thermostat housing. Remove the
air cleaner on the R1181.

3   Remove the top radiator hose at the water pump. In the largest
diameter end should be the thermostat. It does sometimes fall
into its housing if the bottom wormdrive clip is fully undone.
Pull the thermostat out.

4   To test the thermostat, suspend it on a piece of cotton in a
pan of water and see how it behaves at the necessary opening
temperatures. The valve should start to open within $3^{o}$C of the
normal operating temperature. Then, after another 2 to 3
minutes, it should open 6.5 mm (¼ inch) to the "by-pass port

closed" position. After being once more placed in cooler water it
should close within 15 to 20 seconds.

5   If a thermostat does not operate correctly it should be
renewed. If one is not immediately available leave the old one
out to avoid damage by possible overheating of the engine.

6   Refit the thermostat by placing it in its housing checking that
one of its bridges is not obstructing a blocked water circulation
hole and push the radiator hose over it (it is obvious which end
of the hose fits) making sure that it is not necessary, when fitting
the other end of the hose to the radiator, to twist it. Secure the
wormdrive clips, refill the radiator with coolant and check for
leaks. Refit the air cleaner on the R1181.

NOTE: it has been known for the thermostat itself to travel up
the hose about ¾ in when the coolant is hot. To stop excess flow
of coolant, malfunctioning thermostat and hose stretch, lightly
tighten a hose clip around the hose over the thermostat body
located in the hose in its correct place.

7.1 Bottle on R1180. Fixing is sprung slightly

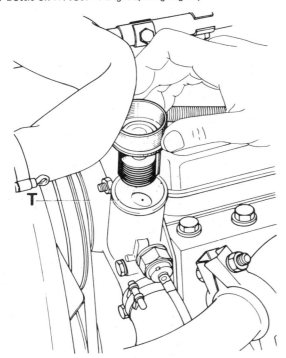

**Fig. 2.6. Position of the thermostat. R1180 illustrated, although R1181 is very similar**

## 9  Water pump - removal and replacement

1  If the water pump leaks or the bearing is obviously worn it will need to be removed for renewal. It can be done with the engine in the car and without removing the radiator or cylinder head. However, it is a nasty job on either car, the R1180 has to have its radiator loosened and the R1181 the centre cross brace pulled forward.

2  Drain the cooling system and then undo the hoses which are connected to the pump.

3  Slacken the generator mounting bolts and belt tension adjuster bolt so that the drivebelts may be removed. The generator should then be allowed to rest down. On some R1180 models a left-hand threaded adjuster bolt is used, identified by a groove in the nut (see Fig. 2.8). On later models, a socket screw is used to tighten the belt idler/tensioner pulley. This is released using a 10 mm Allen key.

4  Disconnect the battery.

5  Loosen the radiator as described in Chapter 1, (R1180) but do not actually remove the radiator. Undo the centre cross brace on the R1181 and pull towards the radiator having unclipped the two radiator hoses on it.

6  Pull the radiator away from the pump so that the fan blades will clear it. (R1180).

7  Remove the water pump securing nuts and bolts. (It is easier to get at all these if the radiator is removed but it is by no means essential). Some bolts do not actually locate the pump to the cylinder head but only the pump backplate to its body.

8  Tap the water pump with a soft faced hammer and draw it out and up, taking care not to hit the radiator.

9  To remove the fan (R1180) and its pulley hold the pulley and the pump in a soft faced vice and remove the Pal locking washer on the centre shaft of the pump at the fan. Remove the securing nut and washer.

10  Take the pump out of the vice and replace in the vice, this time without bearing on the pulley. Lever the pulley/fan off the pump spindle equally all the way round and very carefully. It is located on a woodruff key onto the impeller spindle.

11  To replace a broken fan or pulley undo the two locking tab washers and undo the four setscrews and part one from the other. Replacement of both fan and pulley is a reversal of the removal procedure.

12  Water pumps cannot be repaired. Exchange pumps only are available.

13  Reassembly is a reversal of its dismantling procedure. Make sure the drive pulley nut is torqued to 15 lb ft.

14  Before replacing the pump to the cylinder head the mating faces of both the impeller housing and the head must be perfectly clean and free of traces of old gaskets. Fit a new gasket, using jointing compound, on both sides and tighten the bolts evenly to ensure a watertight joint.

15  Refit the fan and pulley, replace the drivebelts and adjust the tension and connect the water hoses. Refix the radiator on centre cross brace. Refill the system with coolant. Examine for leaks

9.9 Fan removal from the outer pulley

9.10 Outer pulley comes from beneath it

9.14 Note new gasket on cylinder head end

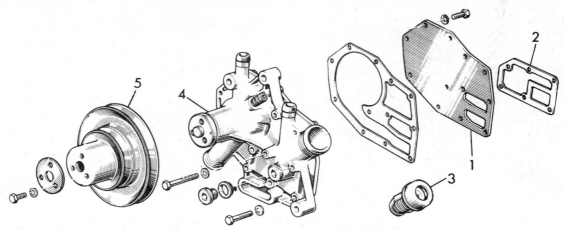

**FIG. 2.7. R1181 WATER PUMP COMPONENTS**
(R1180 is very similar but has temperature sender unit fitted)

| | |
|---|---|
| 1   *Back plate* | 4   *Pump body* |
| 2   *Gaskets* | 5   *Pulley* |
| 3   *Thermostat* | |

*(No further dismantling is possible)*

when cold and at normal running temperature. Make sure that pulleys all run true to each other.

### 10 R1180 Fan belts - removal, replacement and adjustment

1   Two fan belts are fitted, both at the fan end of the engine. Nearest to the cylinder block, a pulley on the end of the camshaft drives the water pump and is adjusted by a jockey wheel just beneath the dynamo. The second belt, the outer, is driven by a second larger pulley on the water pump, and this drives the dynamo pulley, movement of which adjusts this belt.
2   It is fairly easy to replace either belt without removing anything from the engine or its ancillaries but by loosening sufficiently either the dynamo or jockey wheel or both.
3   If the fan belt(s) are obviously worn or stretched so far that they are still too slack at maximum adjustment they should be renewed. In case of breakages it is wise to carry two spares - one of each for they are not interchangeable. Check the engine number of your car before buying fan belts as there are several sizes fitted according to the age of your car.
4   To change the outer or dynamo fan belt, loosen the fixing bolts at either end of the pressed steel rod which holds the top of the dynamo to the water pump. Slacken off the nut at the end of the dynamo pivot bolt on its underside. It helps to take off the handbrake return spring and again pull-on the handbrake so that you can get a spanner to the nut with ease).
5   Remove the old fan belt if not broken, and carefully thread over the new belt, over the four blades of the fan first. Be careful that the fine edges of the fan, radiator cowl or dynamo pulley do not foul and cut it. 'Peel' the belt over the dynamo pulley and tighten up the dynamo, making sure that the belt has the correct tightness. Do not overtighten: deflection should be about ½ inch on its longest run.
6   To change or replace the inner or water pump belt you will obviously have to remove the outer belt and then replace it after removing the inner as described here.
7   Slacken the jockey wheel as far as it will go and with the help of a long screwdriver 'peel' the belt off the jockey wheel outwards towards the radiator. Then pull it further outwards from underneath the camshaft pulley. There is not much room and it becomes fiddly but patience is needed. Once released from the camshaft pulley, pull the belt upwards and over the fan as with the dynamo belt. On some R1180 models a left-hand threaded adjuster nut is used, identified by a groove in the nut (see Fig. 2.8). On later models, a socket screw is used to tighten the belt idler/tensioner pulley. This is released using a 10 mm Allen key.
8   To replace this belt work is the exact opposite to the removal

process up until it is positioned on the camshaft pulley (be sure it is the right belt before starting!) and be especially careful it is not cut on the edges of the pulleys. It is essential to position it under the camshaft pulley before mounting it onto the water pump pulley or the jockey wheel. In fact it is easier to now mount it onto the jockey wheel and then slip it onto the water pump pulley. Do not allow it to twist - it will if it can.
9   Re-adjust the jockey wheel to tension the belt. Do not over-tighten, ½ inch deflection is needed, otherwise it will ruin the jockey wheel and water pump bearing. Replace the dynamo belt as already described.
10  After a new belt has run for a few hundred miles check the tension again as the initial stretch may require re-adjustment. There are no definite rules as regards frequency of checking but it only takes a second every time the oil level is checked.
11  The jockey wheel used to tension the inner belt runs on two small taper roller bearings. Its removal is simple.
12  Remove the outer fan belt but only go as far as to remove the belt from this pulley. Slacken off the tightening nut and remove and pull out the jockey wheel. Its mounting bracket is fixed to the block by three setscrews. However, this only needs to be removed if you are changing the cylinder block, possibly for a new exchange engine.
13  If the bearings in the jockey wheel are worn or the pulley wheel itself damaged there is little point in dismantling to effect a repair unless replacement as a whole is not possible. It is extremely unlikely that internal parts will be readily available rather than the whole unit. It can be dismantled by removing the outer circlip grease cap and the inner circlip and pulling the wheel off the spindle. The two bearings will then have to be extracted with a suitable drift.
14  To reassemble fit a new felt inner pad in the pulley groove and push the pulley onto the spindle. Press on the two bearings and having previously greased them check that the full faces of the bearings face outwards. Refit the small circlip, grease cap and outer circlip.
15  Replace on its mounting and refit and tighten the fan belts.

### 11 R1181 Drivebelts - removal, replacement and adjustment

1   Most of that which has been described in the previous section is pertinent. Remember however that you will be dealing with a alternator - be gentle with it and do not lever on its body.
2   Removal and replacement and then adjustment is exactly as for the R1180 except that a different type of inner belt tensioner is fitted. It is a pulley on the end of a drilled/slotted arm. This arm is adjusted by a threaded screw bolt adjuster from

10.5 This is a tight fit

10.15 Tensioning the inner fan belt

10.6 Inner fan belt replacement. The engine is out of the car here

10.14 Jockey wheel replacement

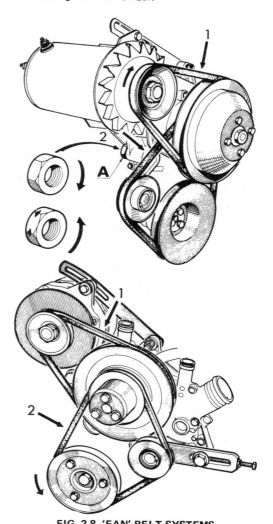

**FIG. 2.8. 'FAN' BELT SYSTEMS**

Top - R1180. 'A' shows possible thread of pivot bolt, indicating visual difference
1   Position of tension testing, dynamo bolt
2   Position of tension testing, camshaft bolt
Lower - R1181
1   Position of tension testing, alternator bolt
2   Position of tension testing, camshaft bolt

the exhaust side of the engine once the through bolt (through the slot) has been loosened. A locknut locks the bolt adjuster once the correct adjustment has been achieved. The through bolt is then tightened; It is a simpler method over that used on the R1180.

## 12 R1181 Electric cooling fan and switch

1  The R1181 is fitted with an electric fan attached onto the radiator; it is thermostatically operated. There is no engine driven fan.

2  A screw-in thermostat switch (Mosta) is fitted into the radiator core next to the fan. This operates the fan at certain temperatures through a relay fitted to the inner wing (early) or crossmember (late) on the opposite side. The switch 'cuts in' when radiator coolant reaches 92°C (197.6°F) and 'cuts out' at 82°C (179.6°F). This switch as well as the relay cannot be repaired - renewal is the only answer.

3  The cooling fan and motor are fixed to the radiator by its surround using three studs and nuts. To remove it (fan and motor complete) undo the three nuts, the electrical connections at the relay and pull away.

4  Further dismantling is feasible. The fan can be removed from the motor which will release the fan surround. The pertinent

illustration gives all that is required.

5  Do not attempt to overhaul the motor. Take this to an auto electrician if in doubt as to its condition. individual parts are not readily available.

6  The obvious sequence of fault diagnosis must be used to check the working. The relay will usually fail first, then the thermostatic switch. The motors are very reliable.

## 13 Water temperature sender unit

1  The water temperature sender unit is located in the bottom of the thermostat housing (R1180). The R1181 fitment is on the rear end of the cylinder head.

2  Whilst operating in the same way in the majority of its applications its actual warning can differ from car to car. Most cars are fitted with a red warning light on the facia panel which is lit by the sender unit when the coolant is cold. It goes out as the car warms up, but will then come on again when the car is overheating. The temperatures at which it operates vary from application to application.

3  If it ceases to work it is easily replaced in a similar method to the thermostat. Drain the coolant sufficiently and unscrew, having removed its connecting wire. Replace with a new unit but make sure that you have also replaced its copper sealing ring.

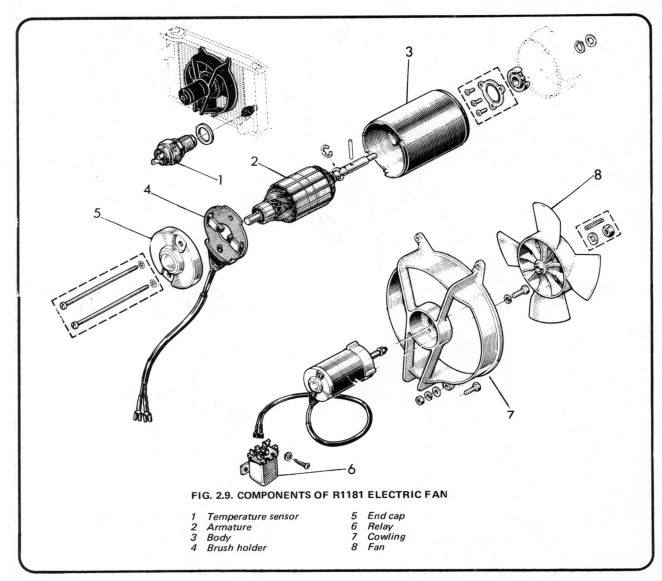

FIG. 2.9. COMPONENTS OF R1181 ELECTRIC FAN

| | |
|---|---|
| 1  Temperature sensor | 5  End cap |
| 2  Armature | 6  Relay |
| 3  Body | 7  Cowling |
| 4  Brush holder | 8  Fan |

## 14 Coolant hoses

1  All Renaults are fitted with 'once only' hose clips when new. If any work is undertaken on the cooling system, buy replacement hose clips to start with. Buy only wormdrive type clips and throw the original fitments away!

2  All coolant hoses are easily and obviously removed and replaced. Never skimp and always use proprietary replacements. The R1180 is fitted with some very 'shaped' hoses whilst the R1181 has some long trunkated ones, also it has a water heated manifold which requires more hoses.

3  A coolant leak is always obvious because of the searching nature of the coloured antifreeze used for all seasons in the Renault engine.

## 15 Water distribution tube and cover plate - removal and replacement

1  At the opposite end to the water pump on the cylinder head is a small retangular cover plate located by four setscrews. The cover plate hides the end of the water distribution tube in the cylinder head. Although the cover plate and a possible leaking gasket can be replaced with the engine and cylinder head in the car, the distribution tube cannot, nor even be inspected.

2  To replace a leaking cover plate gasket drain the coolant from the system and undo the four securing screws. Clean the mating surfaces and using gasket cement replace with the proper gasket and tighten sufficiently.

3  To inspect the water distribution tube, a task only worth doing when the cylinder head or engine are being overhauled, requires the cylinder head to be removed from the block. Remove the cover plate as described and check to see if the cylindrical steel tube, it's end visible through the cover plate end in the circular hole corroded badly, disintegrated or otherwise damaged. If it is damaged it will have to be drifted very delicately from the cover plate end through to the water pump end. This means removing the water pump. Check that replacement parts are available and have a skilled engineer to do the job for you. He should also replace the tube for you in the reverse motion.

4  The holes drilled in the tube should face towards the exhaust valve seats at an angle of 30% to the vertical and the end which has the two holes close together should be positioned at the cover plate end. Peen the ends after insertion to prevent any twisting movement. Replace the water pump and cover plate.

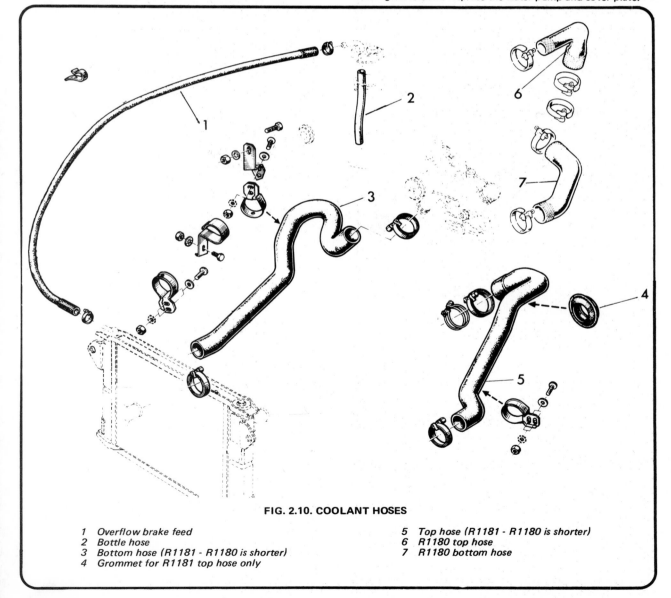

**FIG. 2.10. COOLANT HOSES**

1  Overflow brake feed
2  Bottle hose
3  Bottom hose (R1181 - R1180 is shorter)
4  Grommet for R1181 top hose only
5  Top hose (R1181 - R1180 is shorter)
6  R1180 top hose
7  R1180 bottom hose

## 16 Cooling system - fault diagnosis

| Symptom | Reason/s | Remedy |
| --- | --- | --- |
| Loss of coolant but no overheating provided | Expansion bottle empty<br>Small leaks in system | Half fill expansion bottle.<br>Examine all hoses and connections for signs of cracks and leaks when engine is both cold and hot, stationary and running. If no signs, use proprietary sealer in coolant to stop any invisible leaks. |
| Overheating and loss of coolant only when overheated | Faulty thermostat<br>Fan belt slipping/electric fan faulty<br>Engine out of tune due to ignition and/or fuel system settings being incorrect<br>Blockage or restriction in circulation of cooling water<br><br>Radiator cooling fins clogged up<br>Blown cylinder head gasket or cracked cylinder head<br>Sheared water pump impeller shaft<br>Cracked cylinder body<br><br>New engine still tight | Check and renew if faulty.<br>Check and adjust.<br>Check ignition and fuel systems and adjust as required.<br>Check that no hoses have collapsed.<br>Drain, flush out and refill cooling system. Use chemical flushing compound if necessary<br>Remove radiator and clean exterior as needed.<br>Remove cylinder head for examination.<br><br>Remove pump and check.<br>Remove engine and examine and repair (if possible).<br>Adjust engine speeds to suit until run in. |
| Engine runs too cool and heater inefficient | Thermostat missing or stuck open | Remove housing cover and inspect. |

# Chapter 3 Fuel system

**Contents**

**Specifications**

| Fuel pump | R1180 | R1181* |
|---|---|---|
| Make ... ... ... ... ... ... ... ... | SEV or Guiot, mechanical | |
| Delivery pressure ... ... ... ... ... ... | 50 gm sq cm (0.7 psi) | |

*Early models: some were fitted with SEV electric pumps

| Carburettor | ** Solex 32 PDIS-3 (early) | Solex 32 EISA-3 (early) |
|---|---|---|
| | | (Water heated manifold) |
| | | Solex F32 SEIA (after 1973) |
| Settings: | | |
| Choke tube ... ... ... ... ... ... ... | 24 | 23 |
| Main jet ... ... ... ... ... ... ... ... | 120 | 132 |
| Air compensator jet ... ... ... ... ... ... | 150 | 175 |
| Slow running jet ... ... ... ... ... ... | 47.5 | 50 |
| Needle valve ... ... ... ... ... ... ... | 1.2 mm | 1.5 mm |
| Accelerator pump ... ... ... ... ... ... | 47 | 35 |
| Float chamber fume | | |
| Valve opening ... ... ... ... ... ... ... | | 3 to 4 mm (1/8 in to 5/32 in) |
| Strangler/choke ... ... ... ... ... ... | Manual, by cable | |
| Idling speed (engine) ... ... ... ... ... ... | 675 to 725 rpm | |
| Fuel tank capacity ... ... ... ... ... ... | 8.8 gallons (40 litres) | |
| | (Some early R1180 were fitted with 7 gallon (32 litre) tanks) | |
| Air cleaner ... ... ... ... ... ... ... | Paper element, with 'summer/winter' setting | |
| Exhaust | | |
| R1180 ... ... ... ... ... ... ... ... | Single silencer under inner wing | |
| R1181 ... ... ... ... ... ... ... ... | Two silencers, one under inner wing plus tail silencer | |

**Some R1180 and R1181 may have been fitted with Zenith 32IF or Carter 32RBS. These are similar carburettors to those fitted and are described separately in Chapter 12.

## 1 General description

The fuel tank is mounted underneath the car at the rear and from this fuel is drawn by a mechanical pump (some R1181 models are fitted with an electric pump, see Section 9 and Fig. 3.9) and delivered to the carburettor.

The pump, of either SEV or Guiot manufacture, is operated by an arm actuated by a lobe on the camshaft and is located halfway down the cylinder block on the left hand side, the opposite side of the carburettor. The pump incorporates a filter screen. Fuel is delivered to a single fixed choke carburettor. Two types of carburettor have been fitted, manufactured by Solex depending on model. The output of the pump exceeds all normal requirements of the carburettor and the level of the fuel in the carburettor float chamber is regulated by a float operated needle valve. When the valve is closed, shutting off the flow, the pump freewheels. The diaphragm is held up by the pressure in the line until such time as the carburettor needle valve opens allowing the spring action of the pump to resume oscillating the diaphragm and to deliver more fuel.

The air taken in through the carburettor to mix with the fuel vapour is filtered by a renewable paper element.

### 2  Air filter element - removal and renewal

1  Unscrew the bolt which holds the whole air cleaner assembly to the carburettor. Then disconnect the inlet hose from the air cleaner. (Throw the original hose clip away and refit with a worm drive clip). Once clear the whole unit may be lifted off and separated to give access to the filter element. Clean out the interior of the filter housing. If the same element is to be refitted tap it on a flat surface to remove any loose accumulations of dust. On some models the rocker cover breather pipe feeds into the air cleaner body. Do NOT try and wash the filter element, brush it - or blow it with compressed air.

2  When reassembling the unit make sure that the sealing ring is intact and in place. When fitting the element, it should seat snugly over the locating ridges in the housing.

3  The air intake pipe may be positioned for 'Summer' or 'Winter' conditions by revolving the casing, before the bolt is tightened, so that for 'Summer' conditions the pipe points towards the inner wing at right angles to the exhaust pipe, and for 'Winter' conditions the pipe exits directly above the exhaust pipe to enable it to draw in warm air. NOTE: The stud onto which the whole assembly fits should remain in the carburettor body when the filter is changed. Check that the assembly does not foul the throttle cable.

### 3  Carburettor - descriptions and principle

1  Although each model has a different carburettor Solex 32 PDIS-3 (R1180) and Solex 32 EISA-3 (R1181), they are similar in principal and operation. Apart from their difference in choke size, the basic difference is that the R1181 has a water heated manifold.

2  Petrol is pumped into the float chamber and is regulated by the needle valve. This fuel is sucked into either the main or pilot jet at a rate depending upon the depression in the venturi, or choke of the carburettor, which in turn is controlled by the speed of the engine. It is fed into the venturi as a fine spray to be mixed with air, the flow of which is controlled by the butterfly, and then when mixed, into the combustion chambers of the engine to be combusted. The running of the engine with regard to carburation is controlled by the throttle or butterfly stop screw and its relative position when compared with the air volume control screw. The flow of petrol once past the float chamber is fixed by the jet size and therefore the tuning of the carburettor is totally controlled by the rate of the air flow through the carburettor.

3  At low engine speeds the fuel flows through the pilot jet (idling jet), but as the speed increases there is a point of change over when sufficient depression is available to draw the fuel from the float chamber and bypass the pilot jet through the main jet. The operation of the choke when starting an engine from cold in effect feeds excess petrol, and to a certain extent air, into the venturi through a separate drilling in the carburettor because there is insufficient depression in the engine to draw enough fuel through the idling or main jets. The manual choke is controlled by the driver who can judge when the engine is warm enough not to need this excess of fuel.

### 4  Carburettor - removal and replacement

**R1180**

1  The carburettor may be removed easily with the engine in the car, for inspection and cleaning. Under some circumstances it may be wise to remove it from the manifold before removing an engine from the car.

2  Remove the air cleaner body and with a pair of self-gripping pliers twist out the stud on which the casing sits.

3  Undo the holding bolt on the choke lever arm at the end of the choke cable and the outer cable casing grip on the car-

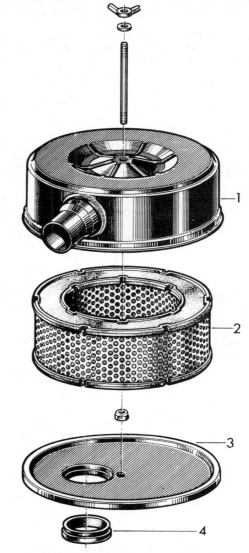

**FIG. 3.1. AIR CLEANER COMPONENTS - BOTH MODELS**

| | |
|---|---|
| 1  Top | 3  Base |
| 2  Paper filter | 4  'O' ring seal |

2.2 Note the centre sealing ring and the locknut on the spindle

burettor. Pull out the cable away from the carburettor and tie back.

4  Unhook the throttle spring and allow to hang on its catch.

5  Pull off the fuel pipe from the carburettor and plug the end with a pencil or suitable instrument to stop fuel dripping out.

6  Release the throttle cable and then the rod from its lever, and tie back. This will be a push-on-ball fit, and a setscrew with a hole drilled through it. Do not be surprised if the throttle pedal rests on the floor of the car. The throttle pedal is described in Chapter 8.

7  With an open ended spanner undo the two fixing nuts from their studs and remove together with their washers.

8  Lift off the carburettor and retrieve the gaskets and fixing bracket. Plug the manifold inlet with some clean rag.

9  Replacement of the carburettor is an exact reversal of removal but you must be sure that the correct number of gaskets have been replaced and that all the operating controls be they cable or rod are fitted in their correct position and that they are not fully tightened up until total adjustment has taken place. It is silly to run with the choke out all the time because you overtightened the cable!

### R1181

10  Removal and replacement of the R1181 carburettor is exactly similar to that of the R1180 except that the water inlet and outlet pipes should be nipped before removal to save yourself the necessity of draining and refilling the cooling system. Use new wormdrive hose clips to secure. Also pull off the vacuum advance pipe.

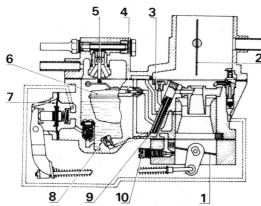

**FIG. 3.2. CROSS-SECTION OF SOLEX 32 PDIS**

| | |
|---|---|
| 1  *Throttle butterfly* | 6  *Float* |
| 2  *Choke flap* | 7  *Accelerator pump* |
| 3  *Air compensator jet* | 8  *Main jet* |
| 4  *Idling speed jet* | 9  *Emulsion tube* |
| 5  *Needle valve* | 10  *Fuel screw* |

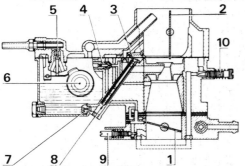

**FIG. 3.3. CROSS-SECTION OF SOLEX 32 EISA**

| | |
|---|---|
| 1  *Throttle butterfly* | 6  *Float* |
| 2  *Choke flap* | 7  *Main jet* |
| 3  *Air compensator jet* | 8  *Emulsion tube* |
| 4  *Idling speed jet* | 9  *Fuel screw* |
| 5  *Needle valve* | 10  *Air screw* |

### 5  Carburettor - setting and adjustment

1  Before making any adjustments to the carburettor settings make sure that your reasons for the adjustment are sound and that you only do one at a time. Check the result of each adjustment after it is made. The carburettor is a finely balanced and a relatively delicate instrument and can easily be put off tune.

2  Control settings are important. Make sure that the operation of the choke cable moves the lever easily throughout its full range of movement and returns to its closed position when the control knob is pushed home. Adjustment can be made by re-positioning the inner cable relative to the operating arm at the clamping screw. The outer cable can be repositioned as necessary where it clips to the bracket on the carburettor.

3  The throttle cable and rod should also be checked for movement throughout its range. Make particularly sure that when the throttle flap is in the fully open position the position of the accelerator pedal is as far down as it could possibly be, even with the cable disconnected. Otherwise pressure on the pedal will impact severe strain on the cable, and more important on the throttle spindle and bearings. Adjustment should be made at the point where the end of the cable outer is located into the bracket near the carburettor. Slacken the locknuts and move the outer cable so that when the accelerator pedal is fully depressed the throttle is just fully open. Twist the head on the end of the rod to achieve the same result. Relock it.

4  Slow running adjustment is controlled by the throttle stop screw for the R1180 which in turn regulates the position of the throttle flap when the accelerator cable is at rest. The R1181 uses an airflow screw instead. This regulates the air mixture with that of the fuel. The single jet screw controls fuel mixture throughout the full operational range. If satisfactory slow-running cannot be achieved with the throttle stop/airflow screw adjustment, then it will be necessary to proceed to the following check which affects the carburettor performance at all speeds.

**Special Note:** Under no circumstances must the settings of the R1181 carburettor throttle bleed screw and cold start setting be altered. These are set at manufacture. If you do you will defeat the fine workings of your carburettor.

5  Make sure that the car has reached its fully operational temperature which should take at least ten minutes from cold.

### R1180

6  Screw in the mixture screw right in with the engine not running. Undo it again three turns.

7  Screw up the idling/throttle stop screw and then unscrew it so that it is just touching the lever.

8  Start the engine and turn this stop screw out until the engine turns over at what you judge to be the normal tickover speed (approximately 700 rpm). The engine should not be too smooth-running at this stage.

9  Now turn the mixture screw either way, probably outwards, until the highest and smoothest tickover speed is obtained. This too should be approximately 700 rpm.

### R1181

10  Turn the air screw to obtain a normal tickover speed (by ear, in fact 675 rpm).

11  Then turn the fuel screw until the engine reaches its maximum speed.

12  Repeat both operations until the maximum engine speed lies between 675 and 700 rpm when turning the fuel screw. Then screw in the fuel screw 'a fraction' to just lower the engine speed but keeping its smoothness.

### Both R1180 and R1181

13  If the tickover setting is not obtainable or is racing the engine then you should recheck your carburettor controls for correctness of fitting and start again. If you are not able to obtain a reasonable tickover such are the variables which can affect the smooth running of the engine that you should look once more at the carburettor and then go on and check the ignition system and other more serious mechanical parts.

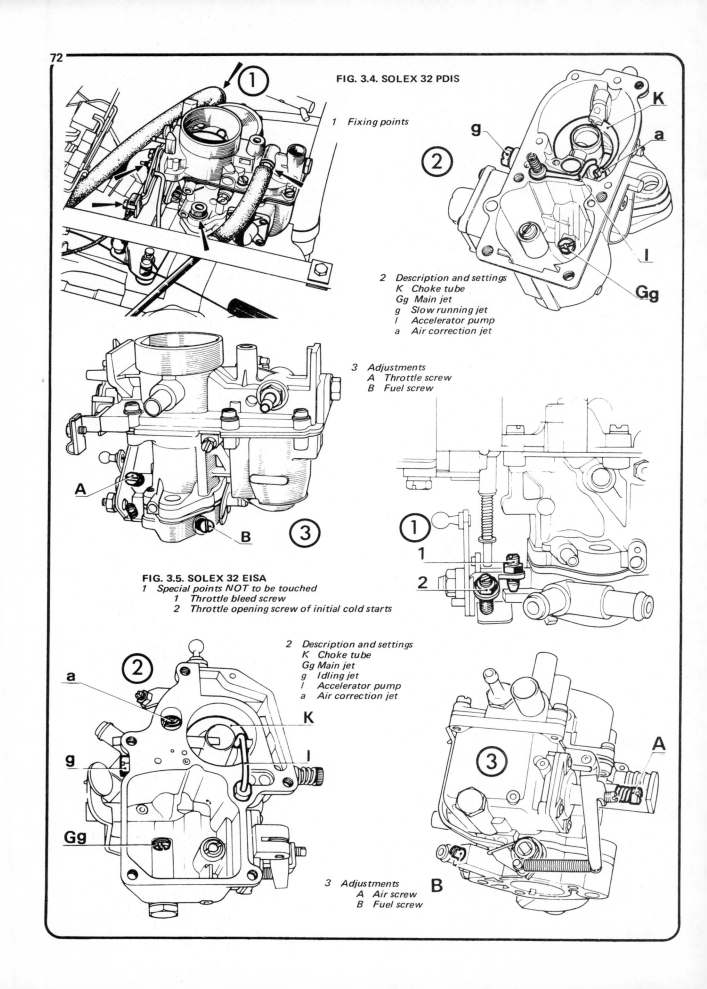

**FIG. 3.4. SOLEX 32 PDIS**

1 Fixing points

2 Description and settings
K Choke tube
Gg Main jet
g Slow running jet
l Accelerator pump
a Air correction jet

3 Adjustments
A Throttle screw
B Fuel screw

**FIG. 3.5. SOLEX 32 EISA**
1 Special points NOT to be touched
1 Throttle bleed screw
2 Throttle opening screw of initial cold starts

2 Description and settings
K Choke tube
Gg Main jet
g Idling jet
l Accelerator pump
a Air correction jet

3 Adjustments
A Air screw
B Fuel screw

## 6 Carburettor - dismantling, inspection and reassembly

1 Do not dismantle the carburettor unless it is absolutely necessary. This should be only for cleaning at intervals of 9000 miles or when systematic diagnosis indicates that there is a fault with it. The internal mechanism is delicate and finely balanced and unnecessary tinkering will probably do more harm than good.

2 Although certain parts may be removed with the carburettor still attached to the engine, nevertheless, it is considered safer to remove it and work over a bench.

3 With the carburettor off the car disassembly is as follows (this covers all carburettors fitted, with slight variations which, because of their simple and obvious nature, are not specifically mentioned each time. Remove the top of the carburettor by undoing its fixing screws with the correct size screwdriver. These screws are made of comparatively soft metal and will damage very easily. With the top should come the choke mechanism (both types), fuel inlet pipe and filter (if fitted), and needle valve. The gasket and float itself should remain in the body of the carburettor. The relevant exploded diagrams will show you specifically what is fitted to each type.

4 Remove the gasket and the float placing bracket or spindle and then the float itself.

5 Remove any jets and their washers which have screwdriver cuts in their heads and are removable from the top and inside of the carburettor.

6 Unscrew all the external adjusting screws but note Section 5, paragraph 4 now. Retain all washers and springs and code for their relevant positions.

7 Turn the top of the carburettor upside down and remove the needle valve and its washer.

8 On Solex carburettors you will be able to remove the choke tube itself from the body of the carburettor.

9 There is no point under any circumstances in removing any more parts from the carburettor. If any of these parts are in need of attention then a complete new carburettor is needed. It is safer and more efficient, if you have reached this stage of need of repair to replace the complete unit.

10 All the parts which have been separated should be thoroughly cleaned in methylated spirit or clean petrol by hand and without the help of anything more than a soft non-fluffy rag. Do not use any scrapers, emery paper, wire wool or hard projections such as a pin on these parts. All have been machined to extremely fine tolerances. Blow all parts dry.

11 Inspect for blockages and scoring, the float for a puncture and the needle valve for easy operation. On floats make sure the metal tag is not bent or distorted. Renew if it is. There is no room for float level adjustment. Renew any parts which are obviously worn or damaged but also do so to any which you even suspect. (Make sure that parts are still available though before throwing away - you may need a temporary repair).

12 Replace all parts in the reverse of their removal using new copper washers and gaskets all the way through. Do not over-tighten anything, and do not use any gasket cement. If the top of the carburettor does not fit flat it needs renewing. SPECIAL NOTE: No mention has been made of throttle, choke and butterfly spindles. As these spindles run directly in the body or top of the carburettor they are likely over a period of usage to wear. It is impractical to replace parts of these and any wear or failure in these parts must mean complete renewal.

## 7 Choke cable

The choke cable should not need touching unless it snaps or receives a permanent kink in it. It is of stiff steel wire. Its removal and replacement is conventional and straightforward. Its pull knob must be removed by unscrewing the nut behind the dashboard. Both inner and outer cable must be removed and replaced from inside the car.

7.1 Thumb is very close to the end of the choke cable

## 8 Throttle cable

The flexible throttle cable is easily renewed if broken. Make sure all the fixings at the carburettor are re-installed. Also make sure it does not 'go through' any tight curves. It helps to lubricate a new cable with light oil. There is a compressing spring at the carburettors end. It should be nearly compressed when the throttle is fully open.

## 9 Fuel pump - removal and replacement

1 The mechanical fuel pump will need removing if it is to be dismantled for overhaul, but the filter can be cleaned in situ. Disconnect the fuel lines on the inlet and outlet sides by pulling off the connector pipes on both sides.

2 Undo the two nuts, one is a nut on a stud the other is a setscrew, holding the pump flange to the crankcase, and take the pump off. Keep the spacer and gaskets together and do not discard them. If necessary blank off the fuel line from the tank to prevent loss of fuel.

3 Replacement is a reversal of the removal procedure. Make sure that the total thickness of gaskets and spacer is the same as came off. Check that the fuel line connections are not leaking after starting the engine.

4 Two types of mechanical pump are fitted. The R1180 is strictly conventional, whilst the R1181 is essentially similar but is fitted 'upsidedown' ie., the operating lever is above the diaphragm and the fuel inlet end outlet below.

5 Some early model R.H.D. R1181s were fitted with SEV electric pumps situated inside a protective shield below the fuel tank filler pipe. They are of the 'short suck, long blow' variety operating on the familiar SU style. Once the protective shield is removed, they are easily removed. Jack up the car: removing the adjacent road wheel will help. Once the electrical connection is pulled off, then the inlet/outlet pipes, they themselves can be inspected.

6 They work if they tick when the ignition key is switched on. No parts are available. If they fail they must be renewed. It is likely that a mechanical pump can be fitted instead because the electric ones were only supplied to ease parts flow on manufacture.

## 10 Fuel pump - inspection, dismantling and reassembly

1 First clean the pump exterior thoroughly and mark the edges of the two halves of the body.

8.1a This shows the correct layout of the throttle cable and its return spring (R1180 rhd)

8.1b The two arrows show the cable stop and its spring outer

9.1 Shows the special stud and the correct gasket

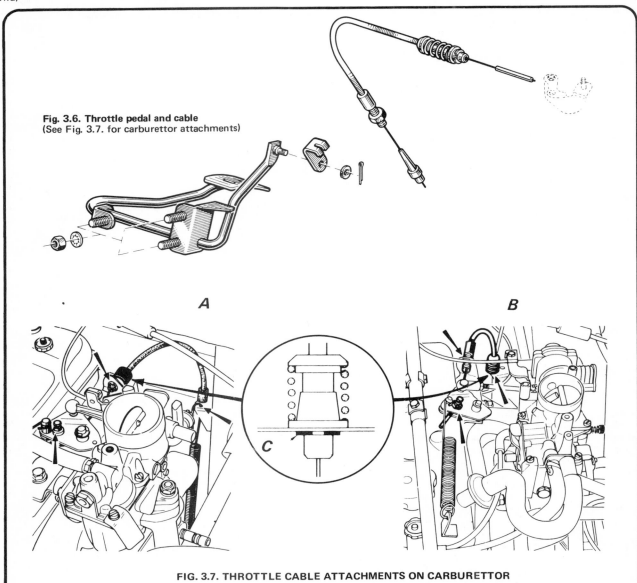

Fig. 3.6. Throttle pedal and cable
(See Fig. 3.7. for carburettor attachments)

A

B

C

FIG. 3.7. THROTTLE CABLE ATTACHMENTS ON CARBURETTOR

A    Early model R1180 - (shows left hand drive version. Rhd is very similar but appears from left of figure)

B    Late model R1180 and all R1181 - again shows lhd but rhd is similar)

C    Shows cross section of spring mounted cable outer and correct fitment

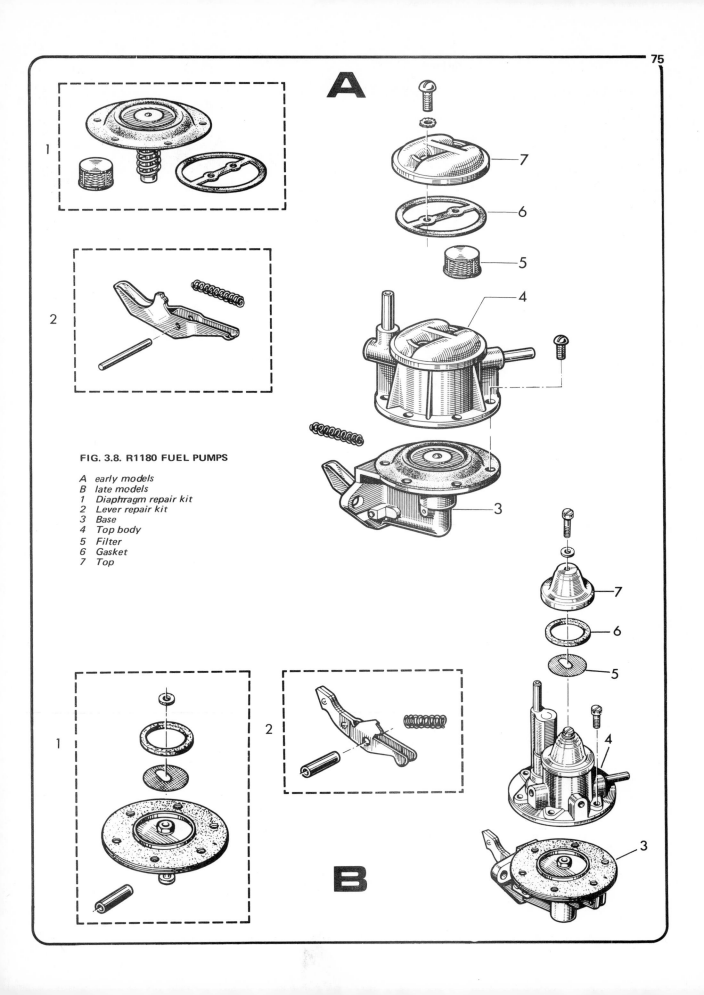

**FIG. 3.8. R1180 FUEL PUMPS**

A  early models
B  late models
1  Diaphragm repair kit
2  Lever repair kit
3  Base
4  Top body
5  Filter
6  Gasket
7  Top

2 Undo the cover retaining clip and lift off the cover. The gasket and gauze filter may then be removed.

3 Remove the screws and washers holding the two halves of the pump together and the top (R1180)/bottom (R1181) half may then be lifted off.

4 The diaphragm and pushrod should be removed next but you will have to remove the pump lever and its spindle to release it. This is done by releasing one of the spindle circlips. This can prove to be very fiddly but with patience and a strong blunt penknife blade the circlip can be 'peeled' off. The R1181 differs slightly here but it will be obvious. Push the spindle through and pull out the lever. Retrieve the lever spring. Lift out the diaphragm and its rod carefully. This spindle is usually known as the rocker arm pivot pin.

5 If there are signs of wear in the rocker arm pivot pin, and rocker arm and link bushes then they should be renewed.

6 The valve assemblies should only be removed from the upper body if renewal is necessary. They are staked into the body and are destroyed when levered out.

7 Examine the diaphragm for signs of cracking or perforation and renew if necessary.

8 Overhaul kits are usually available for all pumps and are supplied with a new diaphragm, valves and sealing rings. Check the manufacture of the pump first as well as the supply.

9 When fitting new valve assemblies to the body, first fit the seating washers and then place the valves, making sure that they are the correct way up according to inlet and outlet. The body will have to be restaked at six (different) places round the edge so that the assemblies are firmly held in their positions. If this is not done properly and leakage occurs between the valve assembly and the seating ring the pump will not operate efficiently.

10 To replace the diaphragm and lever arm it will be necessary to place the diaphragm spring in the body of the pump. Then the diaphragm and its rod. Press the diaphragm spring down and fit the spring, push in the lever (the right way up) and connect over the top of the machined stop on the rod. Push in the rocker arm pivot pin and push through the lever. Replace the circlip on the pivot pin. Always use a new circlip.

11 Fit the upper half of the pump body and line up the mating marks. In order to assemble the two halves and the diaphragm properly push the rocker arm upwards so that the diaphragm is drawn level. Then place the eight screws in position lightly. It is best if the base of the pump is held in a vice whilst the rocker arm is pushed right up to bring the diaphragm to the bottom of its stroke. A short piece of tube over the rocker arm will provide easy leverage. In this position the eight screws should be tightened evenly and alternately.

12 Fit a new filter bowl gasket carefully in the groove of the upper body, making sure that it does not twist or buckle in the process. Replace the cover and screw it tight.

13 When the pump is reassembled the suction and delivery pressure can be felt at the inlet and outlet ports when the rocker arm is operated. Be careful not to block the inlet port completely when testing suction. If the rocker arm were to be operated strongly and the inlet side was blocked the diaphragm could be damaged.

---

## 11 Fuel gauge - tank sender unit

1 The fuel gauge sender unit is mounted on the top of the tank where the fuel outlet pipe connection is also made, sucking up the petrol through a filter on the end of a tube. If the fuel gauge appears faulty first check the wiring connections at the back of the instrument panel, See Chapter 9. Then go on to the sender unit which is a variable resistance giving different readings with both a full and empty tank by the operation of a varnished cork float. If the fault lies here and you are sure that the sender unit was properly connected, you will have to renew the whole unit. It is not possible to replace parts of it.

2 To remove the sender unit pull the rear seat forward, lift the rubber foam covering and prise off the centre panel in the floor.

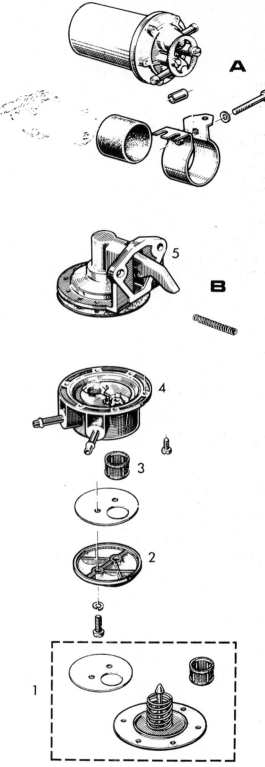

**FIG. 3.9. R1181 FUEL PUMPS**

A  *Electric pump with positioning clamp*
B  *Mechanical pump components*
1  *Diaphragm repair kit*               5  *Top body*
2  *Base cap*
3  *Filter*
4  *Base*

This will expose the top of the unit.

Disconnect the electrical leads from the sender unit, unscrew the three locating screws and lift out carefully turning the body of the unit to release the float and filter tube. When replacing always use a new gasket and do not overtighten. Make sure that the two connections are clean and tight.

3   These are reliable instruments and are usually non-functioning because of some mechanical defect rather than electrical, ie the float arm is bent, or the float has been perforated.

4   Removal of the fuel tank is described in Chapter 11.

## 12 Exhaust system

1   The exhaust system, although peculiar in its arrangement is conventional in its working and extremely simple to repair as it has one silencer for the R1180 and two for the R1181 and either three or four pipe sections. It is wise only to use original type exhaust clamps and proprietary made systems.

2   When any one section of the exhaust system needs renewal it often follows that the whole lot is best replaced.

3   It is most important when fitting exhausts that the twists and contours are carefully followed and that each connecting joint overlaps the correct distance. Any stresses or strain imparted, in order to force the system to fit the hanger rubbers, will result in early fractures and failures.

4   When fitting a new part or a complete system it is well worth removing ALL the system from the car and cleaning up all the joints so that they fit together easily. The time spent struggling with obstinate joints whilst flat on your back under the car is eliminated and the likelihood of distorting or even breaking a section is greatly reduced. Do not waste a lot of time trying to undo rusted and corroded clamps and bolts. Cut them off. New ones will be required anyway if they are that bad.

5   The critical fitting point is the exit hole of the first pipe through the inner wing direct to the silencer. Only adjust this point when the whole system is in place but not fully tightened. The pipe should run through the centre of the hole. Tighten the two exhaust clamps from under the bonnet first, get this right and rigid before finally fixing the rest of the system. Two sorts of exit pipes are in use. One under the rear of the car for the R1180 employing the fourth pipe, and the other exiting at the rear but through another silencer for the R1181. It is possible, if the parts are available, to swop one system for another with the addition or substraction or another clamp and rubber mounting point.

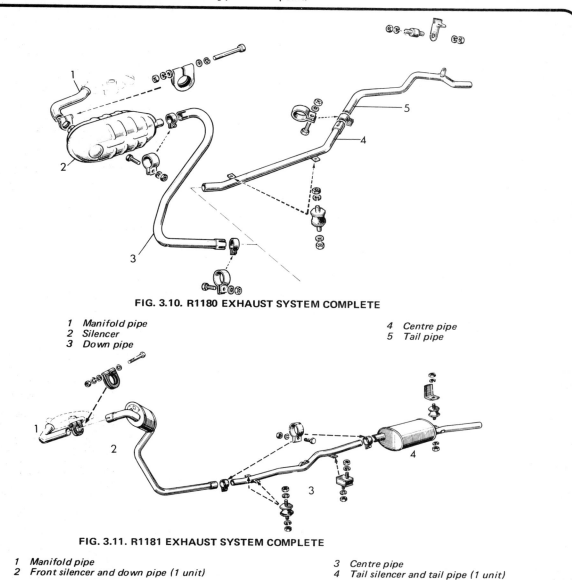

**FIG. 3.10. R1180 EXHAUST SYSTEM COMPLETE**

| 1 | Manifold pipe | 4 | Centre pipe |
| 2 | Silencer | 5 | Tail pipe |
| 3 | Down pipe | | |

**FIG. 3.11. R1181 EXHAUST SYSTEM COMPLETE**

| 1 | Manifold pipe | 3 | Centre pipe |
| 2 | Front silencer and down pipe (1 unit) | 4 | Tail silencer and tail pipe (1 unit) |

## 13 Fault diagnosis - Fuel and exhaust system

Unsatisfactory engine performance and excessive fuel consumption are not necessarily the fault of the fuel system or carburettor. In fact they more commonly occur as a result of ignition and timing faults. Before acting on the following it is necessary to check the ignition system first. Even though a fault may lie in the fuel system it will be difficult to trace unless the ignition is correct. The faults below, therefore, assume that this has been attended to first (where appropriate).

| Symptom | Reason/s | Remedy |
|---|---|---|
| Smell of petrol when engine is stopped | Leaking fuel lines or unions | Repair or renew as necessary. |
|  | Leaking fuel tank | Fill fuel tank to capacity and examine carefully at seams, unions and filler pipe connections. Repair as necessary. |
| Smell of petrol when engine is idling | Leaking fuel line unions between pump and carburettor | Check line and unions and tighten or repair. |
|  | Overflow of fuel from float chamber due to wrong level setting, ineffective needle valve or punctured float | Check fuel level setting and condition of float and needle valve, and renew if necessary. |
| Excessive fuel consumption for reasons not covered by leaks or float chamber faults | Worn jets | Renew jets or carburettor body if not removable |
|  | Over-rich jet setting | Adjust jet. |
|  | Sticking mechanism | Check correct movement of mechanism. |
| Difficult starting, uneven running, lack of power, cutting out | One or more jets blocked or restricted | Dismantle and clean out float chamber and jets. |
|  | Float chamber fuel level too low or needle valve sticking | Dismantle and check fuel level and needle valve. |
|  | Fuel pump not delivering sufficient fuel | Check pump delivery and clean or repair as required. |

# Chapter 4  Ignition system

## Contents

## Specifications

**Spark plugs**

| | |
|---|---|
| Standard ... ... ... ... ... ... ... ... | AC 44F |
| 14mm ... ... ... ... ... ... ... ... | Marchal 35/36R |
| | Champion L87Y |
| Electrode gap ... ... ... ... ... ... ... | 0.5 to 0.7 mm (0.020 to 0.028 in) |

**Coil (12 volt)**

| | |
|---|---|
| Make ... ... ... ... ... ... ... ... ... | SEV type FC with SEV distributor |

**Distributor**

| | |
|---|---|
| Make and type ... ... ... ... ... ... ... | R1180: SEV type 27914 } (Refer also to Chapter 12 |
| | R1181: SEV type 403 035 12 } Specifications) |
| Rotation ... ... ... ... ... ... ... ... | Clockwise |
| Firing order ... ... ... ... ... ... ... ... | 1, 3, 4, 2 |
| Contact points gap ... ... ... ... ... ... ... | 0.4 mm (0.016 in) |
| Ignition timing ... ... ... ... ... ... ... | R1180: 0 mm $\pm$ 1 mm } (Refer also to Chapter 12 |
| (Static at flywheel) ... ... ... ... ... ... | R1181: 0 mm $\pm$ 1 mm } Specifications) |
| Dwell percentage ... ... ... ... ... ... ... | 63 $\pm$ 3 |
| Dwell angle ... ... ... ... ... ... ... ... | 57⁰ $\pm$ 3⁰ |

## 1  General description

In order that the internal combustion engine with spark ignition can operate properly, it is essential that the spark be delivered at the spark plug electrodes at the precise moment it is required. This moment varies - in relation to the position of the pistons and crankshaft - depending on the speed and loading of the engine. This control of the spark timing is automatic. When it is realised that at 50 mph approximately 100 sparks per second are being produced then the importance of the need for precise setting is realised. The majority of minor faults and cases of poor performance and economy can be traced to the ignition system.

The principles are as follows: Battery voltage (12 volts) is fed through a circuit which passes through a coil developing high voltage.

Without going into electrical principles it is sufficient to say that when the 12 volt circuit is 'made', current is fed into a capacitor (condenser). When the circuit is broken the condenser discharges its current into the low voltage line and a high voltage current is boosted from the core of the coil and along the HT lead. This current is delivered to the centre contact of the distributor cap and from there, via the rotor arm, to each of the other four contacts in turn. Each of these is linked by a 'high tension' lead to each spark plug.

Obviously the timing of the break in the circuit decides the moment at which the spark is made. The contact points (or breaker points!) are in effect a switch. Not only do they open and close four times for every 2 revolutions of the crankshaft - delivering a spark to the four plugs in turn - they also open earlier or later in relation to the position of the crankshaft/ pistons. Ignition advance and retard are the terms used to express this condition and it is measured in degrees - being degrees of angle of any crank on the shaft. Zero degrees is top dead centre, being the highest point of the arc made by a crank. Timing setting is therefore expressed as so many degrees BTDC (before top dead centre).

In order to vary the ignition timing the contact opening cam is able to revolve a certain amount around the centre spindle.

This is controlled by spring-loaded weights which move out under centrifugal force. When they move out, the spindle to cam position is altered.

Vacuum advance is fitted to the R1181 but not to the R1180.

Timing varies with different engines (see Specifications). When accelerating and under open throttle conditions the centrifugal control is in operation. The static timing is important of course as the automatic timing advance device starts from this point and consequently if it is incorrect the whole range is affected.

The manual clamp adjustment on the body clamp adjusts the static ignition setting entirely.

Whilst little is in fact identical in the way of components between the R1180 and R1181 the principles, dismantling and reassembly, services and checks are all similar and can be discussed together. Any specific differences are pointed out.

## 2    Rountine maintenance

### a)  Spark plugs

Remove the plugs and thoroughly clean away all traces of carbon. Examine the porcelain insulation round the central electrodes inside the plug and if damaged discard the plug. Reset the gap between the electrodes. Do not use a set of plugs for more than 9000 miles. It is false economy.

At the same time check the plug caps. Always use the straight tubular ones normally fitted. Good replacements can come from a Volkswagen agency.

### b)  Distributor

Every 9000 miles remove the cap and rotor arm and put one or two drops of engine oil into the centre of the cam recess. Smear the surfaces of the cam itself with petroleum jelly. Do not overlubricate as any excess could get onto the contact point surfaces and cause ignition difficulties.

Every 9000 miles examine the contact point surfaces. If there is a build up of deposits on one face and a pit in the other it will be impossible to set the gap correctly and they should be refaced or renewed. Set the gap when the contact surfaces are in order.

Check the proper functioning of the R1181 vacuum advance mechanism.

### c)  General

Examine all leads and terminals for signs of broken or cracked insulation. Also check all terminal connections for slackness or signs of fracturing of some strands of wire. Partly broken wire should be renewed.

The HT leads are particularly important as any insulation faults will cause the high voltage to 'jump' to the nearest earth and this will prevent a spark at the plug. Check that no HT leads are loose or in a position where the insulation could wear due to rubbing against part of the engine.

## 3    Distributor - contact points - adjustment

1    Remove the distributor cap by unclipping, the two leaf springs, one each side of the distributor.
2    Pull off the rotor arm from the cam spindle and remove the plastic dust shield (if fitted).
3    First examine the points by carefully levering them apart with a small screwdriver or something similar. If the faces of the circular contacts are pitted or rough they they cannot be properly set and should be removed for renewal or cleaning up.
4    If the faces are clean then turn the engine so that the moving arm of the breaker rests with the following on one of the four high points on the cam. The engine can be turned by engaging a gear and moving the car.
5    Select a feeler blade (0.4 mm/0.016 in) applicable for both models and place it between the points. If the gap is too great, slacken the fixed point locking screw and move the plate to alter the gap. If the gap is too small the feeler blade may still fit between the points as the spring loaded arm can simply move back. When setting them, therefore, the feeler ·gauge blade should only be a very light touch on each contact face.
6    Lock the fixed plate screw and recheck the gap. Replace the rotor arm making sure that the lug in the rotor recess is fully engaged in the slot on the cam spindle.
7    Check the inside of the distributor cap before replacing it and verify that the four contacts are clean and the centre carbon brush is intact and moves freely.

## 4    Distributor - contact points - removal and replacement

1    The contact points will need removal if the surfaces are bad enough to require renewal or refacing. Generally it is best to renew the contacts completely as refacing never produces a surface as good as the original and they will deteriorate again much more rapidly.
2    Remove the distributor cap, rotor arm and dust shield as described in the previous section and remove the fixed plate locking screw.
3    Remove the small circlip on the terminal post which also secures the end of the spring and lift off the washer. Undo until loose the small nut which secures the lead to the condenser and the spring of the contact breaker arm. Lift upwards the spring contact from the pivot post. Now remove the fixed contact locking screw and lift out this contact. It is wise even for changing contact points to have a set of metric distributor spanners to avoid the use of pliers.
4    Replacement is the EXACT reversal of the removal sequence. Do not get anything muddled and take your time.

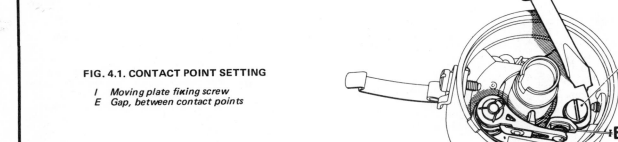

### FIG. 4.1. CONTACT POINT SETTING

*I    Moving plate fixing screw*
*E    Gap, between contact points*

3.2 Pull off the rotor arm

3.5 The feeler blade in place

4.3 The fixed contact locking screw

---

**5  Distributor - condenser - testing, removal and replacement**

1  A faulty condenser causes interruptions in the ignition circuit or total failure. Elaborate testing methods are pointless as the item is cheap to renew.

2  If the contact points become pitted after a relatively small mileage (under 1000) and if starting is difficult then it is a good idea to renew the condenser when replacing the points. Another way to check is to remove the distributor cap, rotor arm and dust shield and turn the engine so that the points are closed. Then switch on the ignition and open the points using an insulated screwdriver. There should be a small blue spark visible but if the condenser is faulty there will be a fat blue spark.

3  The condenser is external to the working of the types of distributor fitted to these engines although it may be in either a vertical or horizontal position. Using the correct spanner undo the lead from the condenser to the fixing post on the side of the distributor. (Some models may be fitted with a metal tag instead). Remove the body of the condenser from the other fixing post which also holds one of the distributor cap clips. Fit a new one in reverse order. Make sure you fit the correct condenser.

5.3 The terminal being loosened using the proper spanner

---

**6  Distributor - removal and replacement**

1  The distributor will need removal if there are indications that the drive spindle is a sloppy fit in the bushes (causing contact

gap setting difficulties) or if it is to be dismantled and thoroughly cleaned and checked. It should also be removed before the oil pump is taken out.

2  Before removing the distributor it is helpful to prevent future confusion if the engine is positioned with No 1 piston at TDC on the firing stroke. This can be done by noting the position of the No 1 plug lead in the cap and then turning the engine to TDC so that the rotor is adjacent to the No 1 plug position in the cap. (The cap of course, will be removed to do this). For details see Section 8 - 'Ignition timing'.

3  Detach the plug leads from the spark plugs and the coil HT lead from the distributor cap or coil. Remove the cap by unclipping the leaf spring clip at each side.

4  Undo the LT lead at the coil - this should be a screw on connector, and pull off the vacuum advance pipe from the R1181 distributor.

5  Undo the one setscrew which locates the baseplate to the cylinder block on the side of the distributor drive casing. Do not at this stage undo the clamp bolt which fixes the baseplate to the distributor body R1180. If this is removed you will have to retime the engine. Of course it may be necessary if a new distributor is fitted, but wait until the distributor is away from the engine.

6  Lift the distributor up and out, the locating flange and sealing ring should come with it. Before proceeding any further, note the position of the eccentric slot in the end of the drive shaft inside the distributor mounting recess in the block. This will give a firm timing reference if the oil pump is to be removed.

7  Replacement is a reversal of the removal procedure. Check that the rubber sealing ring between the flange and block is in good condition. Line up the eccentric tongue on the distributor shaft with the slot in the drive shaft and when the sleeve of the body is being pushed down be prepared to rotate the shaft either way a little so as to engage the drive.

8  Upon camshaft removal and replacement this slotted drive gear will have been removed. Refit into the oil pump drive skew gear in eaxctly the same position from which it was removed.

---

**7  Distributor - dismantling, inspection and reassembly**

1  If the distributor is causing trouble with the ignition system it is often a good idea to fit a completely new unit. Without proper test equipment it is difficult to diagnose whether or not the centrifugal advance mechanism is performing as it should (It is possible to check on the vacuum advance of the R1181). However, play in the shaft bushes can be detected by removing the rotor arm and gripping the end and trying to move it sideways. If there is any movement then it means that the cam cannot accurately control the contact points gap. This must receive attention.

2  With the distributor removed take off the rotor, condenser and contact points as described in Section 4.

3  If, at this stage, you consider that the distributor is in need of

replacement and that you will have to retime the engine then you should remove the base clamp now R 1180 only (the R 1181 has one forked clamp which is always loosened!) otherwise it can be left on throughout the dismantling stages. Release the clamp bolt and pull off the plate.

4   Remove the felt oil-soak washer from the top of the cam.

5   On R 1181 distributors disconnect the vacuum advance piston from the base plate by removing the small circlip from the fixing stud and lifting off. Unscrew the two fixing screws from outside the casing and pull the mechanism out through and away.

6   Remove the contact point baseplate by removing totally the two distributor cap clip fixing setscrews through the side of the distributor body and the condenser/contact spring fixing point. Pull upwards the contact points baseplate and remove.

7   Remove the shaft circlip and washers at the bottom end of the distributor by 'peeling' it off with a penknife.

8   Pull up through the body of the distributor the shaft with the automatic advance mechanism still intact.

9   Remove the advance mechanism springs gently. Do not twist or distort them.

10 It is possible to go further still in the dismantling of the shaft and the advance mechanism by driving out the very small through-pin which holds the cam onto the shaft and extracting the circlips which hold the advance weights onto this shaft. This is not worth doing under any circumstances for if you have reached this stage of dismantling it is only worth renewing the whole distributor. These individual parts may well not be available.

11 To renew the bush first press or drive out the old one from inside the distributor body. Before fitting a new bush it should be soaked in engine oil for at least 24 hours - or hot oil for 2 hours - before fitting. It is made of sintered copper/iron and retains its lubricant due to porosity. The new bush should be pushed in from the lower end. When the shoulder part reaches the body the bush should be pressed in with a shouldered mandrel in a press or vice. Any attempt to drive it in - even using blocks of wood - will almost certainly cause it to break up. The bottom and top of the bush should be flush with the distributor body. When fitted the bush should be drilled through in line with the shaft oil drain hole in the body. Make sure there are no burrs or loose metal particles anywhere in the bush. Refit the shaft, lubricate with engine oil. If it is tight it will need 'running in' by hand until there are no traces of binding. The bush must not be reamed as this will inpair its self-lubricating properties. Do not forget the distance collar on the shaft under the action plate.

12 Reassembly of the distributor is a reversal of the dismantling process. Do not stretch the centrifugal springs. Smear the contact breaker baseplate with a thin film of oil or grease between it and the moving plate.

6.6 The distributor clamp nut has been removed to allow the distributor to be lifted away

## 8   Ignition timing

1   It is necessary to time the ignition when it has been upset due to overhauling or dismantling which may have altered the relationship between the position of the pistons and the moment at which the distributor delivers the spark. Also, if mal-adjustments have affected the engine performance it is very desirable, although not always essential, to reset the timing starting from scratch. In the following procedures it is assumed that the intention is to obtain standard performance from the standard engine which is in reasonable condition. It is also assumed that the recommended fuel octane rating is used. It is possible today to have an engine checked on special equipment designed to indicate where different faults may be. These instruments are excellent for indicating what may be wrong with your engine in a variety of areas. They do not, however, compute the full combination of settings needed to get the best possible performance from your particular engine as it is. The final check for ignition timing depends solely on the perform-ance of the car on the road in all the variety of conditions that it meets.

2   The static or datum timing is getting the spark to arrive at a particular position of the crankshaft. (See Section 1). Most manufacturers stick to the convention of using No 1 cylinder for this adjustment and the Renault is no exception. The flywheel visible between and below the water pump and the radiator (R 1180) and water pump and gearchange (R 1181) has a notch marked on its outer circumference. A pointer is fitted on the cylinder block, just beneath the heater pipe, pointing down on to this outer edge of the flywheel. If the engine is turned, TDC on No 1 piston will be achieved when the pointer is the correct distance from the mark on the flywheel. See specifications for the correct distance according to engine type. Do this and then look at the distributor cap and see at which position the HT lead from No 1 spark plug connects. Then remove the cap and see whether the top of the rotor arm is facing the No 1 plug contact. If it is, good! If not then the engine must be turned another complete revolution to the TDC mark again. The rotor arm should then be in the correct position. Should the rotor arm still be way out, check whether the distributor body can be rotated enough to compensate by slackening the clamp and trying it. It may be possible, with alterations to plug lead lengths.

3   Now the engine should be set at the correct static advance position.

4   As discussed in the opening section the spark is produced when the contact points in the LT circuit open. It is now necessary to slacken the distributor clamping screw so that the body of the distributor may be turned (whilst the rotor spindle stays still). The distributor should now be turned slightly, one way or the other, so that the contact points are just about to open. The contact gap MUST be set correctly. As it is difficult to see exactly when the points are just opening a means of doing this electrically is necessary. Use a continuity tester or 12 volt bulb and a jumper lead. If the latter is used, put one lead to the terminal where the coil LT lead joins the distributor and the other to a good earth on the engine block. With the ignition switched on the bulb will now light. Turn the body of the dist-ributor anti-clockwise until the light just goes out. Then, lightly holding the rotor arm with clockwise pressure, turn the body clockwise again until the light just comes on again. Then tighten the clamping screw. If desired the correctness of the setting can be checked with a stroboscopic timing light but such a device is not essential for accurate setting of the static timing.

5   The performance of the engine should be checked by road testing. Make any adjustments by loosening the clamp screw and moving the distributor body very slightly to the right (anticlockwise) to advance it. Lock it again and retest. If the performance is worse repeat the procedure but turn to the left (clockwise) to retard. After a little time going one way or the other, in very small progression, the 'optimum' timing will result.

6   Should the owner wish, he may check the centrifugal advance

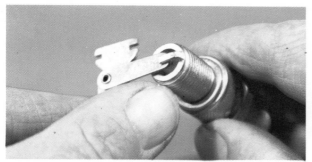

**Measuring plug gap.** A feeler gauge of the correct size (see ignition system specifications) should have a slight 'drag' when slid between the electrodes. Adjust gap if necessary

**Adjusting plug gap.** The plug gap is adjusted by bending the earth electrode inwards, or outwards, as necessary until the correct clearance is obtained. Note the use of the correct tool

**Normal.** Grey-brown deposits lightly coated core nose. Gap increasing by around 0.001 in (0.025 mm) per 1000 miles (1600 km). Plugs ideally suited to engine and engine in good condition

**Carbon fouling.** Dry, black, sooty deposits. Will cause weak spark and eventually misfire. Fault: over-rich fuel mixture. Check: carburettor mixture settings, float level and jet sizes; choke operation and cleanliness of air filter. Plugs can be re-used after cleaning

**Oil fouling.** Wet, oily deposits. Will cause weak spark and eventually misfire. Fault: worn bores/piston rings or valve guides; sometimes occurs (temporarily) during running-in period. Plugs can be re-used after thorough cleaning

**Overheating.** Electrodes have glazed appearance, core nose very white - few deposits. Fault: plug overheating. Check: plug value, ignition timing, fuel octane rating (too low) and fuel mixture (too weak). Discard plugs and cure fault immediately

**Electrode damage.** Electrodes burned away; core nose has burned, glazed appearance. Fault: initial pre-ignition. Check: as for 'Overheating' but may be more severe. Discard plugs and remedy fault before piston or valve damage occurs

**Split core nose (may appear initially as a crack).** Damage is self-evident, but cracks will only show after cleaning. Fault: pre-ignition or wrong gap-setting technique. Check: ignition timing, cooling system, fuel octane rating (too low) and fuel mixture (too weak). Discard plugs, rectify fault immediately

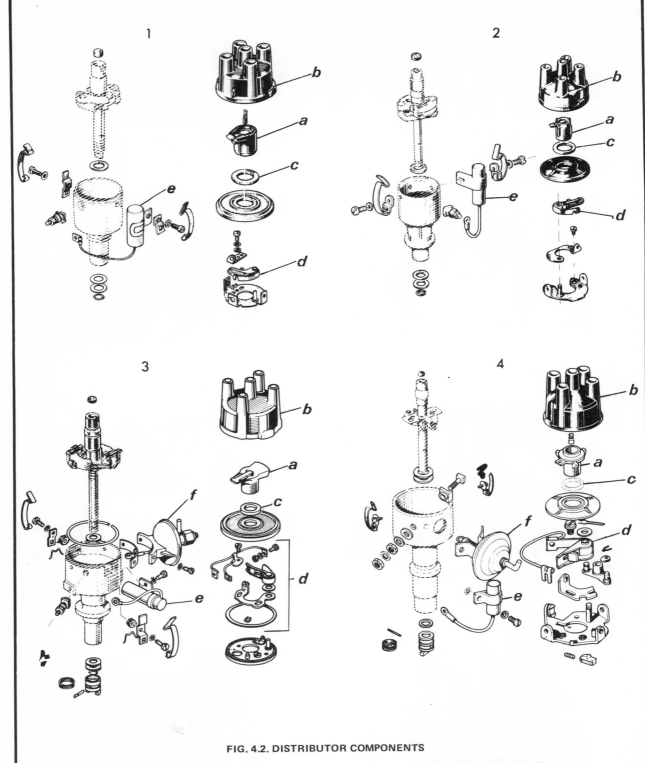

**FIG. 4.2. DISTRIBUTOR COMPONENTS**

1  SEV-Marchal for R1180
2  Ducellier for R1180

3  SEV-Marchal for R1181
4  Ducellier for R1181

A  Rotor arm
C  Felt oil ring
E  Condenser mechanism

B  Distributor cap
D  Contact points mechanism
F  Vacuum advance/retard

characteristics of the distributor, For this he will need to employ an accurate tachometer and a stroboscopic timing light. If the distributor was seriously wrong then the performance of the car would be noticeably affected. Should the distributor be suspected of malfunction in this respect it would be best to get it tested on the specialised equipment available at some garages, or simply fit a new one. Often the cost of thorough checking (which involves removing the distributor if it is to be done very precisely) is not far short of the cost of a new unit.

8.2 TDC on No. 1 piston (R1180)

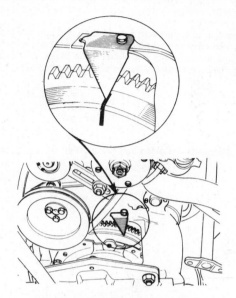

**Fig. 4.3. Ignition timing - R1180**
All UK supplied cars have static ignition timing at the flywheel. Both marks should align

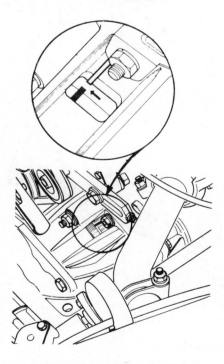

**Fig. 4.4. Ignition timing - R1181**
All UK supplied cars have static ignition timing at the flywheel. Both marks should align

### 9  Spark plugs and HT leads

1  With the development of modern technology and materials, spark plugs are generally very reliable and require minimal attention. When they are due for checking and cleaning it is good practice to have them thoroughly sand blasted, gapped and checked under pressure on the machine that most garages have installed. They can also be used as good indications of engine condition, particularly as regards the fuel mixture being used and the state of the pistons and cylinder bores. Check each plug as it is possible that one cylinder condition is different from the rest. Plugs come in different types to suit the particular type of engine. A 'hot' plug is for engines which run at lower temperatures than normal and a 'cold' plug is for the hotter running engines. If plugs of the wrong rating are fitted they can either damage the engine or fail to operate properly. Under normal running conditions a correctly rated plug in a properly tuned engine will have a light deposit of a brownish colour on the electrodes. A dry black sooty deposit indicates an over-rich fuel mixture. An oily blackish deposit indicates worn bores or valve guides. A dry hard whitish deposit indicates too weak a fuel mixture. If plugs of the wrong heat ranges are fitted they will have similar symptoms to a weak mixture together with burnt electrodes (plug too hot) or to an over-rich mixture caked somewhat thicker (plug too cold). Do not try and economise by using plugs beyond 9000 miles. Unless the engine remains in exceptionally good tune, reductions in performance and fuel economy will outweigh the cost of a new set.
2  The HT leads and their connections at both ends should always be clean and dry and, as far as possible, neatly arranged away from each other and nearby metallic parts which could cause premature shorting in weak insulation. The metal connections at the ends should be a firm and secure fit and free from any signs of corrosive deposits. If any lead shows signs of cracking or chafing of the insulation it should be renewed. Remember that radio interference suppression is required when renewing any leads. NOTE: It is advisable when removing spark plugs from this engine to use a fully cranked 'short' spark plug remover. Be especially careful when refitting plugs to do so without force and screw them  up as far as possible by hand first. Do not overtighten. The aluminium head does not take kindly to thread crossing and extra force. The proprietary non-cranked plug caps should always be used to ease fitting and to ensure against HT lead shorting.

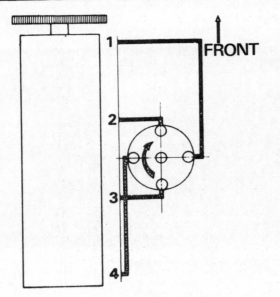

## 10 Coil

1 The coil needs an equal amount of attention to the rest of the ignition system. Testing the coil is dealt with in Section 12.

2 The coil is easily removed by loosening the right hand mounting stud nut, then the left hand one. It can then be swung in a clockwise direction on the right hand stud and lifted upwards. Its actual mounting plate can remain on the cylinder block for R1180. The coil for the R1181 is mounted on the offside inner wing and is more easily accessible. Make sure all the leads are removed.

3 To replace with new unit, unscrew the old coil clamp tightening bolt and remove and place it on in approximately the same position on the new coil and refit to the block. Make sure you have a replacement coil of the correct connector type.

Fig. 4.5. Distributor rotation and firing order

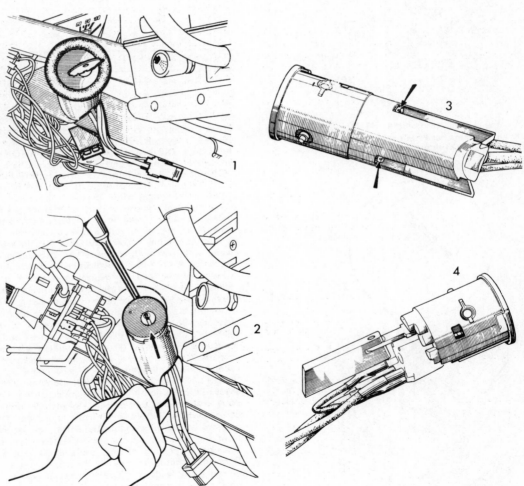

FIG. 4.6. NEIMAN IGNITION/STEERING LOCK

1  Remove panel beneath, disconnect junction box
2  Remove securing screws. Push behind switch, and press on retaining ring
3  Remove key, removing arrowed securing screws
4  Slide switch to rear

10.2 Coil removal (R1180). Its position within its clip is important

## 11 Ignition/starter switch

1   All vehicles are fitted with a switch which is incorporated in the steering column lock. In both cases the switch is in a similar position and can be replaced without removing the locking device.
2   Disconnect the battery, before attempting anything. Before removing to replace check that it is not functioning properly and that there is not a fault either in the starter motor or in the ignition light.
3   Remove the bottom protective panel under the steering column and then remove the steering wheel. See Chapters 11 and 10 respectively.
4   Disconnect the electrical junction box below the switch and unscrew its securing screws.
5   Press on the retaining ring with a screwdriver and push up from behind the switch.
6   Once the total unit is released the switch key is easily removed from the body. Two screws connect it and it slides towards the rear once these are released.
7   Reassembly is a straight reverse sequence.

## 12 Ignition faults - symptoms, reason and remedies

Engine troubles normally associated with, and usually caused by, faults in the ignition system are:
a)  Failure to start when the engine is turned.
b)  Uneven running due to misfiring or mistiming.
c)  Smooth running at low engine revolutions but misfiring when under load or accelerating or at high constant revolutions.
d)  Smooth running at higher revolutions and misfiring or cutting-out at low speeds.

a)  First check that all wires are properly connected and dry. If the engine fails to catch when the starter is operated do not continue for more than 5 or 6 short burst attempts or the battery will start to get tired. Remove the spark plug lead from a plug and turn the engine again holding the lead (by the insulation) about ¼ inch from the side of the engine block. A spark should jump the gap audibly and visibly; if it does not then the plugs are at fault or the static timing is very seriously adrift. If both are good, however, then there must be a fuel supply fault, so go on to that.

If no spark is obtained at the end of a plug lead detach the coil HT lead from the centre of the distributor cap and hold that near the block to try and find a spark. If you now get one, then there is something wrong between the centre terminal of the distributor cap and the end of the plug lead. Check the cap itself for damage or damp, the 4 terminal lugs for signs of corrosion, the centre carbon brush in the top (is it jammed?) and the rotor arm.

If no spark comes from the coil HT lead check next that the contact breaker points are clean and that the gap is correct. A quick check can be made by turning the engine so that the points are closed. Then switch on the ignition and open the points with an insulated screwdriver. There should be a small visible spark and, once again, if the coil HT lead is held near the block at the same time proper HT spark should occur. If there is a big fat spark at the points but none at the HT lead then the condenser is done for and should be renewed.

If neither of these things happen then the next step in this tale of woe is to see if there is any current (12 volts) reaching the coil (+ terminal). (One could check this at the distributor, but by going back to the input side of the coil a longer length of possible fault line is bracketed and could save time.)

With a 12 v bulb and piece of wire suitably connected (or of course a voltmeter if you have one handy) connect between the +or SW terminal of the coil and earth and switch on the ignition. No light means no volts so the fault is between the battery and the coil via the ignition switch. This is moving out of the realms of just ignition problems - the electrical system is becoming involved in general. So to get home to bed get a piece of wire and connect the + terminal of the coil to the + terminal on the battery and see if sparks occur at the HT leads once more.

If there is current reaching the coil then the coil itself or the wire from its - terminal to the distributor is at fault. Check the - or CB terminal with a bulb with the ignition switched on. If it fails to light then the coil is faulty in its LT windings and needs renewal.
b)  Uneven running and misfiring should first be checked by seeing that all leads, particularly HT, are dry and connected properly. See that they are not shorting to earth through broken or cracked insulation. If they are, you should be able to see and hear it. If not, then check the plugs, contact points and condenser just as you would in a case of total failure to start.
c)  If misfiring occurs at high speed check the points gap, which may be too small, and the plugs in that order. Check also that the spring tension on the points is not too light this causing them to bounce. This requires a special pull balance so if in doubt it will be cheaper to buy a new set of contacts rather than go to a garage and get them to check it. If the trouble is still not cured then the fault lies in the carburation or engine itself.
d)  If misfiring or stalling occurs only at low speeds the points gap is possibly too big. If not, then the slow running adjustment on the carburettor needs attention.

# Chapter 5  Clutch system

## Contents

## Specifications

| Clutch | | R1180 | R1181 |
|---|---|---|---|
| Type: diaphragm spring, single plate | ... ... ... ... | 160 DBIR 210 | 160 DBR260 |
| Operation ... ... ... ... ... ... ... ... | | Cable | |
| Plate diameter ... ... ... ... ... ... ... | | 6.3 in | |
| Disc thickness ... ... ... ... ... ... ... | | 7.4 mm (0.291 in) | |
| Thrust bearing ... ... ... ... ... ... ... | | Ball bearing pad | |
| Adjustment ... ... ... ... ... ... ... ... | | End of release fork | |
| | | 3 to 4 mm (1/8 to 5/32 in) | 5 mm (13/64 in) |

| Torque wrench setting | | lbf ft | kgf m |
|---|---|---|---|
| Cover to flywheel | | | |
| R1180 ... ... ... ... ... ... ... ... ... | | 30 | 4.1 |
| R1181 ... ... ... ... ... ... ... ... ... | | 40 | 5.5 |

## 1  General description

The clutch is a cable operated single dry plate diaphragm type.

The clutch pedal pivots on the same shaft as the brake pedal (see Chapter 9) and operates a cable to the clutch release arm. The release arm activates a thrust bearing (clutch release bearing) which bears on the diaphragm spring of the pressure plate. The diaphragm then releases or engages the clutch driven plate which is splined onto the gearbox primary shaft. The clutch driven plate (disc) spins in between the clutch cover and the flywheel face when it is released, and is held there when engaged, to connect the drive from the engine to the transmission unit.

As wear takes place on the driven plate the clearance between the clutch release bearing and the diaphragm increases. This wear is compensated for, up to the point where the driven plate is worn out, by altering the length of the clutch cable. This adjustment takes place next to the release arm with an adjuster nut on the cable.

There is only one fundamental difference in operation between the R1180 and R1181, although few parts are interchangeable. The clutch release arm of the R1180 pivots on the face plate of the transmission unit whilst the R1181 pivots on a rod pressed through the bellhousing of the transmission unit.

Otherwise all operations are similar.

## 2  Clutch cable - removal and replacement

1  The clutch cable travels directly from the end of the clutch pedal to the clutch operating lever. It is very easy to replace. There have been several types of clutch cable fitted from various manufacturers and various types of lever at the release mechanism. It also matters whether the car is left or right hand drive. No cables are interchangeable, it is therefore important that you are certain of the type when ordering a replacement. Generally, cables only need replacing when they have broken. They require no maintenance themselves.

2  To replace a cable first slacken off the clutch release lever completely. See the next section.

3  Depress the clutch pedal inside the car by hand and release that end of the cable. It may be attached to the top of a quadrant or bolted by a U piece to the pedal.

4  From under the bonnet, release the other end of the cable from the rod mechanism. The R1180 threads through the lever arm; the R1181 passes through a ferrule which is slotted into a double drilling.

5  Pull out the outer cable from its fixing in the bulkhead, the other side of the end of the clutch pedal. It is a push-in fit using a special alloy split splined collar to locate the outer cable.

6  Check also at this stage, with the cable removed, the swivel mechansim through which the cable moves. It should not be sloppy.

7 Replacement is an exact reversal of its removal. Adjust the release bearing clearance as described in Section 3.

### 3 Clutch - adjustment

1 Clutch adjustment to compensate for its free play is taken up at the rod connecting the clutch cable to the release bearing arm. Undo the locknut on its end and tighten the inner nut until the correct clearance is made. Retighten the locknut and tighten the two together. There is no compensatory adjustment of the clutch cable outer. The R1180 and R1181 use similar adjusting methods.

2 Clutch adjustment is checked by measuring the free play at the outward end of the fork. Loosen the locknut and screw the adjustment nut in or out to obtain the correct free play, and then retighten the locknut to secure.

2.4 This is the clutch cable support bracket on early R1180s

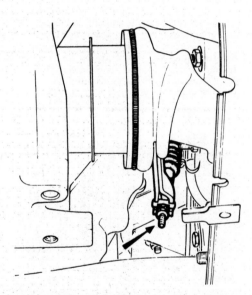

**Fig. 5.1. Clutch adjustment point at end of clutch cable. Principle is same but components are different for two models**

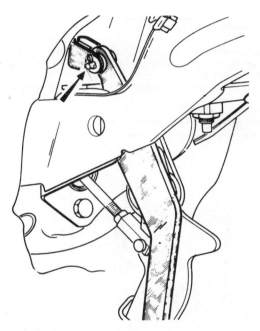

Fig. 5.2. Clutch cable fixing at pedal end

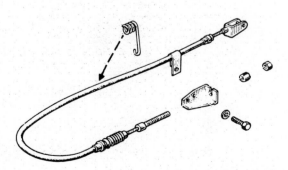

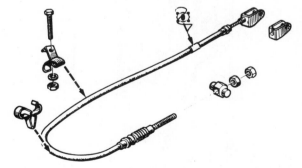

**Fig. 5.3. Left R1180 Clutch cable components
Right R1181 Clutch cable components**

## 4  Clutch - removal

1   If it is necessary to renew the friction plate or examine the clutch in any way it will first of all be necessary to remove the gearbox (see Chapter 6) in order to get at it. If the engine has been removed then the clutch is, of course, accessible. Once the gearbox is removed or the engine taken out the succeeding operations are the same although work is easier with the engine out when no pit or ramp is available. If the engine and gearbox have been removed from the car together they will have to be separated of course.

2   Before removing the clutch cover bolts mark the position of the cover in relation to the flywheel so that it may be put back the same way.

3   Slacken off the cover retaining bolts ½ a turn at a time in a diagonal fashion evenly so as to relieve the diaphragm spring pressure without distorting it.

4   When the bolts are removed the friction plate inside will be released. The cover will then come away easily. The friction plate will fall down from the flywheel face.

## 5  Clutch - inspection and renovation

1   The clutch driven plate should be inspected for wear and for contamination by oil. Wear is gauged by the depth of the rivet heads below the surface of the friction material. If this is less than 0.025 inch (0.6 mm) the linings are worn enough to justify renewal.

   Examine the friction faces of the flywheel and clutch pressure plate. These should be bright and smooth. If the linings have worn too much it is possible that the metal surfaces may have been scored by the rivet heads. Dust and grit can have the same effect. If the scoring is very severe it could mean that even with a new clutch driven plate, slip and juddering and other malfunctions will recur. Deep scoring on the flywheel face is serious because the flywheel will have to be removed and machined by a specialist, or renewed. This can be costly. The same applies to the pressure plate in the cover although this is a less costly affair. If the friction linings seem unworn yet are blackened and shiny then the cause is almost certainly due to oil. Such a condition also requires renewal of the plate. The source of oil must be traced also. It will be due to a leaking seal on the transmission input shaft (Chapter 6 gives details of renewal) or on the front of the engine crankshaft (see Chapter 1 for details of renewal).

2   If the reason for removal of the clutch has been because of slip and the slip has been allowed to go on for any length of time it is possible that the heat generated will have adversely affected the pressure springs in the cover. Some or all may have been affected with the result that the pressure is now uneven and/or insufficient to prevent slip, even with a new friction plate. It is recommended that under such circumstances a new assembly is fitted.

3   Although it is possible to dismantled the clutch cover assembly and, in theory, renew the various springs and levers the economics do not justify it. Clutch cover assemblies are available on an exchange basis. It will probably be necessary to order an assembly in advance as most agencies other than the large distributors carry stocks only sufficient to meet their own requirements. However, it is possible to get assemblies from reputable manufacturers other than Renault; Borg and Beck for instance. Be absolutely sure as to what you are ordering for many types of clutch have been fitted.

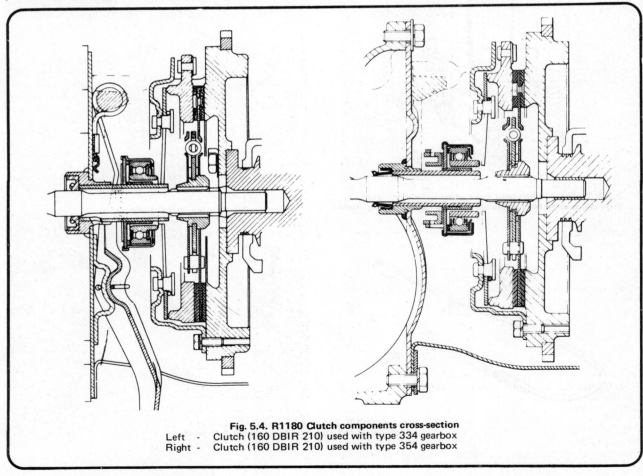

**Fig. 5.4. R1180 Clutch components cross-section**
Left  -   Clutch (160 DBIR 210) used with type 334 gearbox
Right -   Clutch (160 DBIR 210) used with type 354 gearbox

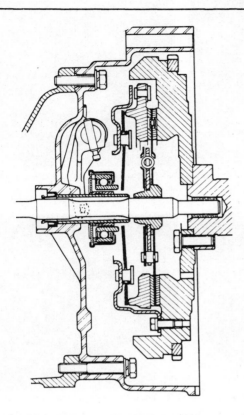

**Fig. 5.5. R1181 Clutch components cross-section**
(160 DBR 260 clutch with type 354 gearbox)

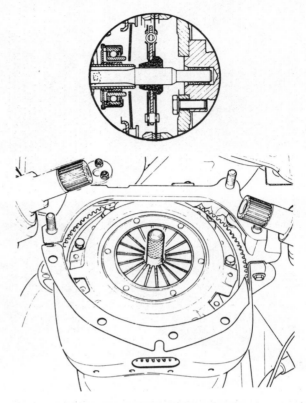

**Fig. 5.6. Centering the clutch driven plate**
(Inset shows correct face of driven plate next to
the flywheel)

### 6 Clutch - replacement

1　If the original cover is being re-used line up the marks made
before removal, and support the friction plate on one finger
between cover and flywheel so that the offset side of the driven
plate, on the side of the boss with the largest diameter, faces the
flywheel.

2　Locate the cover on the flywheel and then place all the cover
bolts in position and screw them up lightly by hand.

3　It is necessary to line up the centre of the friction disc with
the exact centre of the flywheel. This is easily done if a piece of
shouldered bar or an old input shaft can be placed in the counter
bore at the flywheel centre with the larger diameter supporting
the friction disc. If you do not have such a thing, the disc may
be lined up by eye if the engine is out of the car. If this is not
done, great difficulty (and possible damage to the gearbox input
shaft) may be experienced when the time comes to refit the
gearbox to the engine.

4　With the friction plate centralised the cover bolts should be
tightened diagonally evenly and progressively. Be careful with the
diaphragm type so as not to distort it or strip threads in the
flywheel. It is a good idea to replace the fixing bolts with new
each time a new clutch is fitted. Remove the centralising tool.
Before refitting the gearbox to the engine do not forget to check
the clutch release bearing and operating mechanism.

### 7　R1180 Clutch operation lever and release bearing - dismantling, inspection and reassembly

1　When the clutch pedal is depressed the cable actuates the
lever which pivots on the gearbox face and forces a ball release
bearing against the steel boss at the centre of the releasing
mechanism of the clutch cover. The ball bearing release bearing

is unlikely to wear but it may become dry and fail. It is often
very noisy, and should be replaced if it runs out of true.

2　To renew the release bearing the clutch bellhousing/gearbox
must be separated from the engine. The bearing is held to the
actuating arm by two spring steel clips which, when released,
allow it to be drawn off over the gearbox input shaft. Replacement is a reversal of the removal procedure. Should the release
arm require removal the pivot pin clip holding it in position may
be released by unhooking the wire holding spring. With the
release arm removed check its own bearing surface and replace if
very worn. Check also the face of the gearbox at this position
and replace under extreme circumstances. Once again check that
you are using the correct replacement part. This cannot be
overstressed.

6.1a This shows the flywheel side of the driven plate

6.1b The driven plate up onto the flywheel

6.2 A new clutch/cover plate now in place ready for the fixing bolts

6.3 An old gearbox input shaft is used here

7.1 R1180 release lever showing the two springs

7.2a The release bearing going back

7.2b The whole mechanism assembled

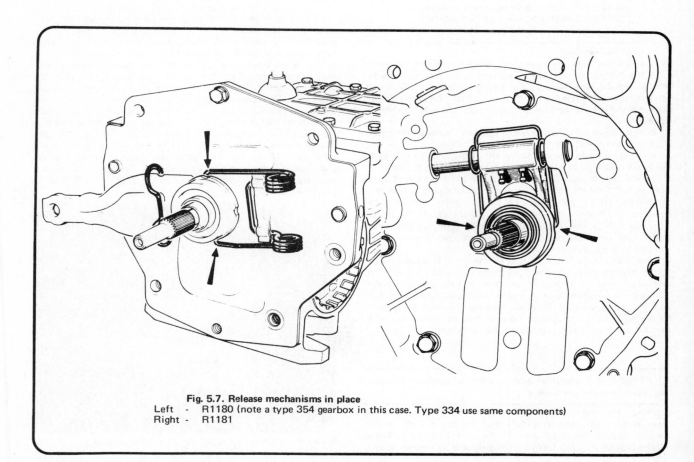

**Fig. 5.7. Release mechanisms in place**
Left - R1180 (note a type 354 gearbox in this case. Type 334 use same components)
Right - R1181

## 8  R1181 - Clutch operation rod/fork and release bearing dismantling, inspection and reassembly

1  Full examination is only possible when the gearbox is removed and is normally undertaken when the clutch is in need of repair. The mechanism is carried in and attached to the transmission casing/bellhousing. Check the bearing itself. The guided ball type should be shiny, and smooth running without any looseness in its revolutions. The retaining spring clips at each side must be a tight fit so that the bearing does not rattle about on its mounting.

2  To inspect the lever fork it is necessary to remove the release bearing by unclipping the holding spring clips and sliding the bearing off the input shaft. Little should go wrong with the lever fork. Renault require a special tool (Emb. 384-01) to withdraw the fork retaining pins, however it should be possible to use a tubular extractor to pull them out

3  Do not clean any parts with any cleaning fluid for it will spoil the release bearing. If in doubt renew the bearing; it is safer and less trouble in the long run.

4  Replacement is a straight reversal of its removal of all components here. To lubricate the lever bearing surfaces and the release bearing faces use a little molybdenum paste - never grease or oil.

Replacing the fork retaining pins is critical. Always use a new rubber seal and then tap the new pins into place. See Fig. 5.9 and leave the shanks protruding 1 mm.

5  Re-adjust the pedal free play once the gearbox is re-installed.

## 9  Fault diagnosis and remedies

| Symptom | Reason/s | Remedy |
|---|---|---|
| Judder when taking up drive | Loose engine/gearbox mountings or over-flexible mountings | Check and tighten all mounting bolts and replace any 'soft' or broken mountings. |
| | Badly worn friction surfaces or friction plate contamination with oil carbon deposit | Remove engine and replace clutch parts as required. Rectify any oil leakage points which may have cause contamination. |
| | Worn splines in the friction plate hub or on the gearbox input shaft | Renew friction plate and/or input shaft. |
| Clutch spin (or failure to disengage) so that gears cannot be meshed | Clutch actuating cable clearance too great | Adjust clearance. |
| | Clutch friction disc sticking because of rust on splines (usually apparent after standing idle for some length of time) | As temporary remedy engage top gear, apply handbrake, depress clutch and start engine. (If very badly stuck engine will not turn). When running rev up engine and slip clutch until disengagement is normally possible. Renew friction plate at earliest opportunity. |
| | Damaged or misaligned pressure plate assembly | Renew pressure plate assembly. |
| | Incorrect release bearing fitted | Renew with correct part. |
| Clutch slip - (increase in engine speed does not result in increase in car speed-especially on hills) | Clutch actuating cable clearance from fork too small resulting in partially disengaged clutch at all times | Adjust clearance. |
| | Clutch friction surfaces worn out (beyond further adjustment of operating cable) or clutch surfaces oil soaked | Renew friction plate and remedy source of oil leakage. |

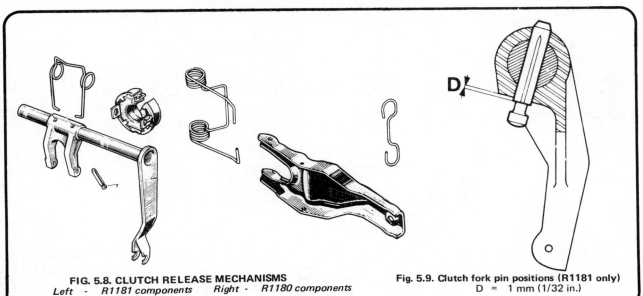

**FIG. 5.8. CLUTCH RELEASE MECHANISMS**
*Left  -  R1181 components     Right  -  R1180 components*

Fig. 5.9. Clutch fork pin positions (R1181 only)
D = 1 mm (1/32 in.)

# Chapter 6 Transmission unit

## Contents

## Specifications

**Gearbox - general**

| | R1180 | R1181 |
|---|---|---|
| Renault type number ... ... ... ... ... ... | 334 up to 1973, 354 after 1973 | 354 |
| Number of gears ... ... ... ... ... ... | 4 forward, 1 reverse | |
| Synchromesh ... ... ... ... ... ... ... | All forward gears | |
| Forward gears ... ... ... ... ... ... | Helical cut gears | |
| Reverse gear ... ... ... ... ... ... ... | Straight cut spur gears | |
| Oil capacity ... ... ... ... ... ... | 2½ pints (1.2 litres) 3 pints (1.8 litres) after 1973 | 3 pints (1.8 litres) |
| Oil grade ... ... ... ... ... ... ... | EP 80 | |

| Ratios: | R1180 Up to 1973 | After 1973 | R1181 |
|---|---|---|---|
| 1st ... ... ... ... ... ... | 3.80 | 3.67 | 3.67 |
| 2nd ... ... ... ... ... ... | 2.05 | 2.24 | 2.05 |
| 3rd ... ... ... ... ... ... | 1.36 | 1.46 | 1.36 (1.46 later models) |
| 4th ... ... ... ... ... ... | 1.03 | 1.03 | 1.03 |
| Reverse ... ... ... ... ... | 3.80 | 3.23 | 3.07 (early) 3.23 (late) |

| | R1180 | After 1973 | R1181 |
|---|---|---|---|
| Speedometer drive gear ... ... ... | 51 x 30 | 6 X 15 then 5 x 12 | 6 x 14 |

**Differential - general** ... ... ... ... ... ... ...    Integral with gearbox, consisting of 2 sun wheels and 2 planet wheels

| | R1180 | R1181 |
|---|---|---|
| Ratio ... ... ... ... ... ... ... ... ... | 33 x 8 (4.125 to 1) | 31 x 8 (early) 33.8 (late) (3.875 to 1) (early) (4.125 to 1) (late) |
| Road speed at 1000 rpm in top gear ... ... ... ... | 14.6 mph | 15.4 mph |
| Casing ... ... ... ... ... ... ... ... | Split (334) One piece (354) | One piece |

Shift pattern ... ... ... ... ... ...

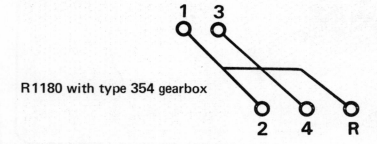

**R1180 with type 354 gearbox**

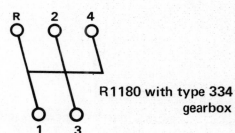

**R1180 with type 334 gearbox**

**Torque wrench settings**

| | lbf ft | kgf m |
|---|---|---|
| **Type 334 gearbox** | | |
| Half casing bolts ... ... ... ... ... ... ... | 20 | 2.8 |
| Intermediate plate bolts ... ... ... ... ... ... | 15 | 2.1 |
| Front cover bolts ... ... ... ... ... ... ... | 15 | 2.1 |
| Gearshift lever housing bolts ... ... ... ... ... | 15 | 2.1 |
| Primary and secondary shaft bolts ... ... ... ... | 60 | 8.3 |
| Differential cover bolts ... ... ... ... ... ... ... | 20 | 2.8 |
| Crownwheel fixing bolts ... ... ... ... ... ... | 80 | 11.1 |
| **Type 354 gearbox** | | |
| Top cover bolts ... ... ... ... ... ... ... | 10 | 1.4 |
| Front cover bolts ... ... ... ... ... ... ... | 15 | 2.1 |
| Primary shaft bearing thrust plate ... ... ... ... | 15 | 2.1 |
| Differential lockplate ... ... ... ... ... ... | 15 | 2.1 |
| Speedo. worm nut ... ... ... ... ... ... ... | 85 | 11.8 |
| Crownwheel bolts ... ... ... ... ... ... ... | 80 | 11.1 |
| Reverse gear securing lever bolt ... ... ... ... | 20 | 2.8 |
| Intermediate plate bolts (10 mm) ... ... ... ... | 30 | 4.1 |
| (8 mm) ... ... ... ... ... | 15 | 2.1 |

## 1 General description

Upon the introduction of the R1180 the transmission unit fitted was that used in the late model Renault 4s; the four speed type 334 which features a split casing and an 'unusual' gear shift pattern. The R1181 appeared with a different unit, new to that model. It is still a four speed gearbox but it has a conventional shifts pattern (all forward speed in an 'H') and a one piece casing. However the 1974 model R1180s have now been fitted with the one piece casing Type 354 gearbox; but with minor differences.

Because the R1180 and R1181 crankshafts revolve in different directions, 845 cc clockwise, 1100 cc anti-clockwise, when viewed from the front of the car, the transmission units have their crownwheel and pinions on opposing sides in the casing. For the same reason 1st, 3rd and 4th gear teeth are cut differently. The final drive is, of course, within the same casing.

The primary shaft transmits motion via four forward gears to the secondary or pinion shaft on which is the main gear cluster and synchromesh. The reverse gear is on a third shaft fixed to the gear casing. Motion is then transmitted when a gear is engaged, by the pinion gear on the end of the pinion shaft to the crownwheel and then to the drive shafts. Gear selector forks are mounted in the top of the casing and are operated by a to-and-fro and sideways motion of the gear lever bolted to the top. These forks select gears on the primary shaft which then mesh with the appropriate gear on the pinion shaft.

Various gear ratios have been used. The speedometer is gearbox driven. Although relatively simple transmission units there are nevertheless a few words of warning which must be stated before any potential dismantlers start work, to let them know what they are letting themselves in for.

First of all decide whether the fault you wish to repair is worth all the time and effort involved. Secondly, if the transmission unit is in a very bad state then the cost of the necessary component parts may well exceed the cost of an exchange factory unit. Thirdly, be absolutely sure that you understand how the transmission unit works.

Returning to the second point just mentioned, it is possible to dismantle the unit with tools from a normal tool kit but only so far. Fortunately this is the point, if further dismantling is decided to be necessary, to check whether an exchange unit would be a cheaper method of repair. Renault cannot supply individual component parts, rather parts assembled into units, past this point.

Check very carefully the availability and cost of transmission unit parts before dismantling.

## 2 R1180 - Transmission unit - removal and replacement

1 The transmission unit can be removed either with the engine, see Chapter 1, or by itself leaving the engine in the vehicle. If only wishing to work on the gearbox or clutch rather than the engine as well it is a simple task to remove the transmission alone. The unit alone is very light and compact.

2 Place the car on level ground and apply the handbrake.

3 Now follow the sequence in Chapter 1 from Section 5, paragraph 3 to paragraph 5 inclusive, the middle exhaust pipe in 11, then again paragraphs 16 to 20, but do not remove the gearshift bracket on top of the radiator. Undo the clutch idler lever as in paragraph 21, the speedometer cable as in paragraph 24, the drive shafts as in paragraphs 25, 26, 27, 28 and 29.

4 Place a support under the front of the engine sump. A screw jack is most suitable for this, with a piece of wood over it, which in turn should be covered with a piece of blanket to avoid damage to the sump.

5 Remove the tubular crossmember.

6 Remove the gearbox front mounting from the gearbox and crossmember and allow the transmission unit to tip downwards slightly by lowering the jack gradually. DO NOT allow the fan blades of the engine to foul the radiator. It may be a good idea to place a piece of blanket over these too.

7 Remove the bolts which attach the sump to the transmission unit. A bracing piece is sometimes fitted here.

8 If possible have an assistant to help you at this point. From the front of the vehicle get him to hold onto the transmission unit with both hands taking some of the weight of the unit from the jack. This will give the required support to the unit when the nuts are removed which connect the unit to the engine block. Once these are removed it will be possible to wriggle the unit down and out, with help from the jack and the assistant. Do not allow the engine to be supported on the primary shaft of the gearbox at any stage and constantly check the fan blades. It is a tight fit. One person can easily carry the transmission unit even if bending right down.

9 Replacement of the transmission unit to the engine and then back into the vehicle is a direct reversal of the removal sequence but an extra special watch must be kept on the primary shaft not being placed under strain. See Chapter 7, for drive shaft reconnection.

10 Refill the gearbox with the correct grade of oil before running the vehicle. It helps in all cases to place the car in reverse gear before filling so to allow a better oil flow in. It is possible, of course, to fill the gearbox when out of the vehicle.

## 3 Type 334 transmission unit - dismantling

1 Before proceeding according to the directions given in this section read the 'General description' section first. It is assumed that the unit is out of the vehicle and on the bench. (It is not advisable to dismantle it on the floor. It will do the kitchen table no harm as it is not heavy). Do not throw away

2.8a Removing the type 334 gearbox from the engine in the car

2.8b The backplate is 'loose' on the engine

2.9a This gasket has to be oil tight

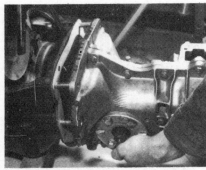

2.9b Push the gearbox fully home before resting

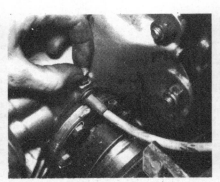

2.9c Locate the speedometer cable

2.10 Be patient when filling with oil

gaskets when dismantling for they will act as a guide for the fitment of the new ones supplied in the gasket set which should have already been purchased. Always renew all gaskets, locking washers and roll pins. Clean the outside casing thoroughly, all the nooks and crannies, and allow to dry. Start work with clean hands and a plentiful supply of clean rag. A set of metric Allen keys will be necessary.

2   Remove the gearshift lever from the top of the gearbox by unscrewing the four locating setscrews. Draw it straight up and out.

3   Remove the clutch end cover plate with the clutch release mechanism still attached. Two bolts locate this to the gear casing together with some dowels.

4   Using a screwdriver in the slots of the starting handle dog on the front end of the unit (early models only) clout fairly sharply the handle of the screwdriver in an anticlockwise direction so to release the dog. Then unscrew it and remove.

5   Remove the front cover plate by releasing and removing the eight fixing setscrews.

6   With a screwdriver select fourth gear and reverse gear and remove the nut which holds the fourth speed gear. Then remove the nut which holds the fourth speed synchro hub. When that is done, select neutral.

7   With the drive shaft roll pin drift, punch out the roll pin which secures the fourth speed selector fork to its shaft. Mark the position of the sliding gear in relation to its hub as they are machine matched and redraw them together with the fourth speed selector fork.

8   Using a proper gear extractor, two or three legged, and taking the load behind the gear, extract the fourth speed gear assembly and synchro hub; remove the friction bush.

9   Using the same method of extraction but placing a protective cap to the end of the primary shaft to protect it from damage, extract the fourth speed gear.

10   Remove the front end spacer plate affixed by Allen screws.

11   Remove the twelve securing bolts which attach the two halves of the casing together placing the gearbox on its right hand side.

12   It is no exaggeration to say that the gearbox will now fall apart! Simply lift out the differential unit from the other, bottom half of the casing. Then lift out the primary shaft complete, making sure all the shims accompany it. Next lift away the speedometer drive cog which was previously hidden under the final drive and primary shaft. Lastly lift out the pinion or secondary shaft again retaining any accompanying shims.

13   At this point read the section on 'Inspection for wear of transmission components'. Section 6 and then in that knowledge carry on as follows, dismantling only if necessary.

14   Punch out with the drive shaft roll pin drift the fourth speed selector fork locking spring plunger and withdraw the selector fork retaining the detent ball and spring. Using the same drift, punch out the roll pin securing the first/reverse and second/third selector fork shaft to the casing. Draw this selector fork shaft out of the casing until the opposite end is flush with the end of the first/reverse selector fork. Remove the shaft guide bush, the shaft and the selector forks in total. Separate the forks from the shaft and retain the detent balls and springs.

15   To remove the reverse gear cluster use the same drift again and drive out the roll pin which locates its shaft to the casing. Push out the shaft and remove the reverse gear and friction washers, having also removed the snap washers from the shaft.

16   The various oil seals in the casing should be renewed as a matter of course. The one in the clutch end plate can be drifted out with a small punch through the provided hole. Do not forget the front end cover too. The differential housing oil seals, one on each side, are removed by undoing the locking washers and removing the six setscrews from the side plates. Retain all the gaskets and shims in their correct order for refitment. Leave the outer half of the differential bearing at this stage,

17   Drive out the roll pin which attaches the clutch half of the primary shaft to the main primary shaft and retain any washers.

18   With the use of a bearing extractor, possibly of the type

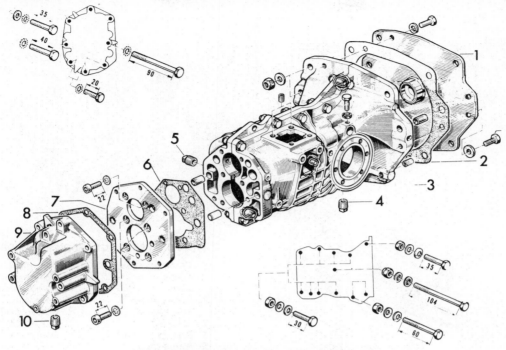

**FIG. 6.1. TYPE 334 GEARBOX OUTER CASING**
(The small numbers indicate bolt lengths in millimetres.
The large numbered are keyed below)

| | | | |
|---|---|---|---|
| 1 Clutch release plate | 4 Main casing drain plug | 7 End plate | 9 End cover |
| 2 Gasket | 5 Filler/level plug | 8 End cover gasket | 10 Secondary drain plug |
| 3 Gearbox casing halves | 6 End plate gasket | | |

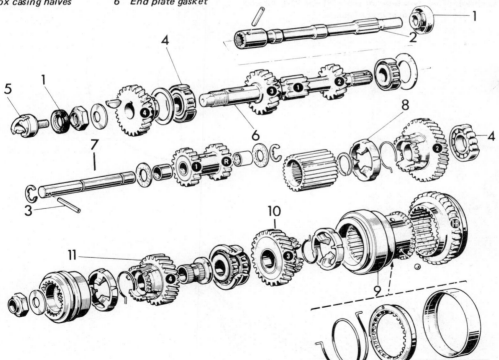

**FIG. 6.2. TYPE 334 GEARBOX GEAR CLUSTER**
(The numbers on the gears indicate the actual gear)

| | | | |
|---|---|---|---|
| 1 Oil seal | 4 Bearing | 7 Reverse idler shaft | 10 3rd gear |
| 2 Extension primary shaft | 5 Starting handle dog (early models) | 8 2nd gear synchro baulk ring | 11 4th gear synchro hub |
| 3 Roll pin | 6 Primary shaft | 9 1st gear synchro hub | |

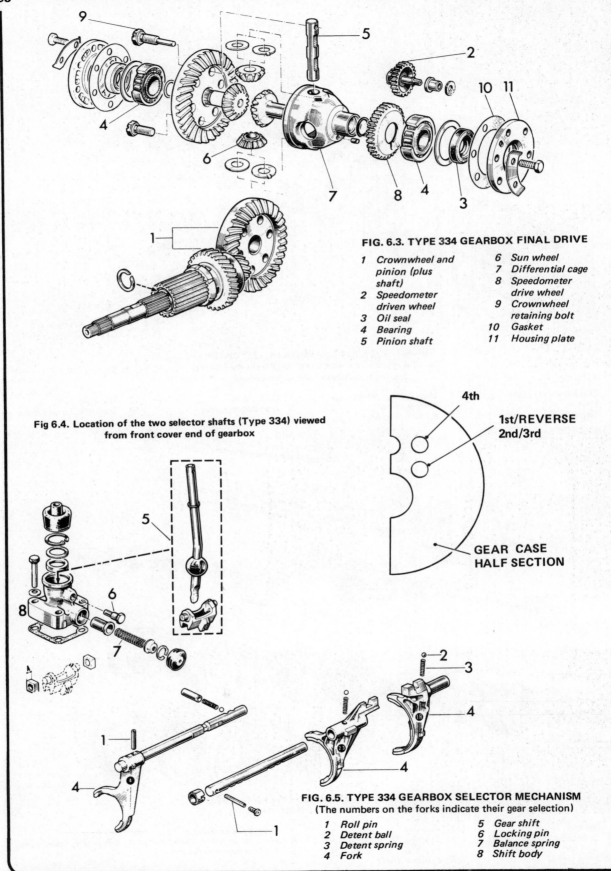

FIG. 6.3. TYPE 334 GEARBOX FINAL DRIVE

1  Crownwheel and        6  Sun wheel
   pinion (plus          7  Differential cage
   shaft)               8  Speedometer
2  Speedometer             drive wheel
   driven wheel         9  Crownwheel
3  Oil seal                retaining bolt
4  Bearing             10  Gasket
5  Pinion shaft        11  Housing plate

Fig 6.4. Location of the two selector shafts (Type 334) viewed
from front cover end of gearbox

4th

1st/REVERSE
2nd/3rd

GEAR CASE
HALF SECTION

FIG. 6.5. TYPE 334 GEARBOX SELECTOR MECHANISM
(The numbers on the forks indicate their gear selection)

1  Roll pin              5  Gear shift
2  Detent ball           6  Locking pin
3  Detent spring         7  Balance spring
4  Fork                  8  Shift body

3.2 Gear shift pulls out

3.4 A sharp knock will loosen

3.5 Note dowel location

3.7a Use a parallel pin punch

3.7b The locking nuts are now removed

3.8a Loosen gently

3.8b The puller is away

3.8c The bearing race now comes away

3.9a We have put back the starter dog to protect the shaft

3.9b The Woodruff key which locates the cog

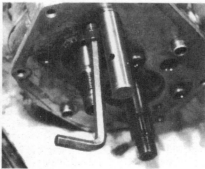

3.10a Always use an Allen key

3.10b The plate pulls off straight

3.11 Lift off one half of the casing

3.12a Lift out the differential carefully...

3.12b ... then the pinion shaft

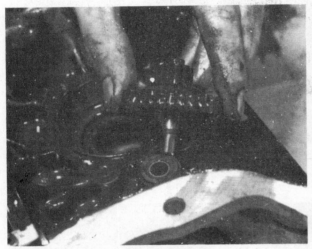
3.12c This is the nylon speedometer driven gear wheel

4.9 Lock tabs are used here

which pushes in two wedges on opposing sides of the bearing, withdraw both bearings from each end of the primary shaft. Mark them for exact replacement. This is important.

19 Unlock and remove the nut on the end of the secondary or pinion shaft, at the opposite end from the pinion, holding the pinion in a soft faced vice.

20 With the use of a bearing extractor already used for the primary shaft, extract the double taper roller bearing from the opposite end to the pinion. Then pull off the 3rd speed gearwheel and synchro ring, then the 2nd and 3rd speed sliding gear and the 1st speed synchro assembly. It will now be possible to pull off the 1st speed gearwheel and its accompanying six detent balls.

21 Place the pinion shaft as it remains, between the two soft jawed faces of a vice. The soft jaws in this case should preferably be wood. Saw the outer track ring of the 1st speed synchromesh with a hacksaw, at the point where the spring hooks locate; this is a small hole. DO NOT saw the synchro ring itself. Then remove from the vice and take off the outer track ring and the synchro ring and its coiled spring. It is again not possible to extract anything further from the pinion shaft as it is a 'sealed' unit.

22 Dismantling of the final drive is not explained here for this is not a task which can be undertaken at home with any likelihood of success. Remove the two rubber 'O' seals from the groove between the inner bearing and the differential spline. These should always be renewed. See Section 6 now. To remove the two differential bearings use a bearing extractor of the type used on the primary shaft and extract the bearings. On the sunwheel side it will be necessary to place the load on it and not the bearing and extract it as well. On bearing replacement drift out the outer cages from both of the casing halves at this point.

## 4   R1181 - transmission unit removal and replacement

1   The transmission unit can be removed either with the engine, see Chapter 1, or by itself. If wishing to work on the gearbox or clutch only remove the gearbox alone. It is fairly simple, the gearbox being light and compact.

2   Place the car on level ground and apply the handbrake.

3   Now follow the sequence in Chapter 1, Section 6, paragraphs 1,2,3,4,5,7,8,12,13,14,16,17,18,21,23,24,25,26,27,28,30.

4   Free the starter motor cable from its clips on the gearbox.

5   Remove the centre cross brace tie rod, the one which links the centre of the cross brace to the chassis side member.

6   Remove the camshaft belt drive pulley and its plate by first removed the three 'outer' bolts and then the centre one.

7   Disconnect the starter motor and pull it towards the bulkhead as far as it will go. It is fixed by three set screws.

8   Take the weight of the gearbox on a jack and remove the front mounting pad with its bracket from the front cross panel.

9   Remove the nuts securing the bellhousing to the engine. A socket wrench is best used - the bottom left hand nut will give most trouble because there is limited access.

10   Ease the gearbox over to the left and then to the right to free each drive shaft in turn. Point the splined ends of the shafts forwards to support them.

11   Remove the tubular crossmember from beneath the gearbox. It pivots on the two rear studs once these are removed it can be swung back and down.

12   With the jack raise the front of the gearbox as high as it will go and then remove from below the five bolts fixing the side stiffeners and the clutch shield. Remove them.

13   Its now a struggle to drop the gearbox out. With two people

its only enough. For one, a hoist is essential at this place, if only to halt its fall if you allow it to slip. Under same circumstances the steering rack must be loosened at its two mounting points. Avoid this if you can. If not mark the shims for exact positioning replacement.

14 Read Section 8 of this Chapter.

15 For replacement of the gearbox read Sections 9 and 10 of this Chapter.

## 5 Type 354 transmission unit dismantling

1 First read Section 1 and paragraph 1 of Section 3, and apply to this transmission unit.

2 Remember that the type 354 used in the R1180 has no bellhousing and that the crownwheel and pinion is on the 'opposite' side in the casing compared with the unit used in the R1181. Once the bellhousing has been removed from the gearbox, (four setscrews) on the R1181 unit, the rest of the unit is the same.

3 Remove the clutch thrust bearing mechanism with the cover plate of the R1180 version. See Chapter 5.

4 Mark the position of the differential adjusting ring nuts relative to the casing. Use a pin punch to dot mark them. Undo the locking tab nut and remove. Now tap gently each ring nut round using a screwdriver and hammer. Count the number of turns the ring nut has to go through to remove. This will enable exact repositioning upon reassembly.

5 To free the primary clutch shaft and thereby the differential pull out the roll pin with a pair of strong grips which locks the two halves of the primary shaft together. Withdraw the shaft. This will now allow the differential to come out of the end of the casing (clutch end).

6 Now remove the top cover. Retain the washers and setscrews. Undo all screws progressively.

7 When the cover is removed three detent springs will appear on the casing edge. Remove these. A small plunger (1st/2nd gear) will be on top of one of these. A small selector shaft locking ball will be below all of these. Turn the casing upside down allowing these to drop out. Retain them.

8 Remove the end cover, its setscrews and washers. Pick out the primary shaft setting shims.

9 Unlock and remove the primary shaft rear bearing retaining plate (bellhousing end). It is held by two setscrews.

10 Punch out (parallel pin punch) the two roll pins holding the reverse gear pinion shaft. Then remove the reverse gear selector shaft.

11 Punch out the roll pins holding the two other gear selector shafts. Remove the 3rd/4th selector shaft and retain the locking disc which appears between the 3rd/4th and reverse gear selector shafts. Remove the 1st/2nd selector shaft. All shafts pull out through the primary end of the gear casing.

12 Select two speeds by sliding two gearshafts along simultaneously so that neither shaft will turn.

13 Using a very wide but thin spanner (a Calor Gas spanner will work) unlock and unscrew the speedometer drive nut from the primary end. Then release the two gears selected.

14 Tap gently with a hide headed hammer the end of the final drive pinion towards the differential end. Remove the taper roller bearing, shims with the final drive pinion.

15 Push the primary shaft towards the differential end so to free its rear bearing cage. Pull out its front bearing plus shims for its a free fit.

16 Pull out of the top of the casing the primary shaft. This will enable the reverse gear shaft to be pulled out of the casing, then the gear itself.

17 Now lift out the 3rd/4th and 1st/2nd selector forks.

18 Mark with punched dot marks the secondary shaft adjusting nut lockplate as you have the differntial housing. Remove the lock tab and nut and then unscrew the adjusting nut counting the number of turns. Remove the 4th speed gear thrust washer, and the 4th gear from the end of the casing.

19 Remove the rest of the gear cluster from the top of the casing.

5.2 The bellhousing is bolted to both engine and gearbox

5.4a Dot marks appear just below the spanner head

5.4b A good method of housing removal

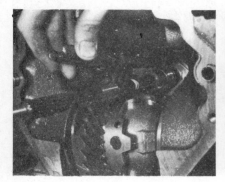

5.5a Remove the roll pin

5.5b Pull out the clutch half of the primary shaft

5.5c Remove the differential from the front

5.7a Lift off the top cover like this

5.7b Pick out the detent springs but do not lose the balls below them

5.8a Lift off the end cover like this

5.8b Retain the shims as shown

5.9 Always retain the tab locks

5.10a The selector shaft roll pins are well illustrated here

5.10b Pull out this selector shaft (Reverse) ...

5.11a ... then this one (3rd/4th) ...

5.11b ... and finally the last one (1st/2nd)

5.11c Do not forget the locking washer

5.13 The speedometer drive gear has flats below it

5.14 Pull out the pinion shaft ...

5.15a ... and then follow it with this bearing ...

5.15b ... and its race

5.16a The primary shaft comes out through the top

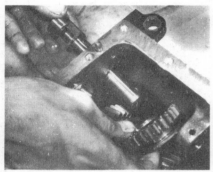

5.16b The reverse gear and its shaft. The roll pin has gone

5.17 Lift out the two selector forks upper 3rd/4th, lower 1st/2nd

5.18 The end housing and the gear below

5.19a The two halves of the main shaft cluster

5.19b The second half of the cluster

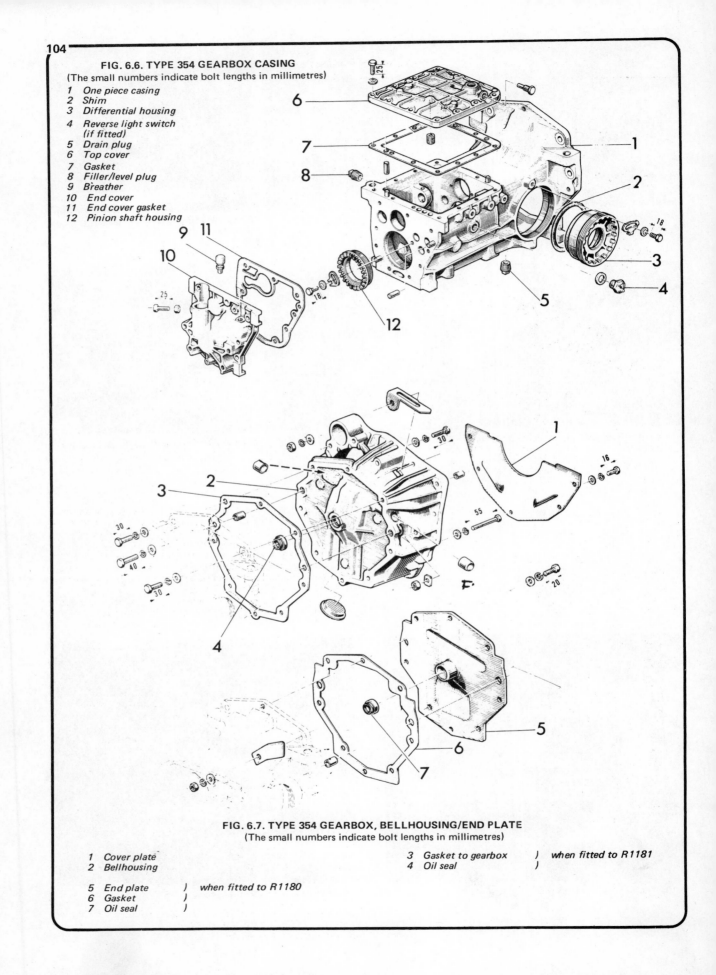

**FIG. 6.6. TYPE 354 GEARBOX CASING**
(The small numbers indicate bolt lengths in millimetres)

1  One piece casing
2  Shim
3  Differential housing
4  Reverse light switch
   (if fitted)
5  Drain plug
6  Top cover
7  Gasket
8  Filler/level plug
9  Breather
10  End cover
11  End cover gasket
12  Pinion shaft housing

**FIG. 6.7. TYPE 354 GEARBOX, BELLHOUSING/END PLATE**
(The small numbers indicate bolt lengths in millimetres)

1  Cover plate
2  Bellhousing

5  End plate          )  when fitted to R1180
6  Gasket             )
7  Oil seal           )

3  Gasket to gearbox  )  when fitted to R1181
4  Oil seal           )

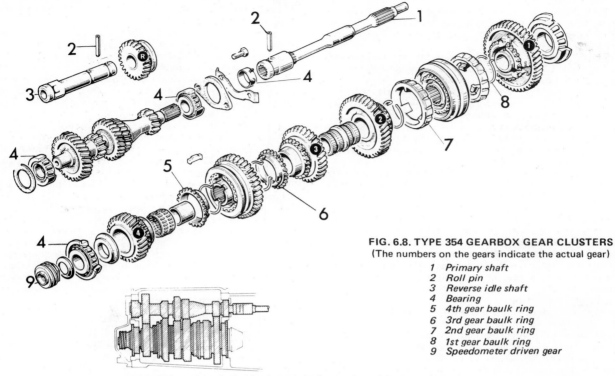

**FIG. 6.8. TYPE 354 GEARBOX GEAR CLUSTERS**
(The numbers on the gears indicate the actual gear)

1 *Primary shaft*
2 *Roll pin*
3 *Reverse idle shaft*
4 *Bearing*
5 *4th gear baulk ring*
6 *3rd gear baulk ring*
7 *2nd gear baulk ring*
8 *1st gear baulk ring*
9 *Speedometer driven gear*

Note: Type 354 gearbox final drive is very similar to that of the Type 334. See Fig. 6.3.

20 Further dismantling is possible of both the gear clusters and the final drive as well as the gear selectors. However, it is not recommended to undertake any further dismantling to the bearings and to the final drive because of the necessity of presses to do the work properly. If at this stage it is found necessary to renew any bearings or the final drive you must seek the services of a Renault agent with suitable equipment. Take him the parts needing work. Read Section 6 now.

21 To replace the synchro units mark the two parts of the synchro ring 1st/2nd and 3rd/4th, then separate them. This will obviously apply when renewing individual gears. Reassembly is covered in Section 8.

22 The top cover is easily dismantled if necessary. See the appropraite illustration to show the components which will enable you to disassemble them.

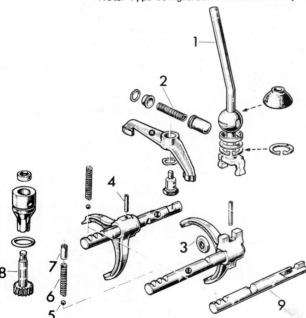

**FIG. 6.9. TYPE 354 GEARBOX SELECTOR MECHANISM**
(The numbers on the forks indicate the gears they select)

1 *Shift lever*
2 *Balance spring*
3 *Spacer*
4 *Roll pin*
5 *Detent ball*
6 *Detent spring*
7 *Plunger (1st and 2nd)*
8 *Speedometer driven gear*
9 *Reverse selector shaft*

---

**6   Inspection for wear of transmission components**

---

Once decided that the transmission unit will have to be stripped down because of some minor irritant or major fault it is still not necessary to strip the unit completely. For example there is no need to remove the reverse gear cluster shaft if the synchromesh is being replaced on an otherwise properly functioning gearbox. Consequently you should go slowly once the three major components are removed from the unit because you may be doing unnecessary work. You may also have to face the fact that even when once dismantled that you will do better to reassemble the box there and then (do it properly though) and exchange it for a replacement unit from Renault. The economics of replacing large components is not always on when compared to a complete exchange unit. Remember also that exchange units are likely to be more readily available than individual component parts and that they will carry a guarantee.

Once dismantled into its three major components, the primary shaft and final drive, inspection should be detailed. Clean the inside of the unit thoroughly first with a mixture of petrol and paraffin and wipe dry.

1   Check the casting for cracks or damage, particularly near the bearing housings and on the mating surfaces. Casings are only available in matched pairs (type 334) so both will have to be replaced.

2   Check all the gears for chips and possible cracks and replace where necessary. You should be able to tell whether this should be so from the inlet diagnosis before dismantling.

3   Check all the shafts and splines for wear and flat spots and replace if necessary. The gears through which the shafts pass should be a good slide fit and not rock about.

4   Check the synchromesh rings and assembly. All models are prone to early synchromesh failure which should really be renewed as a matter of course as it is cheap enough to do so. The springs should also be renewed.

5   Check the bearings: Primary shaft bearings are generally speaking very reliable and long lived and these are the only bearings apart from the double taper roller bearing on the pinion shaft which can be easily and economically replaced. Check them for scoring and 'wobble'. Pinion shaft bearings: The double taper roller bearing at the opposite end from the final drive is easily replaced although generally long lived. Replace it if in any doubt. The pinion bearing next to the pinion wheel is another matter. If this bearing is worn or faulty the pinion shaft will have to be replaced at a cost of approximately one third of an exchange unit. If this has 'gone' and there are other necessary replacements within the transmission unit, then reassemble (properly) the gearbox and exchange the whole unit for a replacement transmission. It is not economic to do otherwise. The two outer differential bearings should be inspected in the same way. These may be replaced by the home mechanic but he may have difficulty in setting up the final drive in the casing afterwards. This was not done on the gearbox we dismantled but it is briefly explained. Again these bearings are usually reliable.

6   Any failure within the final drive unit will mean replacement of the whole unit, crownwheel assembly in total. Under certain circumstances it will mean changing the bearing and speedo drive gear. See the specifications at the start of the Chapter. We did not dismantle the crownwheel and pinion because it is not a task which can be undertaken, at least at the reassembly stage, by the home mechanic. The cost of purchasing a new crownwheel without a new pinion, madness anyway, is again approximately half that of a new exchange transmission unit. Purchasing the two together, crownwheel assembly and pinion assembly, to enable them to mesh and set-up correctly is approximately the cost of the exchange transmission and you will not get the guarantee.

7   Check that the nylon speedometer drive gearwheel is in good condition and running easily in its bush.

8   Check the selector forks for wear. Measure them with a pair of calipers and compare their ends with the thickest point; if in doubt replace. They should be only fractionally worn.

9   Check the gear shift mechanism. The tongue which also slots into the top of the selectors wears quite rapidly often resulting in non-selected gears and sloppy action. Be absolutely sure the correct replacement lever is supplied. Modifications have been made and parts are NOT interchangeable.

Special Note: Such is the construction of these transmission unit that they are generally speaking very reliable but often noisy. They all whine from new to some degree and this should not frighten owners. Obviously it is not possible to detect any increase in whine over a period of time only to suddenly think that it is doing it more than perhaps it should. However this is not good reason in itself to remove and disassemble the unit. The usual reason for discontent is the gradual failure of the synchromesh, particularly on first and second gears. This again is not really good reason for disassembly until it is completely non-functioning and the whine is excessive, from a mechanical point of view. Provided the unit still selects its gears, keeps them there and functions smoothly there is no mechanical reason for worry. Only at a point where it becomes unbearable for the individual owner should this action be taken. See the Fault diagnosis at the end of this Chapter before jumping to conclusions.

## 7   Type 334 transmission unit - reassembly

1   Make sure all the component parts and casing halves are spotlessly clean.

2   Press in the speedometer drive gear bush and fit the gear. A small felt washer should be placed in the outer orifice. Make sure the speedometer outer cable clamp screw is ready fitted.

3   Replace the reverse gear cluster in its housing with the lead on the teeth facing the differential side, and the friction washers with their recessed surface against the gear cluster. Push the shaft through the friction washers and the gear cluster. Lock the shaft in place with a roll pin with the flat of the shaft towards the gasket face of the casing half. Finally position the gear cluster and its friction washers by fitting two snap washers or circlips.

4   Take both selector forks to the local Renault garage and have them fit the locking balls and springs to them for you. It is not an easy task without the special tool to do it and the special tool is not easy to make. Also take along that half of the casing into which the selector forks fit. Once the two selector forks have been fitted into the casing push in the selector fork shaft. This will then drive out the special tools fitted to locate the locking balls and springs yet still hold them in place.

5   Push the shaft fully in and turn it in order to expose the locking plunger hole, with the selector forks in the normal position. Push in the plunger and turn the selector shaft so that the plunger locates in both the selector forks. Drive in the roll pin which locates the selector shaft to the casing.

6   Reassemble the primary shaft. Drive on the bearings to the shaft using an adequate socket with the shaft in a soft faced vice. The socket should be placed over the bearing and tapped with a hammer. MAKE SURE that the bearings are correctly fitted as per the previously made markings if using the same bearings. If using new bearings make sure that the correct ones are fitted for although the packing of the new bearings bears the appropriate number, once out of the packet they cannot be told apart. Fit also the positioning shims and the seal.

7   Measure the primary shaft end float but position the adjusting shims as they were removed with the thinnest innermost, refit the other half of the casing locating with a few of the bolts. The shaft should have an end float of between 0.02 and 0.12 mm and the last shim should protrude 0.1 mm above the gasket housing face. These two measurements should be measurable with feeler gauges and one's finger. If the adjustment is not correct add or subtract shims which are available in seven thicknesses, 0.10 to 3 mm. Once adjusted correctly, remove the

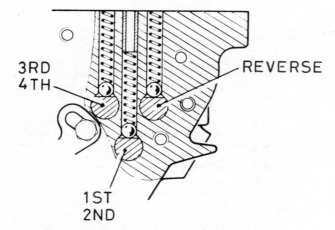

**Fig 6.10. Selector rods viewed from speedometer drive gear end of casing (354 gearbox)**

other half-casing, the primary shaft and proceed to fit the clutch half of the primary shaft.

8  Refit the clutch half of the primary shaft to the main primary shaft simply by pushing one into the other and driving in a new roll pin to make the attachment.

9  Pinion shaft reassembly. If the first speed/synchro ring is renewed as recommended always fit the same type as was removed, ie: with the correct thickness of flange, either 2 mm or 3 mm. Fit the spring as shown in the diagram to the second/ third speed sliding gear with the largest diameter of the spring against the sliding gear selector fork groove. Put the spring tag into the slot. Then place the second/third speed synchro ring onto the sliding gear just mentioned with the flange facing the selector fork groove. Fit the other end of the spring into the hole on the synchro ring and turn it in a clockwise direction until the two ends of the spring are adjacent. Once in this position push the synchro ring onto the sliding gearwheel teeth.

10  Continue to hold this assembly in this same position and slide over the synchro ring outer cage. Make sure this is the right way round.

11  Place the assembly, still properly together, onto the top of an open vice, supporting it with the gearwheel and crimp down the edge of the outer cage with a centre punch. Punch this round uniformly with a gap of about 1/8 inch between each successive punch.            (Renault recommend the use of a press for this, capable of exerting a pressure of 7 tons. The punch method is sufficient however!)

12  Place the six ball bearings in the synchro hub, keeping them there with some grease. Fit the first/reverse gearwheel over the synchro hub with the selector fork groove facing the pinion drive wheel end.

13  Now take the pinion shaft itself and place the assembly just made up, over it, with the first/reverse gearwheel next to the pinion wheel end.

14  Fit the third speed gear wheel moving cone to the pinion assembly with its tapered edge towards the pinion.

15  Locate the spring into the third speed gearwheel, hooking its end through the appropriate hole.

16  Slide this onto the pinion shaft with the actual gearwheel to the rear.

17  Fit the double roller tapered bearing and the locking nut.

18  Place the pinion shaft assembly into the gearbox half-casing alongside the primary shaft.

19  Turning to the final drive, it will be necessary to fit new differential bearings if the old ones were removed although this has previously not been recommended. The roller bearings can be easily drifted onto the crownwheel assembly using the socket and hammer method already described. Make sure that the sunwheel is replaced correctly at the same time. Drift them on as far as they will go. Place the outer half of the roller races in the half-casings. Place new rubber 'O' rings onto the end of the splines of the differential.

20  Place the differential into the casing and place the opposite side of the casing over the top, fit the gasket using gasket cement, and attach all the bolts but do not do them up tight. Make sure that the speedo drive wheel is not fouling on the sun-wheel of the differential. Tighten the casing bolts to a torque of 15 lb ft in the sequence shown in Fig. 6.11.

21  The differential housing should turn freely but without play once the differential housing, the paper gasket and the original number of shims have been replaced each side, provided new differential bearings have not been fitted. Use gasket cement. If this is the case torque the housing bolt to 20 lb ft and bend over their locking washers. The differential housing covers are fitted with oil seals. ALWAYS renew these - failure to do so, and any mishandling, will result in an oil leak.

22  Drift on the fourth speed gear to the primary shaft using the socket and hammer method. It is also possible to thread a bolt through the gearwheel into the shaft, on which, threaded all the way up, is a nut and washer. Tighten the nut holding the bolt and the wheel will slide on.

23  Fit the fourth speed friction bush to the pinion shaft.

24  Then fit on the fourth speed gear and synchro ring onto the same shaft.

25  Drift on using a soft bronze drift the fourth speed synchro hub, again onto the pinion shaft.

26  Together fit the fourth speed sliding gear and the fourth speed selector fork onto their respective shafts interconnected. Make sure that the two marks previously made on the sliding gear and the synchrohub are aligned if no new parts are fitted.

27  Using a screwdriver, select fourth and reverse gear simultaneously to lock the gears. Fit any necessary washers in position and refit the nuts onto the pinion shaft and onto the primary shaft. Torque the pinion shaft nut to 60 lb ft and the primary shaft nut to 45 lb ft and then lock the nuts, using either a screwdriver or a centre punch.

28  Refit the front cover plate having used a new oil seal together with a new gasket and gasket cement. Torque the fixing bolts to 15 lb ft if 7 mm diameter or 20 lb ft if 8 mm.

29  Rethread the starting handle dog and sharply tap to lock it.

30  Select neutral gear.

31  Refit the front/clutch end cover plate having fitted a new oil seal. Use a new gasket and gasket cement.

32  Refit the correct gear shift lever using a new paper gasket and gasket cement, locate the four bolts but leave them loose. The lever stop bolt should face away from the casing split, and the smallest spigot on the lock in the fourth gear selector fork.

33  Final fitment of the lever should proceed as follows: As the lever housing bolt holes are oval and as the notches of the selector forks are not in line it is necessary to make several movements to get all to connect correctly. See Fig. 6.12 and push the housing towards P in the direction of arrow 1 on the casing halves. Place the gear lever (L) in the fourth gear position, arrow 2. tighten the housing bolt further and then draw the housing towards arrow 3 until effectively the latch flange (T) just touches the side of (F) the notch of the gear selector fork. Then draw the housing in the opposite direction, arrow 4, for between 0.10 and 0.30 mm until a side play (J) of about the same figure is felt between (T) and (F). Finally tighten the housing bolts to 15 lb ft torque. Make sure that all can now move freely and gears can be selected.

34  The gearbox is now ready for refitting to the engine. Do not forget to fill with oil before running the car. Treat the gearbox as you would an engine for running-in.

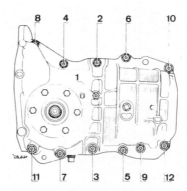

Fig. 6.11. Type 334 casing halves tightening sequence

7.7 Primary shaft joint roll pin

7.18a Locate the pinion shaft

7.18b The primary shaft removed to clarify the speedometer driven gear position

7.18c Main/pinion shaft, primary shaft and speedometer drive gear installed

7.20a The differential. Note the O ring on the spline

7.20b No gasket between the casing halves

7.20c Use new lock tabs

7.21a The same shims replaced

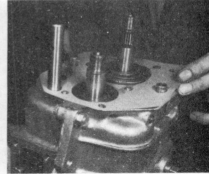

7.21b Always a new gasket

7.21c The end plate ...

7.21d ... the Allen screws and washers and ...

7.22a ... the Woodruff key

7.22b Tap back the gear with a hide hammer

7.22c The lock nut replaced

7.24a Fourth gear pushed on by hand

7.24b 4th gear baulk ring

7.24c The 4th gear synchro hub

7.26 The synchro sleeve with selector fork

7.28a Fitting the end cover

7.28b Left: Late type end cover. Right: Early type with oil seal.
The primary shafts are different

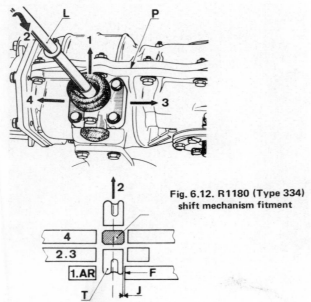

Fig. 6.12. R1180 (Type 334)
shift mechanism fitment

## 8   Type 354 transmission unit - reassembly

1   Make sure all the components are spotlessly clean. Then look at the component drawings relevant to this gearbox. Picture the assemblies in your mind.

2   Make sure the top cover is assembled, complete. Reassemble it in a reverse sequence to its disassembly.

3   Reassemble the two synchro hubs. For the 1st/2nd unit fit the recessed inner of the hub facing towards the 2nd speed sliding gear. Fit the two springs correctly. If original parts are fitted match up the two marks. For the 3rd/4th fit the two springs, positioning each one correctly with the three keys in their recesses. See the diagram. Fit the sliding gear with the groove facing the inner part of the hub with the biggest offset.

4   Put the gear casing on its end; bell housing end down.

5   Fit the secondary/pinion shaft gear cluster into the casing. See the photos.

6   Now fit the 4th gear and ring its split needle roller cage. Hold the cage halves in light grease. Fit the gear sleeve.

7   Screw in the thrust washer and bearing adjusting ring nut. Tighten and lock it using the same number of turns counted and having the dot marks aligned.

8   Turn the gearbox onto its lower side.

9   Insert the 1st/2nd and 3rd/4th selector forks.

10  Insert the reverse gear and its shaft. Punch its roll pins but not too far. See photo.

11  Put in the primary shaft, pushing the reverse gear up and down its shaft to allow it to fit. Punch the reverse gear shaft roll pins home.

12  Refit the rear end plate of the primary shaft and lock it.

13  Insert the pinion shaft gently through the gear cluster. Once inserted tap the taper roller bearing onto the shaft at the other end.

14  Select two speeds simultaneously and lock the gearbox. Refit the speedometer skew gear. Tighten fully. Select neutral. The secondary shaft must now revolve easily and without play. If not something has gone wrong. To rectify unlock the pinion shaft adjusting ring nut and loosen or tighten appropriately. Then relock. If new bearings have been fitted a preload on the secondary shaft of 1 to 3½ lbs will indicate correct fitment. Use a spring balance and cord round the 3rd/4th gear groove.

15  Now refit the selector shafts in the exact reverse order. 1) 1st/2nd selector shaft and roll pin. 2) 3rd/4th selector shaft and roll pin. 3) Locking disc between the selector shafts. 4) Reverse selector shaft and roll pin.

16  Drop the three locking balls above the selector shafts through the edge of the casing. Follow here with the springs and the 1st/2nd spring plunger.

17  Use a new gasket and refit the top cover. Move the end of the selector lever (longest finger) in the top cover towards its nearest corner and having used some gasket cement on both the casing and the cover, place the gasket on the casing and tighten the top cover. If it does not go on easily take it off and slide the reverse gear along so that it rests on the 4th gear on the primary shafts. Make sure the gearbox is neutral. Try again; the selector lever should slide into its correct notch.

18  Now refit the primary shaft front bearing. Tap the outer track ring push with the casing. Refit the same number of shims which were removed.

19  Refit the end cover. Use a new gasket and gasket cement.

20  Replace the differential inside the housing. Make sure the crownwheel is on the correct side. See the appropriate diagram: R1180 is on the opposite side to the R1181.

21  Screw in each adjusting ring nut the same number of turns that were used in its removal. Make sure the dot punch mark aligns. If new bearings have been used your number of turns and dot alignment marks are not valid. Screw in the ring until the differential becomes 'slightly hard' to turn. Then check the preload. Revolve the differential to settle the bearings and then use a spring balance to test. It needs 2 to 7 lb to turn the differential easily. Adjust the ring nuts until all is well. Replace

the lock tab and set screw.

22 Replace the primary shaft using a new roll pin.

23 All is now assembled except for the bell housing of the R1181 model and the cover plate of the R1181. Bolt the relevant part to the gearbox casing in the reverse sequence of its removal.

24 Check that the gears can be selected easily.

## 9 Removal and replacement of gear shift bushes

1 Gearshift mechanisms differ from the R1180 to the R1181; the R1180 early cars were fitted with the 'high' level gear lever knob, this was later lowered. The R1181 is of the 'low' type. However although components are not necessarily interchangeable all the bushes generally are, and the methods of removal and replacement similar.

2 Sloppy gear changes and rattling gear knobs are usually due to worn bushes. The shift rod passes through two nylon bushes, both mounted in rubber, one on the radiator (R1180) or centre cross brace (R1181) and one in a shift tube in the bulkhead. The rod itself has a further bush on its end, over the lever into the gearbox.

3 To renew the cross brace bushes, separate the two halves of the shift control rod (2 bolts) unbolt the bracket from the top of the radiator, remove the radiator stay and free the shift control rod by punching out the roll pin. Lever out the nylon bush through the rubber one and discard both. Lubricate the new nylon and rubber bush as a pair with washing up liquid. Insert one into the other and then push into the bracket. Reassemble the shift rod.

4 The end bush on the shift rod is changed in the same way. At the same time make sure the bias spring is fitted.

5 The bulkhead bush is more difficult to replace. The shift tube must be removed from under the facia. It is fixed by four setscrews. Again the shift rod must be halved under the bonnet. Poke out the bush and push in a new one, inside its keeper. Reassembly is a simple reverse process.

6 Make sure all grommets are fitted to the bodywork where the gearshift passes through the bulkhead. A considerable draught will build up if this is not done! The handbrake lever is another case in point.

## 10 Speedometer cable

1 Speedometer cable removal and replacement is a simple task at the gearbox end but more difficult at the speedometer in the facia panel. A frequent occurrence is inner speedometer cable breakage. If this happens the complete inner and outer cable has to be replaced as a 'sealed' unit.

2 Release the outer cable at the gearbox by undoing the little fixing screw in the gearbox casing.

3 If it is certain the cable is broken cut the inner and outer cable at the bulkhead under the bonnet and remove and discard the rest of the cable.

4 Unscrew the knurled nut behind the facia panel using your fingers. It may be necessary to remove some of the trim first. Remove the now short piece of cable into the vehicle. Take off the two bulkhead rubber grommets.

5 Tape the knurled nut to the end of the new outer cable and thread it through the bulkhead from under the bonnet. Locate this taped end with your fingers from inside the vehicle. Before securing to the facia panel bush on the two rubber grommets.

6 Once located in the facia and screwed tight, locate the rubber grommets and feed the cable to the gearbox. Again locate properly and do up the little fixing screw.

Special Note: These cables are prone to squeaking and causing speedometer needle flutter. There is little that can be done short of replacing the whole cable!

8.5a Position the gear cluster half

8.5b Rest the other half so

8.6a Note the split roller bearing cage

8.6b Back inside the casing

8.7a Screw in carefully

8.7b Replace in its original position and lock

8.9 Rest the selector forks

8.10a Fit the reverse gear and shaft ...

8.10b ... and locate roll pins, but only so far

8.11a Back in with the primary shaft

8.11b Now punch in the roll pins. See photo 8.10b

8.13a Return the pinion shaft very carefully

8.13b Push on the bearing race at the other end

3.13c Tap it home

8.14 Replace the speedometer drive gear

8.15a The 1st/2nd selector shaft back ...

8.15b ... the 3rd/4th shaft and roll pin now ...

8.15c ... and the locking washer, the reverse selector shaft to follow

8.16a Three detent balls and ...

8.16b ....the three springs located

8.17 Replace the top cover with a new gasket not forgetting the 1st/2nd detent plunger

8.18 The same number of shims

8.19 The end cover. Note the driven gear in it

8.20 The differential replaced. Put the right way round according to engine type (see Section 1)

8.21a Note the fine thread. Do not cross

8.21b Reposition exactly as originally

8.22 Tabs locked and a new roll pin

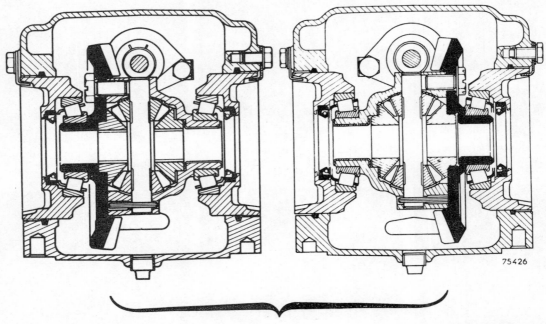

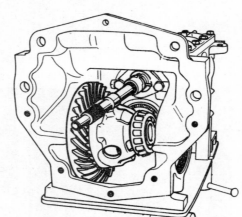

**Fig. 6.13. Type 354 differential placement**
Left: R1181
Right: late model (post 1973) R1180

## 11 Fault diagnosis

1 Faults can be sharply divided into two main groups: Some definite failure with the transmission not working: Noises implying some component worn, damaged, or out of place.

2 The failures can usually be tracked down by commonsense and remembering the circumstances in which they appeared. Thus if the car will not go at all a mechanical failure will occur in different circumstances to a broken linkage from the gear lever!

3 If there is a definite fault within the transmission then it has got to be removed and dismantled to repair it, so further diagnosis can wait till the parts can be examined.

4 But if the problem is a strange noise the decision must be taken whether in the first place it is abnormal, and if so whether it warrants action.

5 Noises can be traced to a certain extent by doing the test sequence as follows:

6 Find the speed and type of driving that makes the noise. If the noise occurs with engine running, car stationary, clutch disengaged, gear engaged: The noise is not in the transmission. If it goes after the clutch is engaged in neutral, halted, it is the clutch.

7 If the noise can be heard faintly in neutral, clutch engaged, it is in the gearbox. It will presumably get worse on the move, especially in some particular gear.

8 Final drive noises are only heard on the move. They will only vary with speed and load, whatever gear is engaged.

9 Noise when pulling is likely to be either the adjustment of preload of the differential bearings, or the crown wheel and pinion backlash.

10 Gear noise when free-wheeling is likely to be the relative positions of crownwheel and pinion.

11 Noise on corners implies excessive tightness or excessive play of the bevel side gears or idler pinions in the differential.

12 In general, whining is gear teeth at the incorrect distance apart. Roaring or rushing or moaning is bearings. Thumping or grating noises suggest a chip out of a gear tooth.

13 If subdued whining comes on gradually, there is a good chance the transmission will last a long time to come.

14 Whining or moaning appearing suddenly, or becoming loud, should be examined quickly.

15 If thumping, or grating noises appear stop at once. If bits of metal are loose inside, the whole transmission, including the casing, could quickly be wrecked.

16 Synchromesh wear is obvious. You just 'beat' the gears and crashing occurs.

# Chapter 7 Drive shafts, hubs, wheels and tyres

**Contents**

**Specifications**

| | |
|---|---|
| **Drive shafts** ... ... ... ... ... ... ... ... | Removable, double universal joints, |
| | Inner end: Spider joint (solid shaft) or |
| | Weiss joint (tubular shaft) |
| | Outer end: "BED" cast iron joint |
| Inner joint oil ... ... ... ... ... ... ... | Specially supplied by Renault |
| **Front hub bearings** ... ... ... ... ... ... ... | Proprietary bearings - 2 ball bearings of Renault manufacture plus 2 taper roller bearings |
| **Rear hub bearings** ... ... ... ... ... ... ... | 2 taper roller bearings |

\* Drive shafts are not interchangeable between R1180 and R1181 vehicles because of differing castor angles and hubs.

| | |
|---|---|
| **Wheels** ... ... ... ... ... ... ... ... ... | Pressed steel disc (slotted, R1180, drilled, R1181), solid centre 3 stud fixing, 13 inch diameter, 4 inch rim (4B) |
| **Tyres** ... ... ... ... ... ... ... ... | Radial 135 or 145 x 13 |
| Pressures | |
| Front - normal ... ... ... ... ... ... ... | 21 psi |
| Rear - normal ... ... ... ... ... ... ... | 24 psi |
| Front (load/motorway) ... ... ... ... ... ... | 24 psi |
| Rear (load/motorway) ... ... ... ... ... ... | 27 psi |

**Torque wrench settings**

| | lbf ft | kgf m |
|---|---|---|
| Front hub nut ... ... ... ... ... ... ... ... | 85 | 11.8 |
| Rear hub nut (initial torque) ... ... ... ... ... ... | 25 | 3.5 |
| Roadwheel nut ... ... ... ... ... ... ... ... | 45 | 6.2 |
| Stub axle nut ... ... ... ... ... ... ... ... | 90 | 12.4 |

## 1 General description

The drive shafts fitted to the Renault 6 drive the front wheels direct from the final drive in the transmission casing. They also undergo the steering movement of the car with the front wheels. Consequently they are fitted with universal joints at the outer (wheel) end and sliding joints at their inner (transmission) end. They are effectively single units, the joints being totally integral with the shafts. Little maintenance can be done on them and when worn out they must be renewed as a whole, although they can obviously be renewed singly.

Several types and lengths of shaft have been fitted with different styles of joint, depending on the model and the length of suspension wishbones fitted. It is most important that you replace the shafts with the correct type. They are not interchangeable, necessarily, from car to car although they are from side to side. BED (cast) universal joints have been fitted at the outer end and Bendix-Weiss with rubber bellows and SPIDER sliding joints have been fitted at the inner end. See the specifications at the start of this chapter for types fitted.

The front wheel hubs themselves run on special Renault manufacture caged ball bearings whilst the rear hubs are conventional taper roller bearings (two). The front hub bearings are not adjustable but the rear ones are (see Section 6).

The disc road wheels are conventional, at least to Renault and French cars in general in that they have solid centres and are three stud fixings. Each model has a different style of wheel. Radial tyres are fitted as standard and must be considered as obligatory on these vehicles.

### 2 Drive shaft - disconnection and connection

1  To be able to remove the engine and transmission unit, the drive shafts have to be disconnected at the inner end and the suspension ball joints at the outer end have to be forced from their mounting points (Section 8, Chapter 10).

2  Before attempting to work on the drive shafts of the early R1180s fitted with the type 334 gearbox it is essential to purchase a special tool kit, which is inexpensive, from your Renault garage. This kit enables the drive shaft roll pins to be driven out, and refitted. There is no other way of doing it short of manufacturing your own version of these tools.

3  Under special tool number B.Vi.318 are three drifts for extracting the roll pins (5 mm), which hold the splines in place on the final drive. With the car jacked up safely supported on stands, drive out the inner roll pins. You will find these located very close to the transmission case, between that and the rubber bellows on the drive shaft. With the appropriate drift drive the pins downwards and throw the two pins (one inside and the other) away. Never re-use old roll pins. For late type R1180 and all R1181s fitted with the type 354 gearbox, the drive shafts are not fixed and can be pulled straight out of the gearbox.

4  Fit retaining clips once you have pulled the drive shaft coupling very gently away from the gearbox. Pull it about one inch only, and fit the retainers to the shaft over the rubber bellows. Be careful, do not stretch the rubber bellows or disconnect the joint inside. Retainers can be manufactured from strong electrical wire and some wormdrive clips approximately 2 inches in diameter. Undo the clip totally and put over the shaft and redo it. Place it about 2 inches  from the bellows. Wind the wire round the shaft, pull it taut and tighten the clips. The inner joint will now not dislodge itself. Do not ignore this stage under any circumstances - it costs money to reconnect the inner joint!

5  To remove the drive shaft completely, refer to the next Section.

6  Replacement of the drive shaft onto the transmission is an exact reversal of the disconnection except that when driving in a new set of roll pins (Early R1180) (always use new ones) use a different and appropriate drift from the tool kit. Grease the splines with Castrol LM Grease. Tap in the large roll pin first, having lined up the splines on the shaft with those on the transmission so that the four holes are all complementary. Then place the second one inside the first with its slot opposite the other, and drive in. Smear the ends of the roll pins once in position with very heavy grease.

2.6b The smaller, inner roll pin inside it. Now tap home

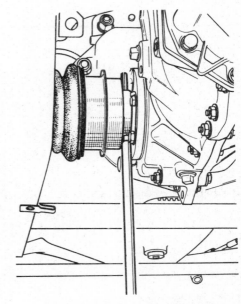

Fig. 7.1 Roll pin punch (334 gearbox)

2.6a The large, outer roll pin first

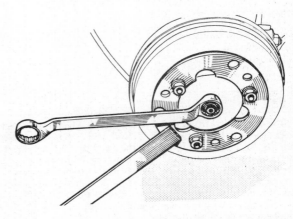

Fig. 7.2. Renault special tool for holding front hub (R1180) to undo shaft nut

### 3 Drive shaft - removal and replacement

1 Total removal of a drive shaft would only need to be done when it was deemed worn out and needing replacement when the inner joint had been disconnected or rubber bellows needed refitting. Obviously crash repairs may necessitate a shaft removal but all other suspension or brake repairs can be undertaken with the shaft remaining in the car.

2 With the purchase or borrowing of two more special tools, one of which is totally unique to this job, the do-it-yourself mechanic can easily replace a drive shaft.

3 Disconnect the inner end of the drive shafts as far as Section 2, paragraph 4. Remove the road wheels. Then disconnect the suspension ball joints as in Chapter 10.

4 With the appropriate sized ring spanner undo the nut on the end of the drive shaft on the outer side of the brake drum or disc. Hold the drum or disc so that you can obtain leverage, by placing a tyre lever on two wheel studs, one on either side, and press in the opposite rotational direction of the spanner. Remove the nut.

5 Borrow or hire a three legged puller (Tool T.Av 235) which you can bolt to the three wheel studs, to enable you to push the end of the drive shaft back through the hub. Fit the puller and firmly screw the bolt in. It should gradually drive out the outer spline through the hub.

6 When released disconnect the steering arm ball joint as you have done the suspension ball joints and remove the drive shaft.

7 Replacing the drive shaft is an exact reversal of its removal except that you will require a special tool from Renault to enable you to pull the shaft through the hub. This is tool No T.Av 236. Slide the drive shaft into the hub stub axle carrier assembly and screw on the fitting tool. Tighten up this tool and it will draw the shaft towards you. Once fully home remove the tool and replace the outer nut and torque to 90 lb ft.

**Note 1**

It is only economic to purchase the tool T.Av 236 if more than one shaft is going to be replaced during work on the car. It is unlikely to be economic to purchase the three legged puller for this purpose. New drive shafts are fitted with an inner joint retaining clip when purchased. It is worthwhile keeping these for they can be used instead of the wire and wormdrive clip when disconnecting a drive shaft in the future.

### 4 Drive shaft joints

As stated in the General description, there is very little maintenance which can be carried out on the drive shaft joints. The outer universal joints are sealed at manufacture and cannot under any circumstances be renewed because the joint itself is

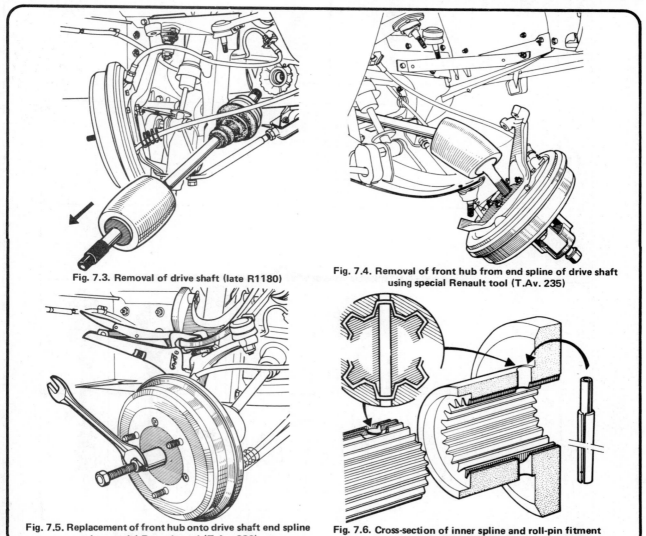

Fig. 7.3. Removal of drive shaft (late R1180)

Fig. 7.4. Removal of front hub from end spline of drive shaft using special Renault tool (T.Av. 235)

Fig. 7.5. Replacement of front hub onto drive shaft end spline using special Renault tool (T.Av. 236)

Fig. 7.6. Cross-section of inner spline and roll-pin fitment (early R1180)

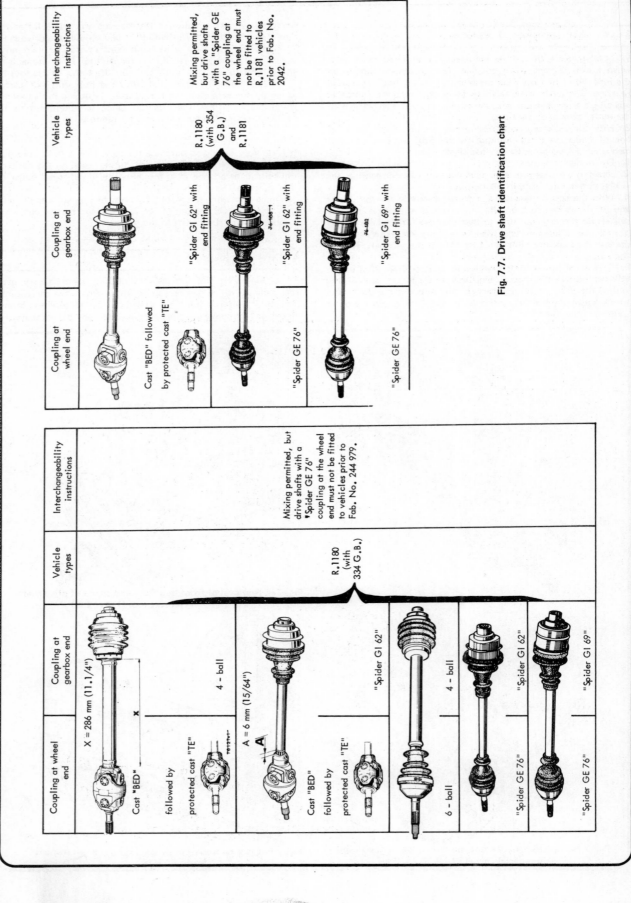

**Fig. 7.7. Drive shaft identification chart**

not available separately. It is unwise and dangerous to attempt any work on these joints. The inner joints can be dismantled by the do-it-yourself mechanic but he will find that he is unable to reassemble them. No matter which type of shaft is fitted special tools are needed to effect a repair. Even replacing the rubber bellows and relubricating the inner joint is beyond the use of ordinary tools. Under all circumstances it is more efficient to remove the drive shaft and then take it to a Renault garage (only) to have them effect any repair or maintenance. With the specific special tools available to them all repairs to the inner joint can be carried out very quickly by an experienced man, and this will always be more efficient and safer than attempting it yourself.

The only repairs available to the Bendix-Weiss joint are reassembly, relubricating and replacement of the outer bellows. When the joints and knuckles themselves wear the whole shaft must be renewed.

For SPIDER joints it is possible to have the bellows, yoke and spider itself replaced, together or separately. Experience shows that unless the bellows are punctured and lubricant allowed to escape and joint to become dry, the outer universal joint wears at a far greater rate than the inner, consequently the shaft is nearly always replaced before the total life of the inner joint is reached. An illustration is given of the various component parts of a drive shaft.

## 5    Front hub bearing - removal and replacement

1    Only ever renew the inner and outer front hub bearings as a pair. It is quite uneconomic to do them singly.

2    Remove the relevant drive shaft as described in Section 2 and 3.

3    Undo the flexible brake pipe from that side as described in Chapter 8.

4    Separate the lower suspension arm ball joint from the stub axle carrier using the same method as used in the drive shaft removal.

5    Remove the suspension stub axle carrier, hub and bearings.

6    Hold the suspension stub axle carrier in a vice and tap out the hub and outer bearing and bearing spacer. Use a soft headed hammer.

7    Extracting the outer bearing can be difficult as there is insufficient room between the bearing and hub to accommodate the feet of a strong conventional three-legged puller. Alternatively break-up the cage of the outer bearing so that the outer track and ball bearings drop out leaving the inner track in position on the hub. Now heat the inner track evenly with a blow lamp and grip it when hot in the jaws of a vice. Using a suitably sized drift and a heavy hammer drive the hub out from the race. Note that several applications of the blow lamp may be required to remove the race.

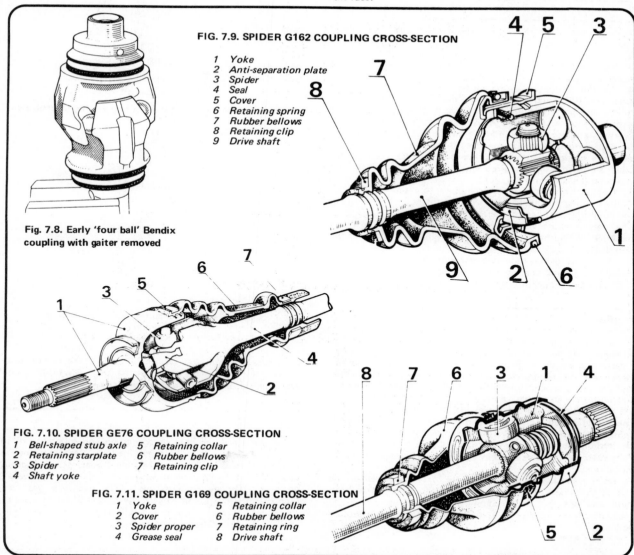

**FIG. 7.9. SPIDER G162 COUPLING CROSS-SECTION**

1    Yoke
2    Anti-separation plate
3    Spider
4    Seal
5    Cover
6    Retaining spring
7    Rubber bellows
8    Retaining clip
9    Drive shaft

Fig. 7.8. Early 'four ball' Bendix coupling with gaiter removed

**FIG. 7.10. SPIDER GE76 COUPLING CROSS-SECTION**

| | |
|---|---|
| 1   Bell-shaped stub axle | 5   Retaining collar |
| 2   Retaining starplate | 6   Rubber bellows |
| 3   Spider | 7   Retaining clip |
| 4   Shaft yoke | |

**FIG. 7.11. SPIDER G169 COUPLING CROSS-SECTION**

| | |
|---|---|
| 1   Yoke | 5   Retaining collar |
| 2   Cover | 6   Rubber bellows |
| 3   Spider proper | 7   Retaining ring |
| 4   Grease seal | 8   Drive shaft |

8   Replacement of the outer bearing to the hub utilises a suitably sized piece of tubing (32 mm) or a socket which should be used to tap in the new bearing. The sealed end of the bearing should be towards the brake drum or disc. Put aside the hub until the inner bearing has been removed from the stub axle carrier.

9   To remove the inner bearing keep the stub axle carrier in the vice and remove the brake backing plate or caliper dust shield by undoing the closure plate nuts and bolts. These are square headed bolts and hexagonal nuts. Remove the backing plate and the bearing closure plate.

10  Push out the inner bearing race by tapping the stub axle carrier onto a piece of suitably sized tube (70 mm).

11  Push in a new bearing, sealed end facing that brake drum, using another piece of tube (58 mm). If a press is available this will ease the task. To ease both bearing races into their respective housings, grease smeared on the outer races will help.

12  Reassemble the stub axle carrier, backing plate and closure plate. Use gasket cement on the closure plate. This will stop water from entering the housing - this is the most usual cause of failure.

13  Reassemble the front hub to the stub axle carrier by pressing it. Do not forget the bearing spacer and place some high melting point grease between the two bearings.

14  Further reassembly is a reversal procedure of the dismantling sequence.

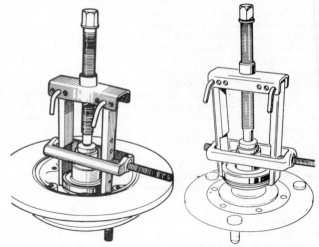

Fig.7.12. Removal of outer hub bearing (front)

## 6   Rear hub bearings - removal and replacement

1   Only ever renew the inner and outer rear hub bearings as a pair.

2   Remove the brake drum as described in Chapter 8.

3   Remove the grease seal from the drum and have a new one ready for replacement. A screwdriver will easily remove this.

4   Tap the two outer bearing housings out of the drum using a large screwdriver and hammer, from the other side of the drum to the bearing. The roller bearing race of the outer bearing is already loose. Extract the inner bearing roller race using a bearing extractor. This could be a simple two legged extractor.

5   Replacement of the races and housing is an obvious reversed sequence of their removal. Tap the inner bearing race onto the stub axle using a suitably sized socket and very carefully ease in the outer housings into the drum.

6   To adjust the hub, tighten the hub nut to a torque of 20 lb ft whilst rotating the brake drum. Unscrew the nut 1/6 turn, which should give an end float of 0.001 to 0.002 in (0.01 to 0.05 mm). The only accurate way to check this is to use a dial gauge mounted on the brake drum with the stylus on the end of the hub shaft.

7   Fit the nut locking cap and a new split pin. Fill the grease cap ¾ full of a general purpose grease and tap it carefully into place. Check the brake operation and adjust if necessary.

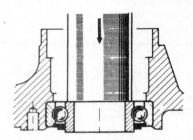

Fig. 7.13. Removal of inner front hub bearing for stub axle carrier

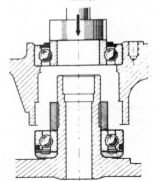

Fig. 7.14. Replacement of front hub bearings
Top half   -   new bearing in stub axle carrier
Lower half  -   new bearing on disc/hub

## 7   Wheels

1   Because of the design of the suspension of the car the strength and the trueness of the road wheels is critical, particularly at the front. A great deal of excessively fast wear on the wheel bearings and universal joints can be attributed to buckled and deformed wheels. Check every 3000 miles or when there is a sudden difference of feeling at the steering wheel that the wheels are not buckled or dented. Check also that the front wheels are balanced. (Remember that the wheels do not have holes in their centres, consequently not all electronic balancing machines can be used on these wheels). If any deformity is noticed the wheel concerned should be replaced by new. Do not attempt to 'repair' wheel rims.

2   Do not overtighten the wheel nuts for this can deform the rim. Always check that the inner side of the wheel is free from mud and grit for the accummulation of these can create inbalance. Never attempt to fit modified wheels for they are sure to 'unset' the car.

3   Grease the hub cap securing thread in the centre of the wheels. The spare wheel soon becomes rusty! Always fit the hub cap with its rubber seal surround firmly fixed.

## 8   Tyres

In the same way that the condition and suitability of the wheels fitted is critical so it is with the tyres. Because of the long suspension travel and fully independent suspension it is always wise to fit radial tyres on all wheels of these cars. Tyre wear is not great under any circumstances but the front tyres wear faster than the rear. Do not fit oversize tyres. The wheel rims are not able to take a larger section tyre. See Specifications for suitability of tyres. Tyre pressures are critical too.

**Fault diagnosis - See the fault diagnosis for Chapter 10.**

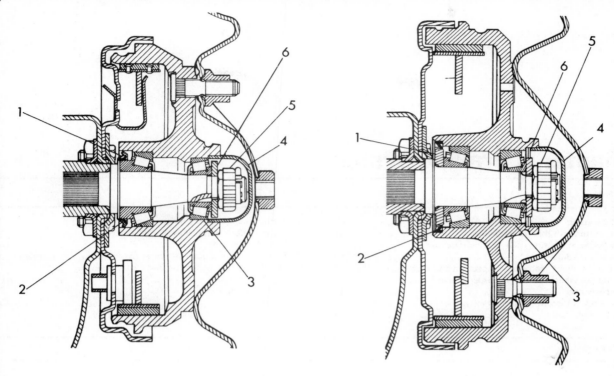

**FIG. 7.15. CROSS SECTION OF REAR HUBS**
Left R1180 with smaller drum brake
Right R1181 with handbrake fitting

1  Oil seal
2  Inner bearing
3  Outer bearing

4  Grease cap
5  Castellated nut lock
6  D washer

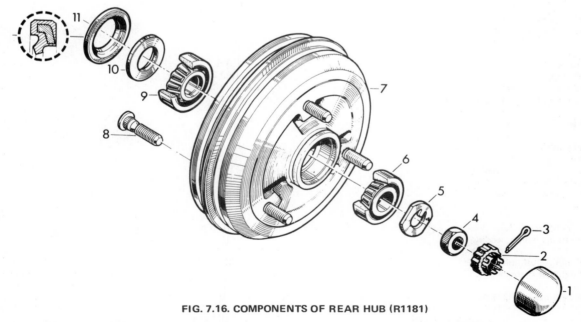

**FIG. 7.16. COMPONENTS OF REAR HUB (R1181)**

1  Grease cap
2  Castellated nut lock
3  Split pin
4  Nut
5  D washer
6  Outer bearing

7  Drum/hub
8  Wheel stud
9  Inner bearing
10  Spacer
11  Oil seal

# Chapter 8 Braking system

## Contents

## Specifications

| | |
|---|---|
| Type ... ... ... ... ... ... ... ... ... | R1180: Hydraulically operated drums all round. Cable operated handbrake to the front wheels<br>R1181: Hydraulically operated disc brakes at the front wheels, drums at the rear. Cable operated handbrake to the rear wheels |

**Front brakes**
**R1180:**
| | |
|---|---|
| Drum diameter ... ... ... ... ... ... | 228.5 mm (9 inch) |
| Brake lining length, leading ... ... ... ... | 244 mm (9 5/8 in.) |
| trailing ... ... ... ... | 189 mm (7 7/16 in.) |
| Brake lining width, both shoes ... ... ... ... | 40 mm (1 9/16 in.) |
| Wheel cylinder diameter ... ... ... ... ... | 23.8 mm (0.937 in.) |

**R1181:**
| | |
|---|---|
| Disc diameter ... ... ... ... ... ... ... | 222 mm (8.9 in.) |
| thickness ... ... ... ... ... ... ... | 10 mm (0.393 in.) |
| Caliper piston diameter ... ... ... ... ... | 45 mm (1. 25/32 in.) |
| Pad thickness (including backing plate) ... ... ... ... | 14 mm (0.551 in.) |

**Rear brakes**
**R1180:**
| | |
|---|---|
| Drum diameter ... ... ... ... ... ... | 160 mm (6 5/16 in.) |
| Brake lining length, leading ... ... ... ... | 152 mm (6 in.) |
| trailing ... ... ... ... | 118 mm (4 5/8 in.) |
| Brake lining width, both shoes ... ... ... ... | 25 mm (6 3/64 in.) |
| Wheel cylinder diameter ... ... ... ... ... | 20.6 mm (0.811 in.) |

**R1181:**
| | |
|---|---|
| Drum diameter ... ... ... ... ... ... | 180 mm (7 1/16 in.) |
| Brake lining length, leading ... ... ... | |
| trailing ... ... ... | |
| Brake lining width, both shoes ... ... ... ... | 30 mm (1 3/16 in.) |
| Wheel cylinder diameter ... ... ... ... ... | 20.6 mm (0.811 in.) |
| | |
| Master cylinder - R1180 single diameter ... ... ... | 20.6 mm (0.811 in.) |
| - R1181 single diameter ... ... ... | 19 mm (0.748 in.) |
| - Dual system diameter ... ... ... | 20.6 mm (0.811 in.) |
| Free play at pedal ... ... ... ... ... | 5 mm (13/64 in.) |
| | |
| Brake pressure limiting valve - R1180 ... ... ... | Pressure 340 to 425 psi |
| - R1181 ... ... ... | Pressure 420 to 448 psi |
| | |
| Brake fluid ... ... ... ... ... ... ... ... | Hydraulic fluid conforming to SAE 70R3 |

**Torque wrench settings**

| | lbf ft | kgf m |
|---|---|---|
| **R1180** | | |
| Brake hose to front wheel cylinder ... ... ... ... | 15 | 2.1 |
| | | |
| **R1181** | | |
| Brake hose to caliper ... ... ... ... ... ... | 15 | 2.1 |
| Brake caliper securing bolt to stub axle carrier ... ... ... | 50 | 6.9 |
| Deflector securing bolt on caliper bracket ... ... ... | 15 | 2.1 |
| Front stub axle nut ... ... ... ... ... ... ... | 90 | 12.5 |
| Disc to hub bolts ... ... ... ... ... ... ... | 20 | 2.8 |
| | | |
| **Both** | | |
| Bleed screws ... ... ... ... ... ... ... ... | 7 | 1.0 |
| Brake pipe unions ... ... ... ... ... ... ... | 10 | 1.4 |
| Roadwheel nuts ... ... ... ... ... ... ... | 45 | 6.2 |

## 1 General description

The braking system of the Renault 6 models is conventional. The R1180 is fitted with hydraulically operated drum brakes at both the front and rear. They are operated by the front pedal whilst an independent parking (hand) brake operates the front wheels only. The R1181 however has front disc brakes and drum rear brakes and the handbrake operates the rear brakes.

Adjustment is done manually at each brake drum individually to compensate for wear on the brake shoe linings. The disc brakes of the R1181 are self-adjusting. The handbrake operation is adjusted automatically by the adjustment of the front brakes although there is a separate method of adjustment for the operating mechanism itself when this wears.

Most models have single hydraulic line braking system. However some models will have dual line with tandem master cylinders. There is little overhaul differences.

A separate restricting valve to the rear brakes is fitted in the hydraulic system. The brake light switch is operated at the master cylinder.

## 2 Routine maintenance

1 Every week remove the hydraulic fluid reservoir cap, having made sure that it is clean, and check the level of the fluid which should be just below the bottom of the filler neck. Check also that the vent hole in the cap is clear. Any need for regular topping up, regardless of quantity, should be viewed with suspicion and the whole hydraulic system carefully checked for signs of leakage.

2 Every 3000 miles adjust the front and rear drum brakes to compensate for wear. Never ignore this task. Lubricate the adjuster EVERY TIME.

3 Every 9000 miles remove the brake drums and examine the shoe linings. They should be renewed when the friction material has very nearly reached the level of the rivet heads or within 1/8 inch (3 mm) if bonded linings are used. If either the rivets or the shoes themselves come into contact with the brake drum they will cause scoring and greatly reduced braking efficiency. Never interchange worn shoes to even-out wear.

For the disc brakes - inspect the disc pad wear, the total pad and backing should not be less than 7 mm. If less they must be replaced in full sets.

Make sure the handbrake functions at all times. At the same time as friction material is examined the hydraulic pipes and unions should be examined for any signs of damage or corrosion. Brake lining pad wear varies according to driving style but no set of brake shoes should be expected to last more than 20000 miles. The front pads are likely to wear at a faster rate than the rear.

4 Every 18 months to 2 years, depending on usage, it is good policy to renew all hydraulic cylinder seals and disc caliper piston seals as a matter of routine, together with the fluid and flexible hoses. Any repair work in the interim should also, of course, be taken into account.

5 If you have just acquired a secondhand car it is strongly recommended that all brake drums and shoes and/or disc and pads are thoroughly examined for condition and wear immediately. Even though braking efficiency may be excellent the friction materials could be nearing the end of their useful life and it is as well to know this without delay. Similarly, the hydraulic cylinders, pipes and connections should be carefully examined for leaks or chafing. Faults should be rectified immediately. It should be remembered that three year old cars will be subject to safety tests and that apart from safety, which is paramount, defects in the system even though they may not yet affect stopping power, will possibly cause the vehicle to fail the test.

## 3 Hydraulic system - bleeding

1 The system should need bleeding only when some part of it has been dismantled which would allow air into the fluid circuit; or if the reservoir level(s) has been allowed to drop so far that air has entered the master cylinder.

2 Ensure that a supply of clean non-aerated fluid of the correct specifications is to hand in order to replenish the reservoir(s) during the bleeding process. It is advisable, if not essential, to have someone available to help, as one person has to pump the brake pedal while the other attends to each wheel. The reservoir level has also to be continuously watched and replenished. Fluid bled out should not be re-used. A clean glass jar and a 9-12 inch length of 1/8 inch internal diameter rubber tube will fit tightly over the bleed nipples is also required.

3 Bleed the rear brakes first as these are furthest from the master cylinder. On dual line systems bleed 'one' system first keeping its reservoir topped up. See Fig. 8.13. Then bleed the by-pass unit circuit from the bleed nipple on the top of the unit.

4 Make sure the bleed nipple is clean and put a small quantity of fluid in the bottom of the jar. Fit the tubes onto the nipple and place the other end in the jar under the surface of the liquid. Keep it under the surface throughout the bleeding operation.

5 Unscrew the bleed screw ½ turn and get the assistant to depress and release the brake pedal in short sharp bursts when you direct him. Short sharp jabs are better than long slow ones because they will force any air bubbles along the line ahead of the fluid rather than pump the fluid past them. It is not essential to remove all the air the first time. If the whole system is being bled, attend to each wheel for three or four complete pedal strokes and then repeat the process. On the second time around operate the pedal sharply in the same way until no more bubbles are apparent. The bleed screw should be tightened and closed with the brake pedal fully depressed which ensures that no

aerated fluid can get back into the system. Do not forget to keep the reservoir topped up throughout.

6   When all four wheels have been satisfactorily bled depress the foot pedal which should offer a firmer resistance with no trace of 'sponginess'. The pedal should not continue to go down under sustained pressure. If it does there is a leak or the master cylinder seals are worn out.

7   Automatic brake bleed valves are available for these cars which will enable you to do this work unaided.

## 4   Drum brake adjustment

1   The procedure for adjusting the drum brakes is exactly the same for both front and rear wheels for all models. It is necessary only to have the correct sized metric spanner to turn the square headed adjuster although the job is always better done with the correct Renault brake spanner which can cover all four sides of this adjuster. The adjusters seize easily and soon become chewed-up if the incorrect tool is used. To this end it is wise to lubricate the adjusters with some penetrating oil in advance of the time you wish to do the task. Soak the adjuster with this fluid at the back of the backing plate. All eight adjusters are exposed to road dirt!

2   Jack up each wheel individually having loosened the hub cap and wheel nuts. Release the handbrake when doing the fronts (R1180) or rears (R1181) and chock the rear wheels, and the opposite for the rears.

3   Remove the wheel and turn the drum with the wheel studs. (At the front the drive shaft will possibly rub on the chassis frame in this position). Place the adjusting spanner on each adjuster in turn, loosen it by turning and then revolve the drum very slowly and tighten up the adjuster until the drum is just locked by the shoe. Slacken it off fractionally so that the drum rotates, just, under slight, but not binding, friction. Proceed with the other adjuster on that backing plate. Then go on and do the other three wheels. Never adjust only one wheel, always do them all.

4   Road test the car and check that it pulls up firmly and straight, without an increase in foot pressure. The pedal should not need pumping.

## 5   Brake drum and shoes - removal, inspection and replacement

1   Jack up the car and remove the road wheel. Block the relevant wheel and release the handbrake.

2   The drums on the front wheels are easily removed. Slacken both adjusters right off. Remove the three holding screws interspaced between the three wheel studs. (These can be Phillips or cut thread screws and are not interchangeable). Pull off the drum over the wheel studs. If it seems stuck fast use a little penetrating oil at the roots of the wheel studs and tap it with a soft headed hammer around the edge. Do not hit the drum with a hammer as it is brittle and may well crack.

3   Removal of the rear drums is a little more complicated. Slacken off the adjusters and then remove the rear drum hub grease cap with a pair of small Stilsons. Wipe any excess grease away from the castellated nut and split pin and pull out the split pin. Undo and remove the castellated nut and D washer. With luck the drum/hub will pull off the stub axle easily together with

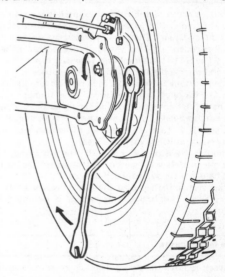

**Fig. 8.2. Brake adjustment - rear R1180**
(Arrows show 'taking up' direction)

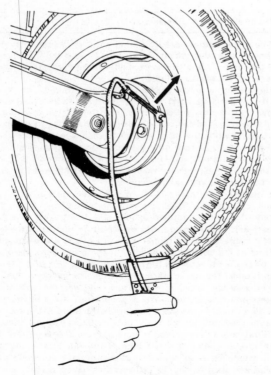

**Fig. 8.1. Brake bleeding. A rear brake illustrated**
(The bleed nipple spanner is arrowed for direction of loosening)

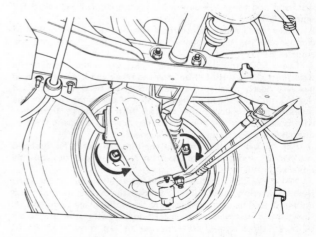

**Fig. 8.3. Brake adjustment - front R1180**
(Arrows show 'taking up' direction)

most of the bearings, inners and outers. If this is not possible a road wheel can be replaced on the hub and this used for something to pull on. Do not waggle the wheel though. Failing both these possibilities a three-legged puller will have to be used fixed to the wheel studs and pushing on the centre of the stub axle. This puller will have to be hired or borrowed.

4 With the drum removed brush out any dust and examine the rubbing surface for any signs of pitting or deep scoring. The surface should be smooth and bright but minor hairline scores are of no consequence and could have been caused by grit or brake shoes with linings just worn to the rivets. A drum that is obviously badly worn should be renewed. A perfectly satisfactory replacement can sometimes be obtained from a breaker's yard. It is no economy having drums turned up on a lathe (unless you can have it done for nothing!). Also, as the radius is altered if the rubbing surfaces are machined out, standard shoes will not match properly until a lot of bedding-in has taken place and re-radiused the linings.

5 The brake shoes should be examined next. There should be no signs of contamination by oil and the linings should be above the heads of the rivets. If the level is close (less than 1/32 inch) it is worth changing them. If there are signs of oil contamination they should be renewed also and the source of oil leakage found before it ruins the new ones as well.

6 To remove the shoes (having, of course, removed the drum) use a screwdriver to push one end of the top inner spring, which pulls the two shoes towards each other to hold-in the two pistons of the wheel cylinder, back through its locating hole in the shoe. This should loosen the spring at the top, the two shoes and the lower shorter spring. Ease each shoe in turn towards the outer rim of the backing plate and then out and away from the anti-rattle clip. The R1181 rear brakes have shoe retaining coil springs which are a push/twist fit through the shoes. Remove this clip before pushing the shoes outwards. Disconnect the lower shorter spring from the shoe. Remove the other shoe, and both springs. This procedure is the same for all the drums but on the fronts (R1180) or rears (R1181) a handbrake steady bar is fitted between the two shoes which the shorter spring rests on. This should come away too. Do not press the brake pedal and use some sort of cylinder holding device to stop the pistons easing out (if possible).

7 Before fitting new shoes check that the wheel cylinder is not distorted and is securely bolted on. Also see that the hydraulic piston moves freely and that there are no fluid leaks.

8 Replacing the brake shoes is almost an exact reversal of removal. Place both shoes under the anti-rattle clips and affix the lower retention spring in place. (On the front (R1180) or rears (R1181) place the steady bar in place underneath it). Place the end of the spring which you originally pushed in towards the backing plate to release the brake shoes in its position under the shoes and hooked in. Wedge it there with a Phillips screwdriver or similar tool. This just holds the little clip firm. With a pair of Stilsons grip the other end of the top spring and squeezing the two shoes together onto the piston faces with the other hand, drag the spring over the other shoe and slot in the curved end into the hole in the shoe. This is quite difficult but not dangerous. It will soon be seen exactly where the grip the spring to do this. Be patient and be sure not to damage the wheel cylinder rubber seals.

9 When replacing the drums try to make sure the drums go back on in the original positions. See Chapter 7 to check on the tightening of the rear/hub bearing.

10 When the drum has been replaced operate the brakes to check that they do not bind. It is possible for light binding to occur initially, in which case they should be checked again after a few miles motoring.

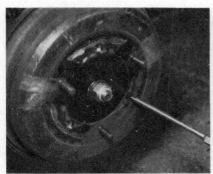
5.2 The three Phillips screws for the front drums of the R1180

5.5 Minimum adjustment, the handbrake off (front R1180)

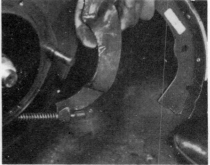
5.6 The handbrake cable fixing (R1180 front, R1181 rear)

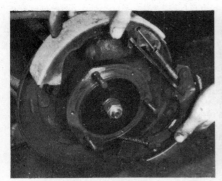
5.8a Starting brake shoe replacement. Top spring is in its place in this case ...

5.8b ... and the leading shoe has now to be placed on the wheel cylinder

5.8c Now the front anti-rattle clips

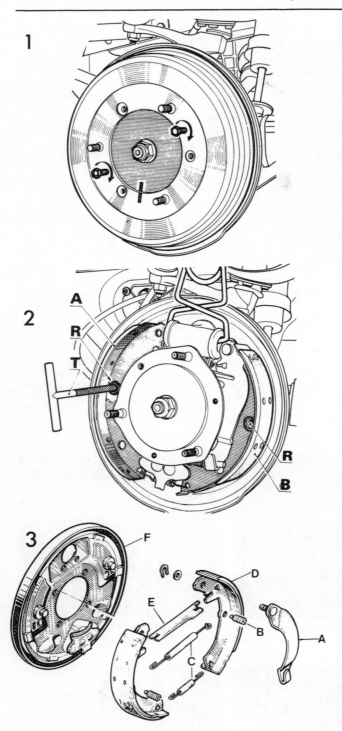

**FIG. 8.4. DRUM BRAKE COMPONENTS - FRONT R1180**

1   *Drum removal showing two setscrews for pushing off.*
     *Note refitment alignment mark*

2   *A: Leading shoe          B: Trailing shoe*
      *R: Shoe retaining spring   T: Tool for removing*
                                       *shoe retaining spring*

3   *A   Handbrake lever      D   Shoes*
      *B   Shoe retaining spring   E   Distance piece*
      *C   Return springs        F   Back plate*

5.8d. The lower spring in place

## 6   Drum brake wheel cylinders - inspection and repair

1   If it is suspected that one or more of the wheel cylinders is malfunctioning, jack up the suspect wheel and remove the brake drum as described in Section 5.

2   Inspect for signs of fluid leakage around the wheel cylinder and if there are any, proceed as described in paragraph 6.

3   Next get someone to press the brake pedal very gently and a small amount. Watch the wheel cylinder and see that the pistons move out a little. On no account let them come right out or it will need reassembly and bleeding. On releasing the pedal pressure, make sure that the retraction springs on the shoes move the pistons back into position without delay. If both pistons move all is well in the cylinder. If only one piston moves, only one shoe has been effective and repair is necessary.

4   If there is a leak, or the piston does not move (or only moves very slowly under excessive pressure) then the rubber piston seals will need renewal at least.

5   Seal the reservoir cap and remove the brake shoes as described in Section 4.

6   Disconnect the brake fluid pipes where they enter the cylinder and plug the ends of the lines to minimise loss of fluid.

7   Remove the cylinder from the backing plate by undoing the two setscrews from the rear side of the backing plate. Remove them and push the cylinder through and away. Do not attempt any cylinder repair with it still in place on the car. It may be necessary to loosen the backing plate to get at the two setscrews.

8   Then pull out the piston, complete with seal and the spring. Examine the piston and cylinder for sings of wear or scoring and if there are any the whole assembly must be renewed. If they are in good condition only the seal needs renewal. Pull the old one off the piston and thoroughly clean the whole asssembly using clean hydraulic fluid or methylated spirit.

9   Fit the new seal to the piston so that the lip faces away from the centre of the piston.

10 Lubricate the components in hydraulic fluid before re-assembly which is carried out in the reverse order. Make sure the lip of the seal on the piston enters the cylinder first.

11 Replace the cylinder back on the backing correctly.

12 Reconnect the hydraulic pipe, replace the brake shoes and drum as described in Section 5. Bleed the hydraulic system as described in Section 3.

Special note: The wheel cylinders are never interchangeable wheel for wheel. They can only be fitted in one place, one way up. Because of the various size changes that have taken place in wheel cylinders be absolutely sure any replacement cylinders or cylinder kits are of the correct size and type.

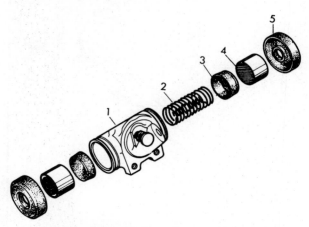

**FIG. 8.5. DRUM BRAKE CYLINDER COMPONENTS**

1 *Cylinder*
2 *Spring*
3 *Cap*
4 *Piston*
5 *Boot*

## 7   R1181 - disc pad - inspection and replacement

1   Before dismantling any parts of the brakes they should be thoroughly cleaned. The best cleaning agent is a stiff brush followed by a rag soaked in methylated spirit. Do not use petrol, paraffin or any other solvents which could cause deterioration to the friction pads or piston seals.
2   Jack up the car and remove the wheel.
3   Inspection does not necessitate the removal of the disc pads themselves. The pads abut the disc surface at all times. Therefore it is possible to put the end of a steel rule (the measure must start at the end of the rule) into the recess above the caliper and the tops of the pads. It should then be evident where the outer edge of the pad comes to, on the rule, from the surface of the disc outwards. The total thickness of the pad, and its backing, must be not less than 7 mm (9/32''). If less than this figure the pads must be renewed.
4   To remove the pads take out the four clips which hold the caliper locking blocks in place. Hold the caliper and punch out the locking pins and then remove the second pin, and swing the caliper out to one side out of the way, and then hang with a piece of string without straining the flexible hose.
5   The pads may be taken out of the caliper support bracket. If they are not being renewed note which side they come from so they may be put back in the same place. The pad friction material plus the backing should be no less than 7mm (9/32''). If the pads are not worn out but have a black and shiny surface it is helpful to roughen them up a little on some emery cloth before replacing them. Disc pads last normally about 12,000 miles.
6   Behind the pads on the carrier bracket are two pad anchor springs. Remove these and clean them up after ensuring that they are intact. Renew them otherwise.
7   Check the disc and caliper before replacing the original on new pads.
8   Replacement of the pads and calipers is a reversal of the removal procedure, but when fitting new pads certain additional matters must be attended to.
9   Make sure that the new pads are exactly similar to the ones taken off. Push back the piston in the caliper with a suitable blunt instrument to provide the necessary clearance for the new thicker pads.
10   Make sure the pads are the correct way up. The drilling on the back is downwards.
11   Refit the pads into the carrier, after the two pad anchor springs. The longest spring goes on the outside whilst the shortest on the inside.
12   Fit one side of the caliper between the spring and the keyway on the caliper bracket and then fit the other side of the caliper by compressing both springs.
13   Punch in the first locking pin. Using a screwdriver press in the other keyway and then in the second locking pin.
14   Refit the four spring clips with their flat portion facing the caliper bracket.
15   Refit the road wheel, lower the car and pump the brake pedal.
NOTE: Disc pads must be renewed in sets. Always renew pads on both front wheels - never just one.

## 8   R1181 - caliper and disc - removal, overhaul and replacement

1   Remove the caliper from the car as described in Section 7 which is necessary when changing the disc pads. Then remove totally by undoing the flexible hose from the caliper end. This is simpler than disconnecting the flexible hose from the rigid pipe-line. Let the hydraulic fluid drain into a container.
2   The caliper is constructed in two parts. The cylinder body is connected to the mounting bracket by a pin. Before overhauling the assembly always separate the cylinder from the bracket. To do this, spread the legs of the bracket very slightly using a wedge and then using a rod depress the spring-loaded plunger and slide the cylinder body from its bracket.
3   If the pistons are seized solid it is more than likely that you will be unable to get the piston out without damaging the cylinder or piston. However it is worthwhile having a go. Pull out the rubber dust seal and leave the whole assembly to soak in methylated spirit for a time. If this does not soften things up then a new caliper assembly will have to be bought.
4   Assuming the pistons have been removed without difficulty, clean them thoroughly with methylated spirit and remove the seal from the annular groove in the cylinder bore. Any hard residue deposits may be removed with careful use of some 600 grit wet and dry paper. If there are any ridges or scores in the cylinder or on the piston the parts must be renewed.
5   Fit new seals in the cylinder groove, lubricate the cylinders and pistons with hydraulic fluid and replace the pistons. Fit the dust seals so that they fit in the cylinder groove and on the piston.
6   When the calipers have been reassembled and fitted back to the car bleed the hydraulic system as described in Section 3.
7   Discs do not last forever. Under ideal conditions and with proper and regular maintenance of caliper pistons and brake pads they will last a long time. Under other circumstances they can warp, wear irregularly, get rusted and pitted, develop score lines and as a result provide poor braking and rapid consumption of pads. Remember, disc brakes are only better than drum brakes if they are in good condition.
8   A disc in good condition should have a smooth, shiny bright surface on the pad contact area. Do not hope to improve a deteriorated disc by the burnishing effect of new pads! Another fault which a disc may have, even though the surfaces are good, is a warp (or run-out). This means it does not run true. If bad it can be seen when the wheel is spun. However, to measure the run-out accurately a dial gauge pointer should be set against one face. The deviation should not exceed 0.15 mm/.006 ins. If you do not possess a dial gauge it is worth holding a steel pointer firmly on a nearby support with the point up to the disc face. Variations can be detected in this way also. Remember that the wheel bearings must be completely devoid of any end float in order to check disc run out. Worn or maladjusted bearings can be a contributory factor in disc deterioration.
9   To renovate a disc calls for either refacing or renewal and for this they must be taken off as described next. The cost of

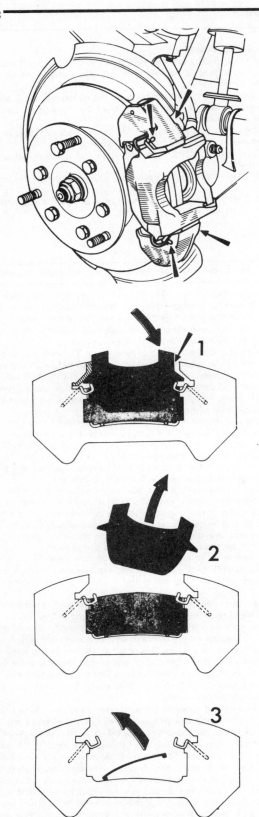

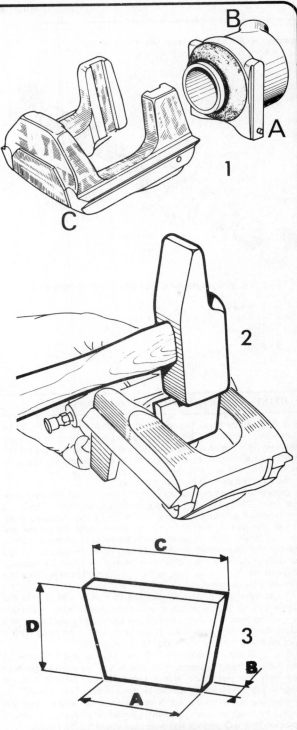

**FIG. 8.6. A: DISC CALIPER/PAD SPRING CLIPS**

1 Pad removal started
2 Pad away
3 Anti rattle shim

**FIG. 8.7. CALIPER SPLITTING USING THE PROPER WEDGE**

1 The caliper parts
A Bracket
B Cylinder
C Spring-loaded plunger
2 Spreading bracket legs
3 Wedge dimensions - for spreading bracket legs
   A: 2 1/32 in. (51.5 mm)
   B: 5/16 in. (8 mm)
   C: 2 7/32 in. (56 mm)
   D: 1 3/8 in. (35 mm)

refacing should be checked against the cost of a new disc. Remember also that the thickness of the disc should not be less than 10 mm/.39 ins. If it is very deeply scored or pitted, or the run-out is excessive the only remedy may be a new one. If the disc is too thin it loses some of its capability to disperse heat and also its rigidity.

10 To remove a disc, a difficult task, first remove the road wheel and the caliper. Hang the caliper up so that the flexible hose is not strained.

11 Remove the caliper bracket by removing the two deflector securing bolts and then the two bracket to stub axle carrier bolts. Free the bracket; no shimming is necessary on refitment.

12 Unscrew three of the six disc to hub securing screws. Obtain three other 8 mm setscrews about two inches long and three pieces of steel rod about 4 mm in diameter, two inches long.

13 Place one piece of rod in each of the drillings from which the bolts have just been removed. Then screw in a new setscrew pushing them through to the face of the stub axle carrier.

14 Remove the stub axle nut (90 lb f ft is needed). Hold the hub with a tyre lever placed appropriately across the wheel studs.

15 Now progressively tighten the three setscrews and push the hub/disc off the stub axle carrier. It is not easy and quite a crude but effective method.

16 Once off the disc can be separated from the hub quite easily. Hold the disc in padded jaws of a strong vice.

17 Replacement is almost a direct reverse motion of the removal except that hub/disc must be replaced using the method described in Chapter 7 for refitting a drive shaft.

Note: Only use high tension bolts for the hub to disc fitment. (Y3 should be stamped on their heads).

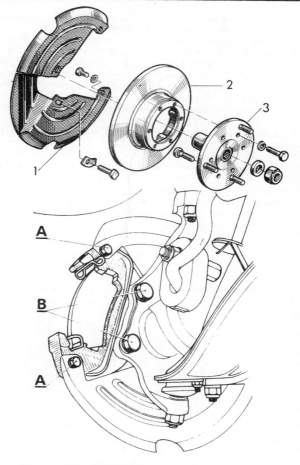

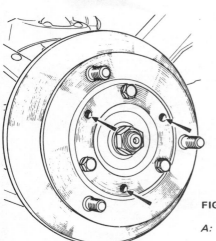

Fig. 8.8. Caliper piston seal being peeled out of its groove

**FIG. 8.9. DISC COMPONENTS**

| | |
|---|---|
| 1 Dust shield | A Caliper carrier/dust shield fixing bolts |
| 2 Disc | B Caliper carrier mountings |
| 3 Hub | |

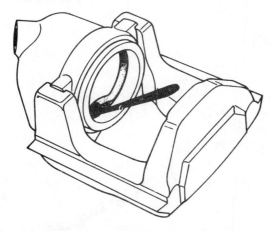

FIG. 8.10. REMOVING DISC FROM HUB

A: Temporary extractor bolts

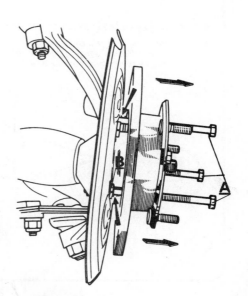

## 9  Master cylinder - removal and replacement

1   If the wheel hydraulic cylinders and/or caliper pistons are in order and there are no leaks elsewhere, yet the brake pedal still does not hold under sustained pressure then the master cylinder seals may be presumed to be ineffective. To renew them the master cylinder must be removed.

2   Disconnect the master cylinder pushrod from the brake pedal by removing the clevis pin.

3   Unscrew the hydraulic pipe union(s) and push the pipe to one side.

4   Remove the two nuts and washers holding the master cylinder to the bulkhead, one inside the car the other under the bonnet, and lift the unit away. Empty the contents of the reservoir into a clean container.

5   Replacement is a reversal of the removal procedure, after which the braking system must be bled completely and the pedal clearance checked. See Section 17.

## 10  Master cylinder - dismantling, overhaul and reassembly

1   Unless there are obvious signs of leakage any defects in the master cylinders are usually the last to be detected in the hydraulic system.

2   Before assuming that a fault in the system is in the master cylinder the pipes and wheel cylinders shuold all be checked and examined as described in Section 6.

3   Remove the master cylinder from the car as described in the previous section.

4   Single or dual line master cylinders are similar in principle. The tandem cylinder has a by-pass unit fitted to it. Dismantle and reassembly in the same way as you would a wheel cylinder, with the same care and cleanliness. Note however the additional final circlip which holds the piston and spring and seals in the cylinder. You will need to remove the stop light switch (Section 14).

5   Adjust the brake pedal rod as described in the next section.

6   Completely bleed the hydraulic system.

Special note: Be absolutely sure you have repaired the master cylinder with the correct repair kit. Some kits which will physically fit some master cylinders are dangerous.

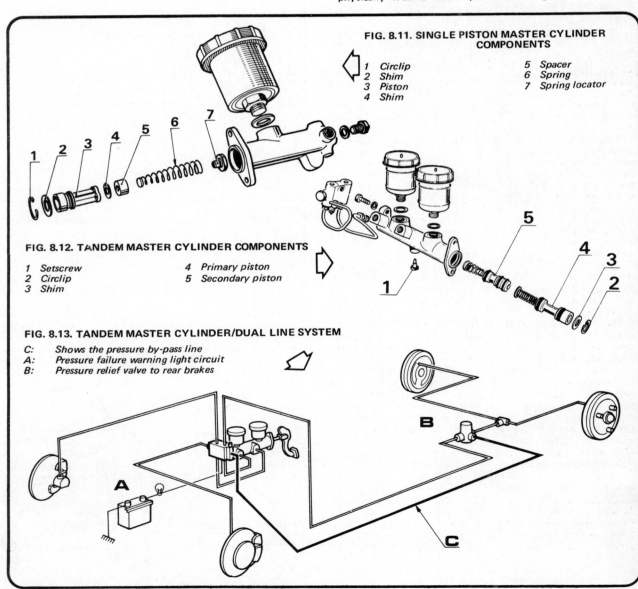

**FIG. 8.11. SINGLE PISTON MASTER CYLINDER COMPONENTS**

1  Circlip
2  Shim
3  Piston
4  Shim
5  Spacer
6  Spring
7  Spring locator

**FIG. 8.12. TANDEM MASTER CYLINDER COMPONENTS**

1  Setscrew
2  Circlip
3  Shim
4  Primary piston
5  Secondary piston

**FIG. 8.13. TANDEM MASTER CYLINDER/DUAL LINE SYSTEM**

C:  Shows the pressure by-pass line
A:  Pressure failure warning light circuit
B:  Pressure relief valve to rear brakes

## 11 Hydraulic fluid pipes - inspection, removal and replacement

1 Periodically and certainly well in advance of the MOT test, if due, all brake pipes, connections and unions should be completely and carefully examined.

2 Examine first all the unions for signs of leaks. Then look at the flexible hoses for signs of fraying and chafing (as well as for leaks). This is only a preliminary inspection of the flexible hoses as exterior condition does not necessarily indicate interior condition which will be considered later.

3 The steel pipes must be examined equally carefully. They must be thoroughly cleaned and examined for signs of dents or other percussive damage, rust and corrosion. Rust and corrosion should be scraped off and, if the depth of pitting in the pipes is significant, they will need replacement. This is most likely in those areas underneath the chassis and along the rear suspension arms where the pipes are exposed to the full force of road and weather conditions.

4 If any section of pipe is to be removed, first of all take off the fluid reservoir cap, line it with a piece of polythene film to make it airtight and screw it back on. This will minimise the amount of fluid dripping out of the system when the pipes are removed.

5 Rigid pipe removal is usually quite straightforward. The unions at each end are undone and the pipe drawn out of the connection. The clips which may hold it to the car body are bent back and it is then removed. Underneath the car exposed unions can be particularly stubborn, defying the efforts of an open ended spanner. As few people will have the special split ring spanner required, a self-grip wrench (mole) is the only answer. If the pipe is being renewed new unions will be provided. If not then one will have to put up with the possibility of burring over the flats on the union and use a self-grip wrench for replacement also.

6 Flexible hoses are always fitted to a rigid support bracket where they join a rigid pipe, the bracket being fixed to the chassis or rear suspension arm. The rigid pipe unions must first be removed from the flexible union. Then the locknut securing the flexible pipe to the bracket must be unscrewed, releasing the end of the pipe from the bracket. As these connections are usually exposed they are more often than not rusted up and a penetrating fluid is virtually essential to aid removal (try Plus-Gas). When undoing them, both halves must be supported as the bracket is not strong enough to support the torque required to undo the nut and can easily be snapped off.

7 Once the flexible hose is removed examine the internal bore. If clear of fluid it should be possible to see through it. Any specks of rubber which come out, or signs of restriction in the bore, mean that the inner lining is breaking up and the pipe must be replaced.

8 Rigid pipes which need replacement can usually be purchased at any local garage where they have the pipe, unions and special tools to make them up. All that they need to know is the pipe length required and the type of flare used at the ends of the pipe. These may be different at each end of the same pipe.

9 Replacement of pipes is a straightforward reversal of the removal procedure. It is best to get all the sets (bends) in the pipe made preparatory to installation. Also any acute bends should be put in by the garage on a bending machine otherwise there is the possibility of kinking them and restricting the bore area and fluid flow.

10 With the pipes replaced, remove the polythene from the reservoir cap and bleed the system as described in Section 3.

## 12 Brake pressure limiting valve and by-pass unit

1 All models are fitted with a brake pressure limiting valve which is fitted in the hydraulic circuit to limit the maximum amount of fluid pressure going to the brakes at the rear and thereby distribute pressure between front and rear to ensure a balanced and effective braking effort at all times. Several different types have been fitted. If it is suspected of malfunctioning it is important that it is replaced with the correct one. It is located in the hydraulic pipe circuit on the chassis at the rear right hand side at the end of the torsion bars. It has a special steel cover plate. It is not possible to dismantle this unit and not practical to test it.

2 Always fit a new unit. Removing the old unit is a similar operation to the removal of rigid hydraulic pipes as described in Section 12. Try to bleed the unit before actually fitting to ease the system bleeding and to ensure satisfactory operation immediately. It is never wise to leave it out of the system - in fact it is positively dangerous.

3 It is not practical to adjust the adjustable limiting valves at home. Once a new unit is fitted and the hydraulic system bled, have it adjusted by a reputable Renault agency. It does not take long and is easy for them.

4 Those cars fitted with tandem master cylinders are fitted with by-pass units. It enables pressure to the rear wheels to be increased in the event of a leak in the front wheel circuit. Both this unit and the pressure limiter are fitted.

5 The by-pass unit is attached to the tandem master cylinder by conventional hydraulic system fittings. It is not repairable and can only be checked by a Renault agency. If in doubt replace the fitting.

6 Bleed the by-pass system from the bleed screw on the top of the unit once the four road wheels have been bled.

## 13 Stop light switch

1 The stop light switch is located on the outer end of the master cylinder just below the fluid reservoir. It can be removed with the master cylinder still in the car.

2 To remove, only when it is absolutely certain it in itself is malfunctioning and there is not some other electrical fault, disconnect the two cables and mark their position. Place a piece of polythene sheet over the reservoir and replace its cap - this will stop, to some extent, the loss of fluid. Place a rag underneath the switch and with the correct sized open ended spanner unscrew the switch.

3 Replace, always using a new copper washer and tighten sufficiently. Replace the cables and bleed the brakes, having removed the polythene sheet. (Try and leave the replacement of this switch to another time when you have to bleed the brakes anyway. However, do not contravene the law).

## 14 R1180 - handbrake

1 The handbrake adjustment is normally taken up when the front brakes are adjusted, consequently the only reason that the mechanism itself would need adjusting would be to compensate for a stretched cable or to fit replacement parts. (Correct lever travel is 6 notches). A rod type of operating linkage have been used apart from the actual cable itself.

2 Small amounts of adjustment can be taken up at 1 in Fig. 8.14. Larger measures of adjustment can be taken up at 2. (Always make sure that you have adjusted the parts of the system in the right order).

3 The handbrake cable going to the brake drums is in two parts and easily removed and replaced. Jack up the front of the car and place on stands. Remove the wheels and the drums.

4 Remove the split pins, circlips and tension springs from the operating mechanism under the bonnet. Remove the stirrup piece pin and disconnect the stirrup piece and its holding piece from the two ends of the cable.

5 Remove the front brake shoes and then pull out the captive end of the handbrake cable from the operating mechanism by prising open the two lips with a screwdriver. Pull the end of the cable through the backing plate. With this done on both wheels the cables should be ready to be taken off the chassis. Replace-

ment is quite simply the reversal of the removal. (Coiled wire cable holders at the rear side of the backing plate have been fitted. Make sure these are in their correct positions).

6 The lever arm on which the stirrup piece sits is easily removable when the stirrup piece is taken off as described previously. This hinges in the centre of two hooks. Pull it out and up. The two hooks are attached to the chassis by two setscrews. Both are easily removed and replaced.

7 The handbrake handle tube can be pulled away from inside the car once the operating mechanism under the bonnet is removed. A plastic sealing tube should then come away. The rest of the handle control bracket can then be removed from inside the car under the facia by undoing the four setscrews which hold the whole mechanism to the bulkhead. Be careful of the flasher and any wiring which may be in the vicinity and held to the mounting plate.

8 The normal reason for having to remove this bracket is to replace the ratchet spring for the fly-off operation. This is held by a pin and spire nut. Replacement is obvious for the whole mechanism and is a reversal of the removal sequence. Grease the handle very lightly before inserting into the bracket. Never operate the handbrake without the ratchet spring working properly. Always replace the handbrake handle tube plastic sealing tube on the bulkhead. Without it the driver gets very cold!

14.3 The two cables below the flexible coupling

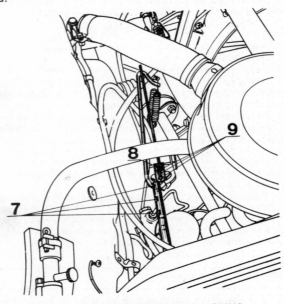

FIG. 8.14. R1180 HANDBRAKE ADJUSTING

7    First stage adjustment
8/9    Second stage adjustment

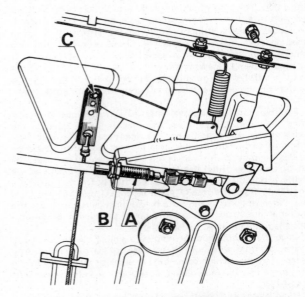

FIG. 8.15. R1181 HANDBRAKE ADJUSTMENT

A    Secondary cable adjuster
B    Secondary cable adjuster lock nut
C    Primary cable adjustment

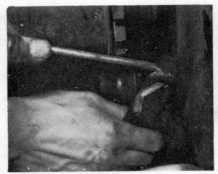

14.4a The first adjuster rod

14.4b The necessary return spring. It's very strong

14.4c The second adjuster pivot

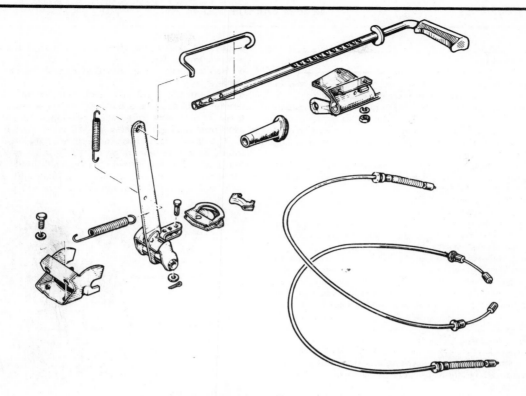

Fig. 8.16. Handbrake components (R1180)

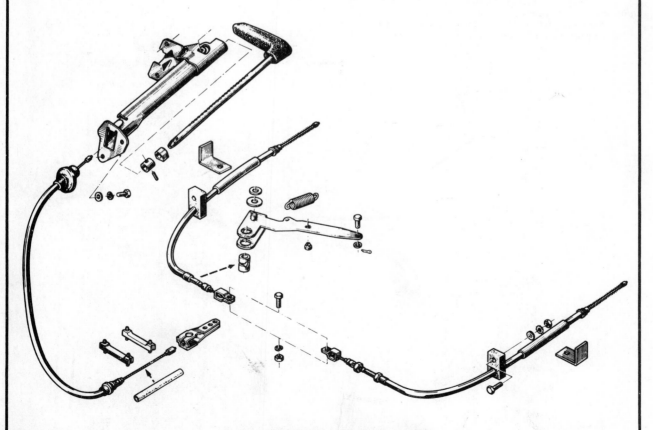

Fig. 8.17. Handbrake components (R1181)

### 15 R1181 - handbrake

1  Read paragraph 1 of the previous section first, but bear in mind the handbrake operates on the rear wheels.

2  Adjustment can only be carried out in two places, the second to be done if the first is not satisfactory; All to be done after brake adjustment at the drums. Screw up the threaded end fixing under the car in the centre of the secondary cable (going across the two rear drums).

Tighten this fitting until the rear shoes just touch the drums to hold the car, but only just. Make sure the handbrake is in the 'off' position. Tighten the locknut.

3  Now try the handbrake. If all is ok and the car is held approximately half way up its travel (3 clicks!) adjustment is finished. If not, return to the underside of the car and pull up the notch on the fork end of the primary cable to the handbrake cradle; again handbrake off! All should now be well.

4  The cables are easily replaced, the illustration shows clearly how the parts fit together. The umbrella handle is held to the facia by two captive setscrews only. The centre lever mechanism is fixed to the underside of the car by captive setscrews also. The more grease on this part of the mechanism the longer it will last!

### 16 Brake, clutch and throttle pedals

1  The brake and clutch pedals pivot on the same shaft and one cannot be removed without the other. The throttle pedal is mounted separately.

2  To remove the pedals (necessary together) unclip the two pedal return springs from the arms, having once removed the glove tray. Punch out the roll pin, to the right of the brake pedal, on the pivot. Push out the pivot shaft to the left.

3  Let the pedals fall away. Disconnect the clutch cable from the clutch pedal by pulling out the split pin and locking pin. The pedals will now come off the pivot shaft. Note the order of washers, springs etc.

4  Replacement is the reverse of removal but be sure to pre-grease everything.

5  The throttle pedal is integral with its pivot bracket. The bracket is fixed to the bulkhead by three studs. The nuts of these are accessible from under the bonnet. Remove the throttle cable from the pedal in the same way as for the clutch.

6  The brake pedal push-rod clearance must be checked. It should have a clearance of 5 mm (13/64''). There is a locknut on the pushrod. This should be loosened until the clearance (between pushrod end and master cylinder) is correct at the pedal end. Tighten the locknut when all is correct.

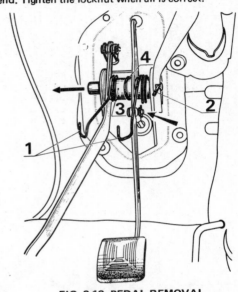

**FIG. 8.18. PEDAL REMOVAL**

1 & 4  *Pedal return springs*
2        *Roll pin*
3        *Outer bush*

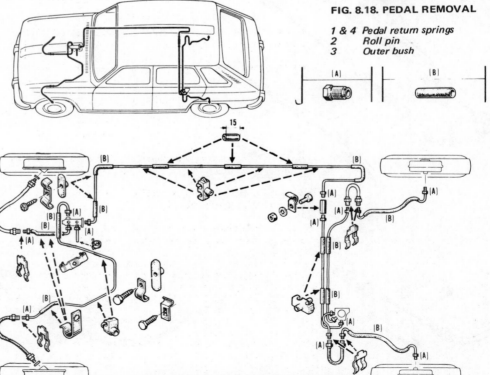

**FIG. 8.19. BRAKE PIPE LAYOUT (R1180 illustrated)**

A        *Joints*
B        *Rubber hose covering*

## 17 Fault diagnosis

Before diagnosing faults from the following chart, check that any braking irregularities are not caused by:—

1 Uneven and incorrect tyre pressures
2 Incorrect 'mix' of radial and cross-ply tyres
3 Wear in the steering mechanism
4 Defects in the suspension
5 Misalignment of the chassis

| Symptom | Reason/s | Remedy |
| --- | --- | --- |
| Pedal travels a long way before the brakes operate | Brake shoes set too far from the drums | Adjust the brake shoes to the drums. |
| Stopping ability poor, even though pedal pressure is firm | Linings/pads and/or drums/disc badly worn or scored | Dismantle, inspect and renew as required. |
| | One or more wheel hydraulic cylinders or caliper pistons seized, resulting in some brake shoes not pressing against the drums/discs/pads | Dismantle and inspect. Renew as necessary. |
| | Brake linings/pads contaminated with oil | Renew linings/pads and repair source of oil contamination. |
| | Wrong type of linings/pads fitted (too hard) | Verify type of material which is correct for the car, and fit it. |
| | Brake shoes/pads wrongly assembled | Check for correct assembly. |
| Car veers to one side when the brakes are applied | Brake linings/pads on one side are contaminated with oil | Renew linings/pads and stop oil leak. |
| | Hydraulic wheel cylinder(s)/caliper on one side partially or fully seized | Inspect wheel cylinders/pistons for correct operation and renew as necessary. |
| | A mixture of lining materials fitted between sides | Standardise on types of linings fitted. |
| | Unequal wear between sides caused by partially seized wheel cylinders/pistons | Check wheel cylinders/pistons and renew linings/pads and drums/discs as required. |
| Pedal feels spongy when the brakes are applied | Air is present in the hydraulic system | Bleed the hydraulic system and check for any signs of leakage. |
| Pedal feels springy when the brakes are applied | Brake linings/pads not bedded into the drums/discs (after fitting new ones) | Allow time for new linings/pads to bed in after which it will certainly be necessary to adjust the shoes to the drums as pedal travel will have increased. |
| | Master cylinder or brake backplate mounting bolts loose | Retighten mounting bolts. |
| | Severe wear in brake drums/discs causing distortion when brakes are applied | Renew drums/disc and linings/pads. |
| Pedal travels right down with little or no resistance and brakes are virtually non-operative | Leak in hydraulic systems resulting in lack of pressure for operating wheel cylinders/caliper pistons | Examine the whole of the hydraulic system and locate and repair source of leaks. Test after repairing each and every leak source. |
| | If no signs of leakage are apparent all the master cylinder internal seals are failing to sustain pressure | Overhaul master cylinder. If indications are that seals have failed for reasons other than wear all the wheel cylinder seals/piston seals should be checked also and the system completely replenished with the correct fluid. |
| Binding, juddering, overheating | One or a combination of causes given in the foregoing sections | Complete and systematic inspection of the whole braking system. |

# Chapter 9 Electrical system

## Contents

## Specifications

| | | |
|---|---|---|
| All cars ... ... ... ... ... ... ... ... | | Negative (—) earth, 12 volt system |
| Battery ... ... ... ... ... ... ... ... | | Tudor 30 amp GRF3 or<br>Fulmen 30 amp 809R |
| Generator | - R1180 ... ... ... ... ... ... | Dynamo: Ducellier type 7346 (22 amp) |
| | - R1181 ... ... ... ... ... ... | Alternator: SEV-Motorola type 34838 (1st)<br>type 71227912 (2nd)<br>(30/40 amp) |
| Control box | - R1180 only ... ... ... ... ... ... | Ducellier 8311A (sealed type) |
| | - R1181 only ... ... ... ... ... ... | SEV 033546 or Ducellier 8364 |
| Starter motor | - R1180 ... ... ... ... ... ... | Ducellier 6185 |
| | - R1181 ... ... ... ... ... ... | Ducellier 6172 or 6187 |
| Windscreen wipers: motor ... ... ... ... ... ... | | SEV type 11 6007 |
| Flasher unit ... ... ... ... ... ... ... | | Flaxon 40/45 watt |
| Brake light switch ... ... ... ... ... ... | | Torix or LMP mechanical switch |
| Headlamps ... ... ... ... ... ... ... | | Cibie standard round 5 inch (pre 1973)<br>Cibie special 'square' 5 inch headlight (post 1973) |
| Horn ... ... ... ... ... ... ... ... | | Flaxon 12 volt |
| Oil pressure sender switch ... ... ... ... ... ... | | Jaeger |
| Temperature sender switch ... ... ... ... ... ... | | Jaeger, operates at 115° C ± 5° C (240° F) |
| R1181 cooling fan and switch | | |
| Motor ... ... ... ... ... ... ... ... | | Ducellier type 4921 or<br>SEV-Marchal type VR12 or<br>Paris-Rhone type M7C1 |
| Switch ... ... ... ... ... ... ... ... | | Mosta |

## 1 General description

The electrical system is 12 volt DC, negative earth and apart from the ignition system which is dealt with in Chapter 4, the main items are:
1 Battery (12 volt).
2 R 1180 - Dynamo (generator) driven by the fan belt, coupled with an integral voltage and current regulator; or R1181. Alternator (generator) again driven by the fan belt.
3 Pre-engaged starter motor.
4 Windscreen wipers.
5 Lights.
6 Heater motor.
7 Heated rear window (R1181).
8 Thermostatically controlled electric cooling fan (R1181).

The battery supplies current for the ignition, lighting and other circuits and provides a reserve of power when the current consumed by the equipment exceeds the production of the generator.

The starter motor places very heavy demands on the power reserve. The generator uses engine power to produce electricity to re-charge the battery and the rate of charge is automatically controlled by a regulator. This regulator keeps the power output of the generator within its capacity (an uncontrolled generator can burn itself out) and also adjusts the voltage and current output depends on the state of the battery charge and the electrical demands being made on the system at any one time.

## 2 Battery - removal and replacement

1 The battery is situated at the front right hand side of the engine compartment.
2 Disconnect the earth lead (negative) from the terminal by unscrewing the shackle or centre screw and twisting the terminal cover off. Do not use any striking force or damage could be caused to the battery. Then remove the positive lead in the same way. Always remove the earth coil first.
3 Slacken off the nuts holding the battery clamp stays until the assembly can be disengaged sufficiently to lift the battery out.
4 Lift the battery out, keeping it the right way up to prevent spillage of the electrolyte.
5 Replacement is a reversal of this procedure. Replace the positive lead first and smear the terminal posts and connections beforehand with petroleum jelly (not grease) in order to prevent corrosion.

## 3 Battery - maintenance and inspection

1 Any new battery, if properly looked after, will last for two years at least (provided also that the generator and regulator are in correct order).
2 The principal maintenance requirements are cleanliness and regular topping up of the electrolyte level with distilled water. Each week the battery cell cover or caps should be removed and just enough water added, if needed, to cover the tops of the separators. Do not overfill with the idea of the topping up lasting longer - it will only dilute the electrolyte and with the level high the likelihood of it 'gassing' out is increased. This is the moisture one can see on the top of the battery. 'Little and often is the rule'.
3 Wipe the top of the battery carefully at the same time removing all traces of moisture. Paper handkerchiefs are ideal for the job.
4 Every three months disconnect the battery terminals and wash both the posts and lead connectors with a washing soda solution. This will remove any corrosion deposits. Dry them off and smear liberally with petroleum jelly - not grease, before re-connection.
5 If a significant quantity of electrolyte is lost through spillage

it will not suffice to merely refill with distilled water. The battery will have to be emptied and refilled by your garage or service station.

## 4 Battery - charging

1 In winter certain conditions may result in the battery being used in excess of the generators ability to recharge it in the running time available. This situation does not occur however on cars fitted with alternators which have a much higher rate of output at low revolutions.
2 Where necessary therefore, an external charging source is needed to keep the battery power reserve at the proper level. If batteries are being charged from an external source a hydrometer is used to check the electrolyte specific gravity. Once the fully charged reading is obtained. Most battery chargers are set to charge at 3-4 amps initially and as the battery charge builds up this reduces automatically to 1-2 amps. The table following gives details of the specific gravity readings, at 21$^\circ$C/70$^\circ$F. Do not take readings just after topping up, just after using the starter motor, or when the electrolyte is too cold or too warm. The variation is SG readings is .004 for every 6$^\circ$C/10$^\circ$F charge - the higher readings being for the higher temperatures.

| Specific gravity | Battery state of charge |
|---|---|
| 1.28 | 100% |
| 1.25 | 75% |
| 1.22 | 50% |
| 1.19 | 25% |
| 1.16 | Very low |
| 1.11 | Discharged completely |

## 5 Generator (dynamo) - description, maintenance and testing

1 The DC generator or dynamo consists of an armature running in bearings. It is surrounded by field coils bolted to the outer casing or yoke. At one end of the armature is the commutator consisting of copper segments. Two carbon brushes, spring loaded and in holders run on the commutator.
2 The only maintenance required is to check that the fan belts are correctly tensioned. The armature runs in ball bearings with sealed in lubrication. Some owners may wish to check the carbon brush length and this can be done by seeing that the ends are not below the ends of the brush holders. If they are new brushes should be fitted.
3 A generator normally works properly or not at all. There are few instances of poor performance. A quick check can be made if a voltmeter is available. Disconnect both leads from the dynamo and join the two terminals together with a piece of bare wire. From the centre of the wire run a lead via the voltmeter to earth. With the engine running at a fast tickover there should be a reading of about 15 volts. If there is no voltage then suspect the carbon brushes. If the voltage is low - 208 volts then suspect the field windings or armature. Either of the latter will require renewal or re-build by specialists.

## 6 Generator (dynamo) - control box

1 The regulator box regulates the voltage and current, according to the demands of the system. It also prevents feed back from the battery when the generator is producing voltage less than battery voltage. The unit is not designed for adjustment or repair and under normal circumstances it will function perfectly

and last indefinitely.

2   If the charging system is not working correctly, indicated by the warning lamp not going out when the engine speed increases the generator should first be checked as this is the most usual cause of the trouble.

3   If the generator is found to be satisfactory make a careful check of the connections on the control box to make sure they are tight and corrosion free. If the vehicle has been standing unused for a long time in a damp climate the control box will probably be defective.

4   Where a control box is defective the whole unit must be renewed.

---

**7   Generator (dynamo and/or alternator) - removal and replacement**

1   Slacken the one dynamo retaining bolt and the nuts on the sliding link, and move the dynamo in towards the engine so that the fan belt can be taken off the dynamo pulley. This is most easily done by removing the handbrake tension spring and then placing the handbrake on again. This allows the necessary room to get full leverage on the nut of the retaining bolt underneath the dynamo with an open ended spanner.

2   Push the dynamo as near to the rocker cover as possible and gently ease the fan belt off its pulley. Sometimes a screwdriver can be used effectively as a 'shoe-horn'.

3   Still holding the dynamo with the left hand undo the two terminal leads from the dynamo. Always use the correct spanners on these two.

4   Now hold the dynamo in the same position with the right hand and carefully unclip the distributor cap but leave it attached still to the plug leads resting on its edge on the rotor arm. Also unclip the throttle cable from its retainer.

5   Swing the dynamo down now so that it rests gently on the steering column. Take off the retaining nut and slide the bolt through towards the distributor. Pull out the bolt (this is why the distributor cap is off) with the left hand and remove the dynamo with the right.

6   Replacement is a reversal of the above procedure. Do not finally tighten the retaining bolt and the nut on the sliding link until the fan belt is at its correct tension.

7   Removal and replacement of the alternator is basically similar except that the electrical contacts are push-on. Be most careful to reconnect properly first time and do not use any force on the casing of the alternator - do NOT use the lever.

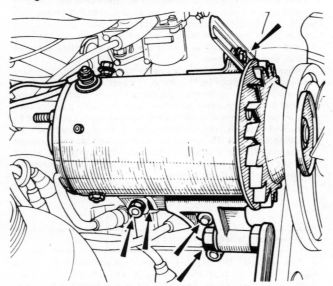

Fig. 9.1. R1180 dynamo and jockey wheel fixing points

7.1a The three dynamo connections

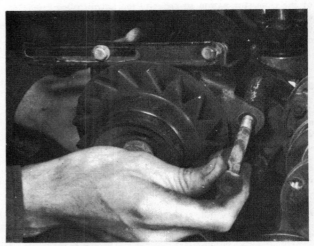

7.1b The pivot bolt for the dynamo. It could be left or right hand thread

---

**8   Generator (dynamo) - dismantling, repair and reassembly**

1   It is likely that once the dynamo is beyond just the replacement of brushes, it is more economic to have the whole unit overhauled or replaced. Overhauling should only be undertaken by qualified auto-electricians. Its total overhaul is not really a home mechanic's task.

2   Grip the pulley of the dynamo in a vice and loosen the pulley retaining nut. Then remove the nuts from the two studs at the other end of the dynamo to release the commutator end bracket.

3   Pull off the commutator end bracket.

4   Pull out the armature, pulley and end bearing cap from the body of the dynamo but hold the brushes, still attached to the body, away from the armature to avoid their damage. (Shim steel or feeler blades do this adequately). Place the armature aside for inspection.

5   Remove the brushes from the body of the dynamo by undoing the DYN and EXC terminal nuts and thereby releasing the brush contact wires and the brushes from their seating bodies.

6   Never attempt to release the field coils by dismantling the field terminals of both types of dynamo because an impact screwdriver is necessary. If the dynamo is in need of new field

coils it should be renewed complete.

7   Do not dismantle further still at this stage. Examine the carbon brushes. The length of the brushes should be no less than 7/16 inch. If required fit the correct new ones which are supplied with new leads.

8   Examine next the commutator end of the armature. This should not be burnt or scored in any way. First clean it off with a little petrol on a rag. Any traces of pitting, scoring or burring, if slight, can be cleaned off with fine glass paper. Do not use emery paper. Make sure that there are no flat spots, by tearing the glass paper into strips and use it by drawing it round the commutator evenly. Do not try and clean off too much by this method as the commutator must remain circular in section.

9   To test the armature is not difficult but a voltmeter or bulb and 12 volt battery are required. The two tests determine whether there may be a break in any circuit winding or if any wiring insulation is broken down. Fig. 9.3 shows how the battery, voltmeter and probe connectors are used to test whether (a) any wire in the windings is broken or (b) whether there is an insulation breakdown. In the first test the probes are placed on adjacent segments of a clean commutator. All voltmeter readings should be similar. If a bulb is used instead it will glow very dimly or not at all if there is a fault. For the second test any reading or bulb lighting indicates a fault. Test each segment in turn with one probe and keep the other on the shaft. Should either test indicate a faulty armature the wisest action in the long run is to obtain a replacement dynamo altogether. The field coils may be tested if an ohmmeter or ammeter can be obtained. With an ohmmeter the resistance (measured between the terminal and the yoke) should be 6 ohms. With an ammeter, connect it in series with a 12 volt battery again from the field terminal to the yoke. A reading of 2 amps is normal. Zero amps or infinity ohms indicate an open circuit. More than 2 amps or

less than 6 ohms indicates a breakdown of the insulation. Unless you can get the field coils readily repaired it is better to obtain a replacement unit.

10 The drive end bearing should have no play but in the event that it also needs renewal (very rare except where the fan belt has been persistently overtight), first remove the pulley nut and washers and draw off the pulley. Then tap the Woodruff key out of the shaft using a screwdriver under one end. Be careful to guard against it flying off and getting lost. If the end cover is now supported across the jaws of a vice, with the armature hanging down, the end of the shaft may be tapped with a soft faced mallet to drive it out of the bearing housing with the bearing. The bearing itself can next be taken off the shaft by the same method. When fitting a new bearing make sure it is thoroughly packed with grease and fit it into the end cover first making sure that the pressure ring and retaining plate are all assembled correctly. Then place the retaining cup over the armature shaft so that the open end faces the armature. Then the end cover may be supported over the vice jaws and the armature carefully tapped through the bearing with a mallet. Refit the spacer, then the Woodruff key, followed by the pulley, washer and nut.

11 Reassembly is a straight reverse sequence of the disassembly just described. Note: always replace the armature before refitting the brushes.

Replace the through bolts and before tightening them right up, check that the end plates are fully and correctly in position. Spin the armature to ensure it is not binding or touching the field coils and then unhook the brush springs and lower the brushes onto the commutator with the springs on top. Finally place a few drops of engine oil in the oil hole of the commutator bearing bush.

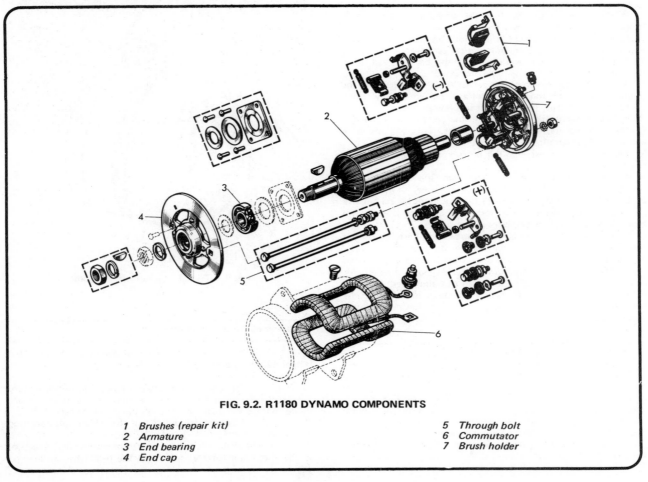

**FIG. 9.2. R1180 DYNAMO COMPONENTS**

| | |
|---|---|
| 1   Brushes (repair kit) | 5   Through bolt |
| 2   Armature | 6   Commutator |
| 3   End bearing | 7   Brush holder |
| 4   End cap | |

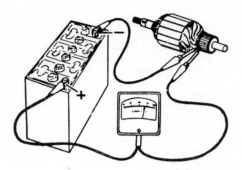
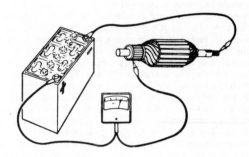

**FIG. 9.3. ARMATURE WINDING TESTS**

1  *Testing the armature for a broken wire*
2  *Testing the armature for insulation between windings*

### 9  Generator (alternator) - descriptions and precautions

The R1181 imported into the United Kingdom is fitted with an alternator in place of the more generally wellknown DC 'dynamo'. The alternator generates alternating current (AC) which is rectified by diodes in DC and is the current needed for battery storage.

The regulator is a transistorized unit which is permanently sealed and requires no attention. It will last indefinitely provided no mistakes are made in wiring connections.

Apart from the renewal of the rotor slip ring brushes and rotor shaft bearings, there are no other parts which need periodic inspection. All other items are sealed assemblies and must be replaced if indications are that they are faulty.

If there are indications that the charging system is malfunctioning in any way, care must be taken to diagnose faults properly, otherwise damage of a serious and expensive nature may occur to parts which are in fact quite serviceable.

The following basic requirements must be observed at all times, therefore, if damage is to be prevented:

1  ALL alternator systems uses a NEGATIVE earth. Even the simple mistake of connecting a battery the wrong way round could burn out the alternator diodes in a few seconds.
2  Before disconnecting any wires in the system the engine and ignition circuits should be switched off. This will minimise accidental short circuits.
3  The alternator must NEVER be run with the output wire disconnected.
4  Always disconnect the battery from the car's electrical system if an outside charging source is being used.
5  Do not use test wire connections that could move accidentally and short circuit against nearby terminals. Short circuits will not blow fuses - they will blow diodes or transistors.
6  Always disconnect the battery cables and alternator output wires before any electric welding work is done on the car body.
7  Never lever on the alternator body when adjusting its fan belt drive. The casing is easily fractured. Fault diagnosis on alternator charging systems requires sophisticated test equipment and even with this action required to rectify any fault is limited to the renewal of one or two components. Knowing what the fault is is only of academic interest in these circumstances.

### 10 Starter motor - general description

1  The starter motor is mounted on the engine block where the bellhousing would be on a conventional car. It is secured by two bolts on the left hand side of the engine under the exhaust manifold. It has four field coils and four commutator brushes, two of which are earthed. The switch, in addition to making the electrical connection, also operates a lever which moves the pinion into mesh with the ring gear just before the power is switched to the motor. This results in quieter operation and

reduces much of the shock loading on the starter motor. To prevent the engine driving the starter, should the pinion stick, the drive is through a one-way roller type clutch. Also, the pinion is spring loaded, so that in the event of an exact abutment of gear teeth preventing engagement the switch will still continue and make power contact and the pinion will move into engagement automatically as soon as the shaft moves. The operating lever, which connects the plunger to the pinion, pivots on an eccentric pin so that the pinion engagement may be set correctly in relation to the switch contacts. The switching method is by solenoid plunger (electrically activated).

2  Although the starter motors of the two engines are different components they can be dealt with as if they were actually the same.

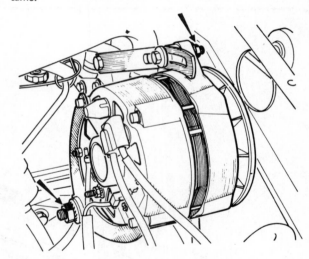

**Fig. 9.4. R1181 alternator fixing point**

### 11 Starter motor circuit - testing

1  If the starter motor fails to turn the engine when the switch is operated there are four possible reasons why:
a)  The battery is no good.
b)  The electrical connections between switch, solenoid, battery and starter motor are somewhere failing to pass the necessary current from the battery through the starter to earth.
c)  The solenoid switch is no good, or the cable is not operating properly.
d)  The starter motor is either jammed or electrically defective.
2  To check the battery, switch on the headlights. If they go

dim after a few seconds the battery is definitely unwell. If the lamps glow brightly, next operate the starter switch/cable and see what happens to the lights. If they go dim then you know that power is reaching the starter motor but failing to turn it. Therefore, check that it is not jammed the starter will have to come out for examination. If the starter should turn very slowly on to the next check.

3   If when the starter switch is operated, the lights stay bright, then the power is not reaching the starter. Check all connections from battery to solenoid switch or cable to starter for perfect cleanliness and tightness. With a good battery installed this is the most usual cause of starter motor problems. Check that the earth link cable between the engine and frame is also intact and cleanly connected. This can sometimes be overlooked when the engine is taken out.

4   If no results have yet been achieved turn off the headlights, otherwise the battery will go flat. You will possibly have heard a clicking noise each time the switch was operated. This is the solenoid switch operating but it does not necessarily follow that the main contact is closing properly. (NB if no clicking has been heard from the solenoid it is certainly defective). The solenoid contact can be checked by putting a voltmeter or bulb across the main cable connection on the starter side of the solenoid and earth. When the switch is operated, there should be a reading or lighted bulb. If not, the solenoid switch is no good. (Do not put a bulb across the two solenoid terminals. If the motor is not faulty the bulb will blow). If finally, it is established that the solenoid is not faulty and 12 volts are getting to the starter then the starter motor must be the culprit.

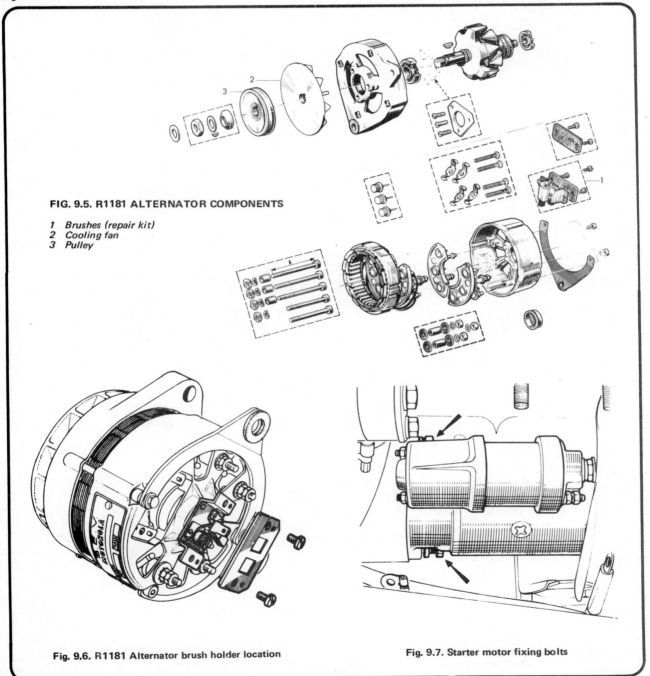

**FIG. 9.5. R1181 ALTERNATOR COMPONENTS**

1   *Brushes (repair kit)*
2   *Cooling fan*
3   *Pulley*

**Fig. 9.6. R1181 Alternator brush holder location**

**Fig. 9.7. Starter motor fixing bolts**

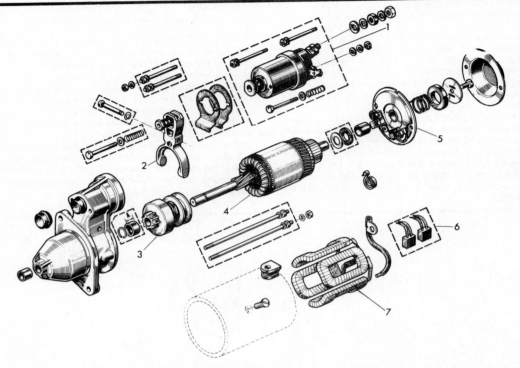

**FIG. 9.8. R1180 STARTER MOTOR COMPONENTS**

1  Solenoid
2  Yoke
3  Drive
4  Armature

5  Brush holder
6  Brushes (repair kit)
7  Commutator

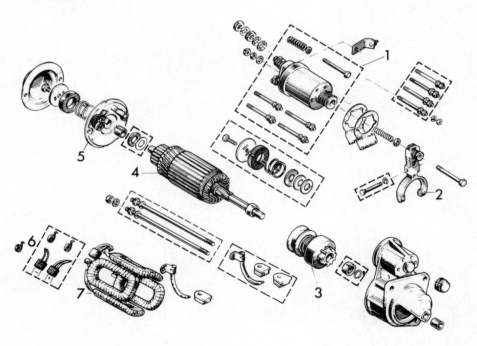

**FIG. 9.9. R1181 STARTER MOTOR COMPONENTS**

1  Solenoid
2  Yoke
3  Drive
4  Armature

5  Brush holder
6  Brushes (repair kit)
7  Commutator

## 12 Starter motor - removal and replacement

**Note:** Before removing the starter motor from the car make sure it is absolutely necessary. With the engine in the car on the R1181 it is not a nice job; its really no better on the R1180.

Starter motor removal with the engine out of the car is however, simple. (The engine is easily removed with the starter left in place. Just the electrical and/or cable connections removed). Always disconnect the battery first.
1   With the engine in the car proceed as follows:
Undo the electrical cable from the starter motor and tape back to the bulkhead. Undo and remove the two (R1180) or three (R1181) fixing bolts and remove the starter motor back, up (forwards) and out. Be patient with the two fixing bolts, it is quite fiddly. A tubular spanner is easiest.
2   You may find it easier if you remove the carburettor air cleaner and the exhaust pipe between the manifold and silencer. It gives more working room. On the R1181 further ease of working, depending on the type of spanners available, to remove the engine support arm on that side.
3   Replacement is in each case a reversal of removal. Be sure to tighten the fixing bolts well.

12.2 The starter motor goes under the brace

## 13 Starter motor - dismantling and reassembly

1   Such is the inherent reliability and strength of the starter motors fitted that it is very unlikely that a motor will ever need dismantling until it is totally worn out and in need of replacement. It is not a task for the home mechanic because although reasonably easy to undertake the reassembly and adjustment before refitting is beyond his scope because of the need of specialist equipment. It would under all circumstances be realistic for the work to be undertaken by the specialist auto-electrician. It is possible to replace solenoids and brushes on starter motors quite easily.
2   Remove the solenoid by, undoing the two holding nuts and unhooking the solenoid plunger from the lever. This may mean pushing out end locating pin in the plunger. Then lift away.
3   To remove the brushes undo the two nuts at the opposite end to the pinion and remove the end cap. Pull off the insulation and spring and ease out the commutator end bracket. On this bracket are located the brushes. Remove and inspect in the same way and renew if necessary. Do not disrupt the rest of the starter motor. Replacement is the direct reversal on all starter motors.

Solenoids should always be renewed if they have ceased to function properly - there is little that can be done to them in the way of repair.
4   If the motor has been disassembled right down to its component parts the checking of the armature field coils and subsequently bearing bushes should be carried out as described in Section 7.
5   Reassembly of a totally dismantled starter motor is easy for the experienced auto-electrician but not for the home mechanic if he is to have any measure of success. Each type of starter motor has a different bearing and pinion adjustment which you will find impossible to measure without costly equipment. It is better even at this stage of disassembly to realise, that to pay for the work to be done on this unit is more economic than to do it yourself.

## 14 Starter motor drive pinion - inspection and repair

1   Persistent jamming or reluctance to disengage may mean that the starter pinion assembly needs attention. The starter motor should be removed first of all for inspection.
2   With the starter motor removed thoroughly remove all grime and grease with a petrol soaked rag, taking care to stop any liquid running into the motor itself. If there is a lot of dirt this could be the trouble and all will now be well. The pinion should move freely in a spiral movement along the shaft against the light spring and return easily on being released. To do this the spiral splines should be completely clean and free of oil. (Oil merely collects dust and grime and gums up the splines). The spring should be intact.
3   If the preceding cleaning and check does not actually remove the fault the starter motor will need to be stripped down to its component parts and a further check made. This, as has been explained in the preceding section, is really beyond the scope of the home mechanic and should be left to the professional auto-electrician. Removal of the pinion itself from the armature is not difficult but requires skill and special tools to replace. If you think that the starter motor needs further insepction take it to the auto-electrician.

## 15 Fuses

The electrical system of the UK import vehicles is fused. All vehicles are fitted with a four fuse system which is deemed sufficient for the whole vehicle. The fuse box is mounted under the instrument panel. The top can be lifted off and inspected easily. Always replace fuses with the correct type, see the end of this section. They are a straight pull-out/push-in fit. Never think that you can leave them out, by-pass them or substitute a fuse for a piece of tin foil or other conductive material unless in a real emergency. Replace the blown fuse as soon as possible.

**Fuses:**
3 x 15 amp fuses protect the instruments, stoplights, windscreen wipers, interior light and heater fan.
1 x 5 amp fuse protects the indicator system.
The R1181 has a single fuse for the heated rear window, isolated from the others, but under the dashboard.

## 16 Direction indicator flasher circuit - fault tracing and rectification

1   The unit which causes the lights to flash intermittently is contained in a two inch long box clipped under the dashboard. It has three terminals.
2   If the flashers fail to work properly first check that all the bulbs are serviceable and of the correct wattage. Then check that the screws which hold the lamp bodies to the car are tight and free from corrosion. These are the means by which the circuit is completed and any resistance here could affect the proper

working of the coils in the flasher unit.

3 If there is still no success, bridge the COM amd REP terminals on the flasher unit. When the switch is operated the lights should go on (on the appropriate side) and stay on. If they do the flasher unit is faulty. If they do not go on first make quite sure that with the ignition switched on current is reaching the COM terminal at the flasher circuit. If it is then the indicator switch is faulty. If it is not, then the connection from the ignition switch to the flasher unit is faulty (via a fuse - 5 amp).

## 17 Windscreen wipers and drive motor - fault diagnosis

1 If the wipers fail to operate first check that current is reaching the motor. This can be done by switching on and using a voltmeter or 12 volt bulb and two wires between the (+) terminal on the motor and earth.

2 If no current is reaching the motor check whether there is any at the switch. If there is then a break has occurred in the wiring between switch and motor.

3 If there is no current at the switch go back to the ignition switch and so isolate the area of the fault.

4 If current is reaching the motor but the wipers do not operate, switch on and give the wiper arm a push - they or the motor could be jammed. Switch off immediately if nothing happens otherwise further damage to the motor may occur. If the wipers now run the reason for them jamming must be found. It will almost certainly be due to wear in either the linkage of the wiper mechanism or the mechanism in the motor gearbox.

5 If the wipers run too slowly it will be due to something restricting the free operation of the linkage or a fault in the motor. In such cases it is well to check the current being used by connecting an ammeter in the circuit. If it exceeds three amps something is restricting free movement. If less, then the commutator and brush gear in the motor are suspect. The shafts to which the wipers are attached run in very long brushes and often suffer from lack of lubrication. Weekly application to each shaft of a few drops of glycerine, preferably, helps to prevent partial or total seizure. First pull outwards the rubber grommets, afterwards, wipe off any excess.

6 If wear is obviously causing malfunction or there is a fault in the motor it is best to remove the motor or wiper mechanism for further examination and repairs.

## 18 Windscreen wiper motor and mechanism - removal, replacement and overhaul

1 The windscreen wiper mechanism must be removed from the car separately from the wiper motor. Both fortunately are fairly simple, if a little fiddly, to remove.

2 To remove the mechanism first remove the wiper arms. Open the bonnet and disconnect, just below the centre of the windscreen, the motor drive arm from the driving link. Its a push fit only.

3 Unscrew the four mounting plate fixing screws, two are easily visible. Remove the plate and linkage by turning it towards the top, having pushed the wiper arm spindles through their drillings.

4 Replacement is a straight reverse process.

5 Fortunately wiper motors are very reliable: failure is usually in the linkage. Check the fuses before attempting necessary overhaul. Disconnect the battery.

6 Open the bonnet and disconnect the linkage as in paragraph 2.

7 From inside the car get a clear view of the motor underneath the facia just above the heater 'on-off' switch. Remove any panelling surrounding to clear the working area.

8 Undo the four nuts which affix the motor to its mounting plate. This will be very fiddly. Once undone wriggle the motor out having disconnected its three feed wires.

9 Replacement is a reverse sequence; patience is needed because of the restricted room.

10 The motor is secured to the plate by three screws. Check the

operation of the spindles. They go rusty and therefore seize very quickly. The individual spindles are available as a spare. Retain the small fixing circlips.

11 Failure of the motor, even brush deterioration, is rare. If this does not happen, either exchange the motor or have it rebuilt by an auto electrician - its an intricate mechanism with its 'Park' facility.

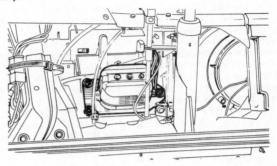

**Fig. 9.10. Windscreen wiper motor location under the facia**

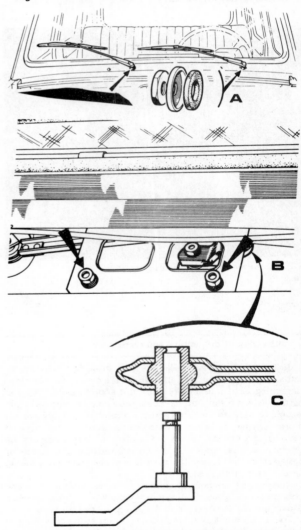

**FIG. 9.11. WIPER MECHANISM COMPONENTS**

A    *Spindle outer fixing*
B    *Mechanism plate fixing (under bonnet)*
C    *Cross-section of the drive spindle*

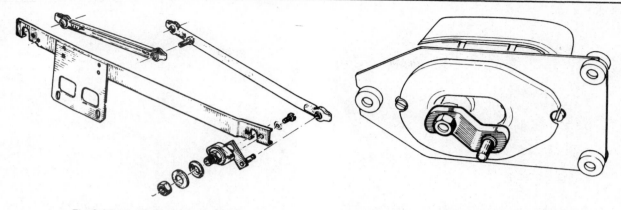

**Fig. 9.12. Wiper operating mechanism**          **Fig. 9.13. 'Park' position of motor drive spindle**

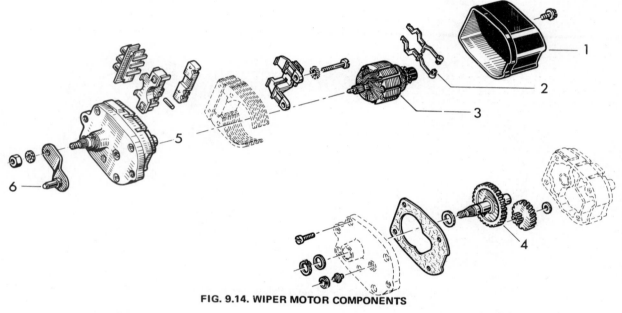

**FIG. 9.14. WIPER MOTOR COMPONENTS**

1  End cap                          4  Gear drive
2  Brush holder                     5  Commutator/body
3  Armature

## 19 Horn

1  The horn fitted to the Renault 6 is a very reliable unit. If it fails to operate check all the other parts in the circuit first - the push is much more likely to fail.

2  Should the horn fail to work the first thing to do is make sure that current is reaching the horn terminal. This can be done by connecting a 12 volt test lamp to the feed wire and pressing the horn button with the ignition switch on. If the bulb lights then the fault must lie in the horn or the horn mounting. The tightness and cleanliness of the horn mounting is important as the circuit is made to earth through the fixing bolt. The connections should, of course, be a clean, tight fit on the horn terminals.

3  If no current is reaching the horn check wiring connections as indicated in the wiring diagram.

4  If it is found that the fault lies in the horn unit then it will have to be renewed. Removal of all types of horn is simply the undoing of the nut which secures the horn to the mounting arm. The horn is located on the front cross panel adjacent to the gearbox. It is not important to replace the horn with exactly the same type.

5  A horn cannot be adjusted or repaired.

## 20 Headlights and bulbs - adjustment, removal and replacement

1  The headlight is of the pre-focus type fitted with a replaceable bulb held by spring clips.

2  It is not necessary to remove the headlamp shell to renew the bulb. Open the bonnet and gently grip the black plastic rear covering and pull away, but remember that the wing still passes through the cover.

3  Pull off the three-way connector and then unclip the two wire springs which hold the rear of the bulb base in the shell. Pull off the bulb.

4  Replacement is exactly a reverse procedure. There is no need to re-adjust the headlight after bulb replacement.

5  To renew a headlamp shell first remove the bulb. Then remove the headlamp rim panel by unscrewing the four fixing screws at the front panel.

6  With the thumb of the left hand push upwards the metal clip on the top left hand side of the lamp unit retainer and with the right hand pull the lamp away from this retainer hinging it at the opposite edge. Lift out the lamp by releasing the hook from the wire bracket at this hinging point.

7  Replacement of the headlight units is a reversal of their removal in each case. Units are interchangeable side to side.

20.3a Pull off the three-way connector

20.3 Unclip two wire springs and pull off rear of bulb base

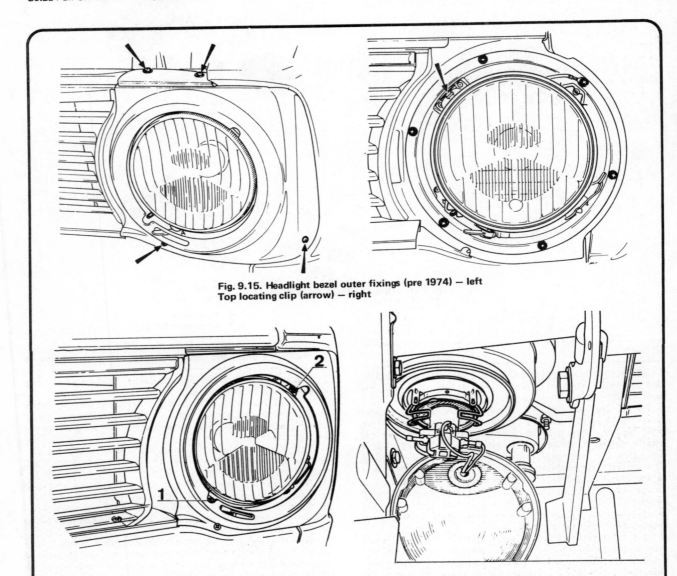

**Fig. 9.15. Headlight bezel outer fixings (pre 1974) — left**
**Top locating clip (arrow) — right**

**Fig. 9.16. Headlight alignment screws**
1 & 2      Both given height and direction

**Fig. 9.17. Behind the headlamp lens. Connection with covering unclipped**

8  The headlight retainers themselves are simply attached to the front panel by a number of setscrews and are easily removed.

9  Headlamp adjustment should be undertaken only with the proper optical equipment. This is therefore best left to your local Renault garage. The Renault 6 is fitted with a load adjuster for the headlights. This allows the headlight beams to be adjusted down once the vehicle has been filled with a heavy load by the use of one external switch under the lamps. On all light retainers this will be a plastic lip. Check that you have the switch in the correct position under all circumstances - this will ensure that you do not dazzle oncoming traffic or have insufficient beam throw. Also fitted to many headlight units is a small switch below the bulb orifice which allows differing beam dipping direction. Make sure this is in the correct position under all circumstances. Full instructions should be stuck to the rear of the unit.

10  As a temporary measure it is possible to adjust the direction and height of the headlights with a small screwdriver. Always adjust on main beam, and blank off one headlight while the other is being adjusted. Place the vehicle 25 feet square, away from a wall and turn the adjusting screws in either direction until the lamp is adjusted. Then do the other one. When finally adjusted oil the adjusting screws (they often rust solid).

11  Check the condition of the bulbs once removed and renew if doubtful. Any discolouring is an indication of present or potential malfunction. Make sure you purchase the correct type of bulb. Take the old bulb along to the stores and match it with the replacement.

Special Note: If there is any kind of malfunction of the head-lights always check the wire at the headlamp.

## 21 Front, side and flasher lights

1  The combined front side and flasher light unit (pre 1973 in the body panel, post 1973 in the front bumper) lens is a combined orange/white lens with a divided fixing base and two bulbs.

2  The lens is removed by unscrewing its two fixing screws which are captive through the lens on early models. On post 1973 the screws are fixed through the lower edge of the bumper.

3  The individual bulbs are a bayonet fitting.

4  The unit itself is removed once having removed the lens and bulb by unscrewing the two fixing self-tapping screws visible around the circumference of the bulb orifice. Pull the unit away from the bonnet and carefully slide it from its rubber cover. The electrical connection(s) is then easily removed.

5  Replacement of the unit is exactly a reversal of the removal but make sure you do not overtighten the fixing screws and that the rubber cover is correctly positioned around the lens.

6  Early models had flasher/repeater lights in the side of the front wings. Their fixings are similar to the front side/flasher lights.

## 22 Rear side, stop, flasher and reflector lights

All that has been said in Section 21 for the front lights applies for those at the rear.

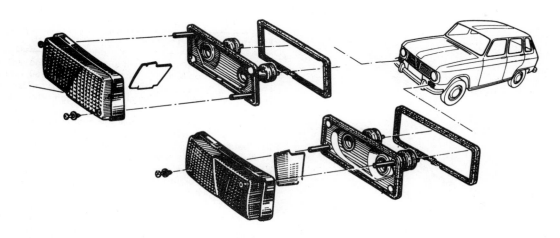

**Fig. 9.18. Front/flasher side lights (pre 1974)**

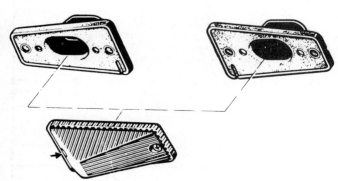

**Fig. 9.19. Side wing flasher lights (early models only)**

## 23 Number plate light

1  The number plate light is situated in the centre of the tailgate. Its lens can be removed by unscrewing the two visible Phillips screws.

2  The bulbs are a push-in-and-twist fit.

3  The unit as a whole can be removed completely after the lens and bulbs have been removed by releasing the electrical connection and unscrewing the two locating self-tapping screws visible.

4  Replacement is a reversal of removal. Check again that you have the correct replacement parts.

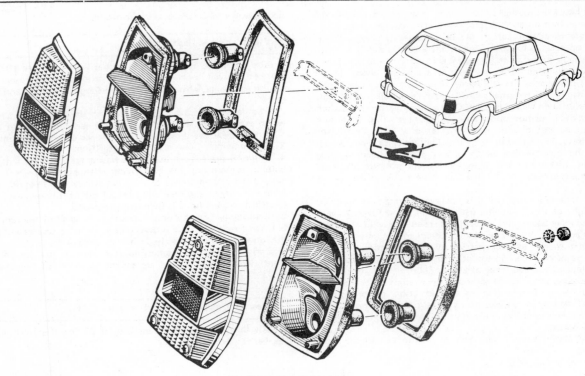

**Fig. 9.20. Rear light clusters**

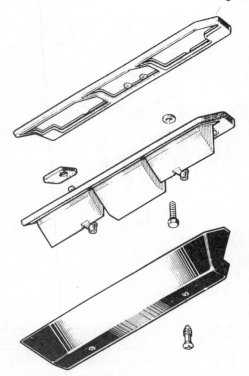

**Fig. 9.21. Number plate light on tailgate**

### 24 Ignition switch

See Chapter 10 on steering as this unit is an integral part of the steering column. It is a simple switch with three electrical contacts.

### 25 Interior light and switches

1  The interior light is situated in the centre of the roof in early models. It can be activated by the three way switch on the light or by the door plunger switches. On late models the switch is the light, above the offside door. It rocks in the centre but is only, off-on manually.
2  Bulb replacement is simple by removing the lens; its a push-on fit. The bulb is then clipped out and in.
3  The door plunger switches - in the front door pivots are fixed by one screw each. Once the screw is removed, the switch pulls out. The wire connection is behind it.
4  There is no facility for the repair of either of the switches - roof or door. They must be renewed.

### 26 Lighting - dip, main beam, horn and indicator switches

1  The light and horn switch uses one stalk whilst the indicator uses another, however both are part of the same switch body. If any part fails the whole switch must be renewed. No repair is possible - these switches are expensive.
2  Disconnect the battery before undertaking any work. To remove start by removing the lower protective panel under the instrument panel. Lift the top panel and remove the securing screws.
3  Leave the Lucar clips on the rear of the switch (s) attached and uncouple the junction blocks plus the two loose connections. The new switch comes with junction blocks attached.
4  Replacement is a straightforward reverse sequence.

### 27 Other switches

The switches are located singly on the facia panel and are a push-in spring fit. Lever them out carefully with a broad bladed screwdriver. To refit push them gently in with the terminals correctly wired.

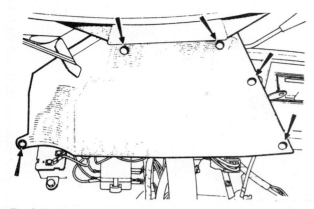

Fig. 9.22. Switch panel/steering column lower protective panel

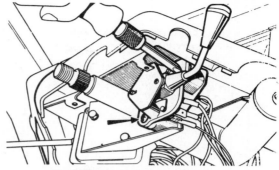

Fig. 9.23 Early lighting switch removal

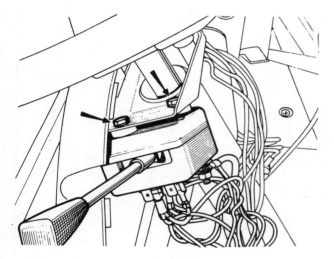

Fig. 9.24 Early flasher switch removal

### 28 Instrument panel, imstruments and bulbs

1   The instrument panel, instruments and their bulbs are easily removed. Little can be done in the way of overhaul; replacement of components only is feasible.

2   Always disconnect the battery. From below the facia disconnect the junction blocks which feed the instrument panel.

3   Disconnect the speedo cable at the speedometer head by undoing the knurled outer ferrule.

4   The panel is located by two dowels and clipped top and bottom by four plastic clips. Push in top and bottom to release the clips and removed down from below.

5   Speedometer removal is easy once the front glass has been unclipped. It is fixed by two securing screws. The gauges are removed by unscrewing the five gauge/lamp assembly screws. The gauges, available separately, are fixed to a printed circuit.

6   Bulbs are a push in and twist fit.

7   Replacement is straightforward. Remember however that all parts will be expensive.

### 29 Heated rear window (R1181)

The R1181 can be fitted with a heated rear window. This consists of a special tailgate glass with five wires threaded in its centre - as if it were an electric blanket. It is fused. You are advised not to fiddle with it. Replace the fuse - but do not attempt anything more. If it is found to be faulty take the car to a Renault agency or preferably to an auto-electrician who can test it. Let them advise to its removal and replacement - it is very costly and delicate.

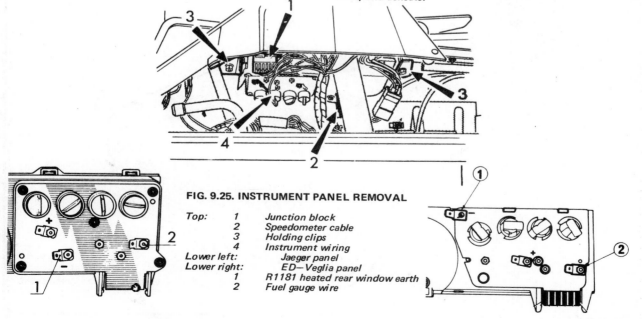

**FIG. 9.25. INSTRUMENT PANEL REMOVAL**

| | | |
|---|---|---|
| Top: | 1 | Junction block |
| | 2 | Speedometer cable |
| | 3 | Holding clips |
| | 4 | Instrument wiring |
| Lower left: | | Jaeger panel |
| Lower right: | | ED—Veglia panel |
| | 1 | R1181 heated rear window earth |
| | 2 | Fuel gauge wire |

### FIG. 9.26. JAEGER INSTRUMENT PANEL
(ED—Veglia is very similar)

1   Headlight main beams 'on' warning light
2   Oil and water warning light
3   + after ignition switch
4   Instrument panel earth
5   Panel light bulb
6   Direction indicator tell-tale

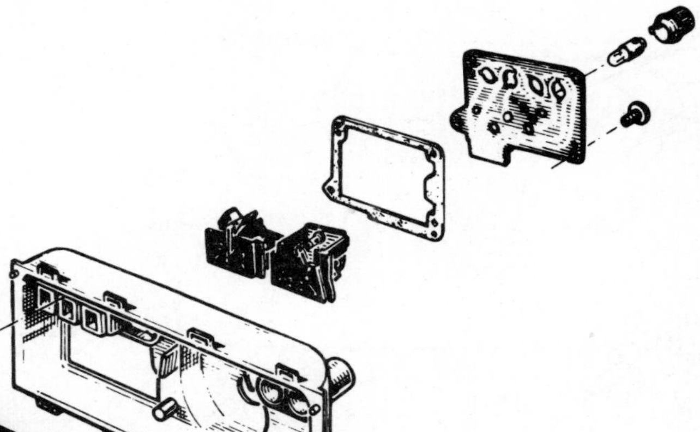

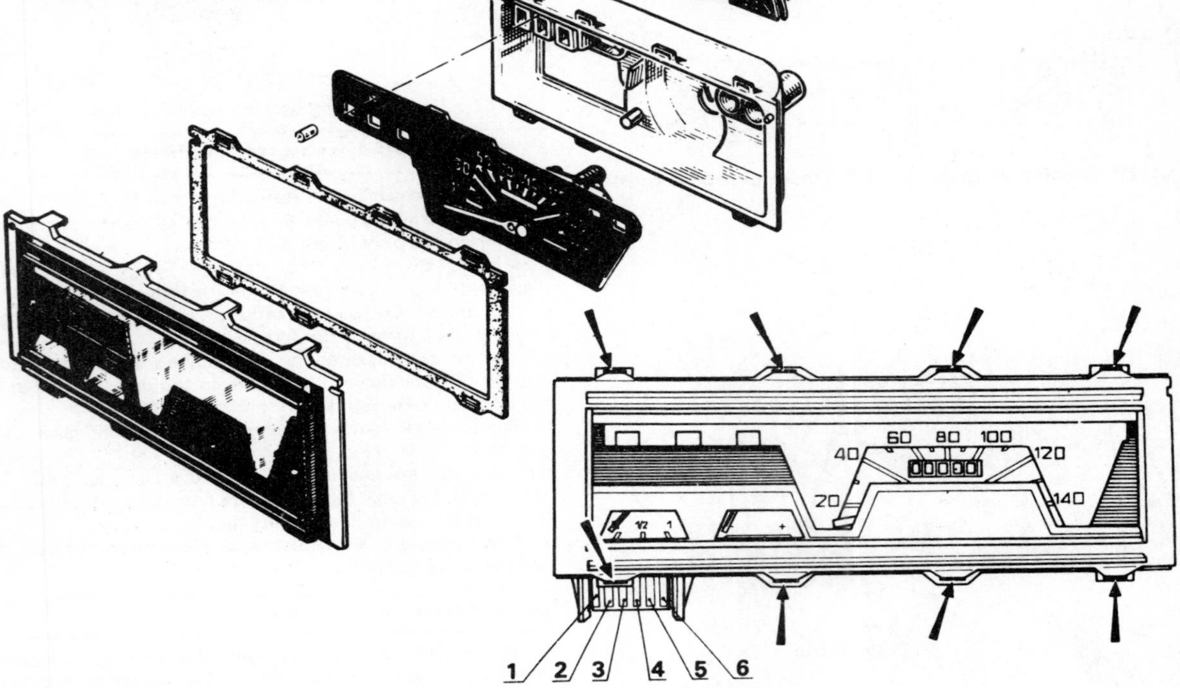

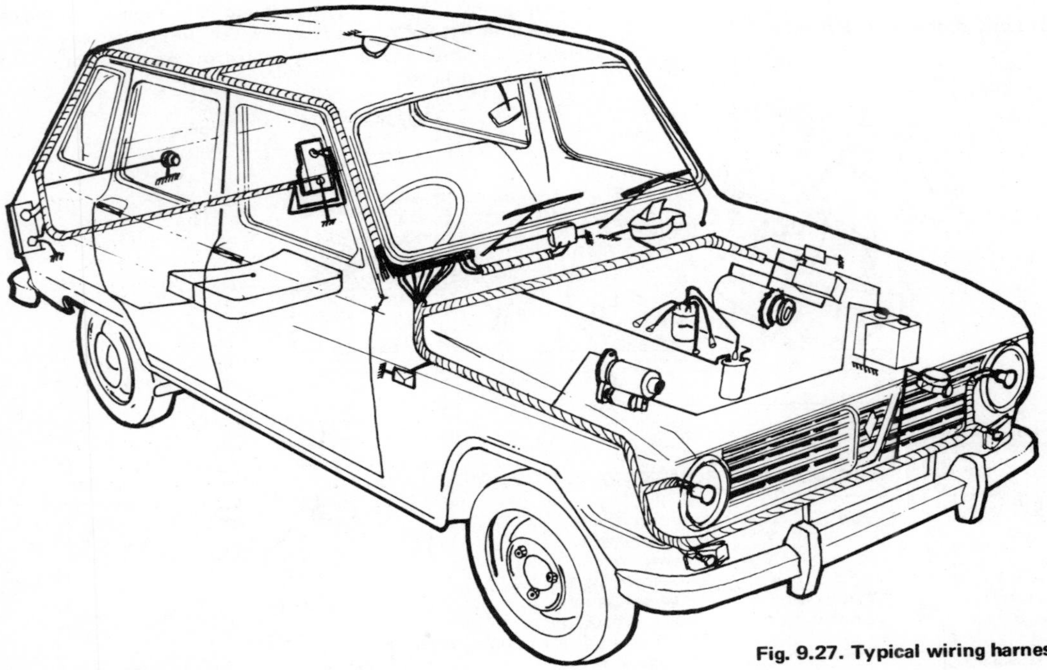

1  2  3    4  5  6

Fig. 9.27. Typical wiring harness location layout

**FIG. 9.28. ELECTRICAL CONNECTIONS**

This is a breakdown of the pre 1974 model R1180 connection up to part 19 inclusive. Part 20 is for the R1181. Parts 21 to 23 are for post 1972 models of the R1180. All other models will have similar fittings. See the wiring diagram for exact wiring layout.

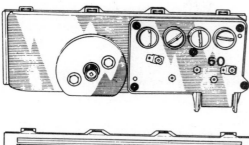

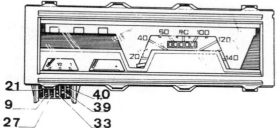

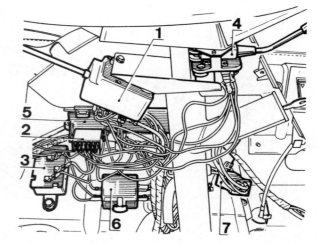

**1 Instrument panel and location of units**

1 Lighting switch
2 Instrument panel junction box
3 Flasher unit
4 Flasher control
5 Instrument panel
6 Fuses
7 Neiman junction box

| No. | Colour | Description |
|-----|--------|-------------|
| 60 | White | Feed to petrol gauge |
| 21 | Blue | Pilot light of headlamp |
| 9 | Green | Feed to pressure sender switch and temperature sender switch |
| 27 | Grey | Feed to instrument panel |
| 33 | Yellow | Instrument panel earth |
| 39 | White | Instrument panel light |
| 40 | Black | Pilot light of flasher |

**LIGHTING**

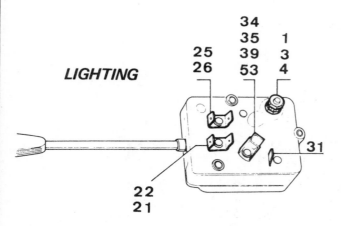

**2 Lighting switch and flasher switch**

| No. | Colour | Description |
|-----|--------|-------------|
| 1 | White | Main feed |
| 3 | Beige | Feed to Neiman switch |
| 4 | Salmon pink | Main feed to fuses |
| 21 | Blue, clear sleeve | Pilot light for headlight |
| 22 | Blue, clear sleeve | Main feed to headlight |
| 25 | Salmon pink | Dipped beam LH side |
| 26 | Salmon pink | Dipped beam RH side |
| 39 | Grey | Horn |
| 34 | White | Front LH side light |
| 35 | White | Front RH side light |
| 39 | White | Instrument panel light |
| 53 | Black | Rear lights |
| 32 | Salmon, clear sleeve | Feed to flasher unit |
| 36 | Blue, clear sleeve | Front LH flasher unit |
| 37 | Red, clear sleeve | Front RH flasher unit |
| 58 | Blue, clear sleeve | Flasher rear left-hand |
| 59 | Red, clear sleeve | Flasher rear right-hand |

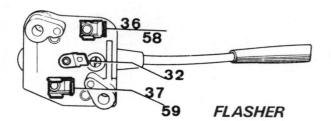

**FLASHER**

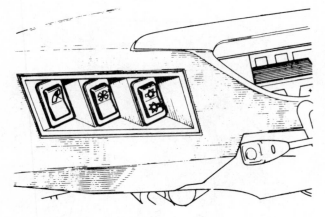

### 3 Instrument panel switches

| No. | Colour | Description |
|---|---|---|
| 12 | Black | Parking light left-hand |
| 13 | Black, brown sleeve | Parking light right-hand |
| 14 | Yellow | Feed to heater motor |
| 20 | Yellow | Feed to heater motor switch |
| 15 | Salmon pink | Feed to windscreen wiper switch |
| 17 | Green | Feed to windscreen motor |
| 18 | Grey | Windscreen wiper 'Arefix' |
| 75 | Blue | Feed to parking light switch |

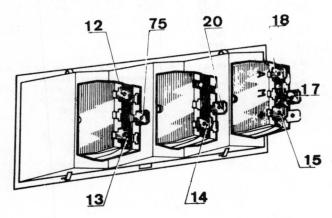

### 4 Roof light switch

| No. | Colour | Description |
|---|---|---|
| 49 | White, blue sleeve | Feed to roof light |
| 50 | White | Earth to front LH door switch |
| 86 | White | Earth to front RH door switch |

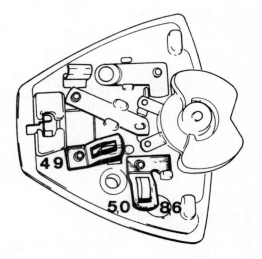

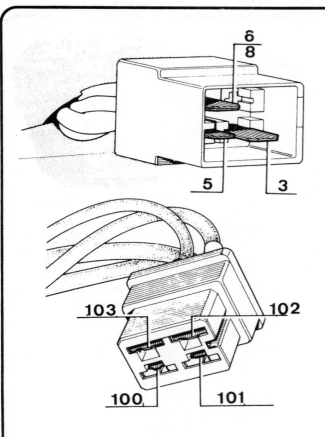

### 6 Neiman ignition and starter switch

| No. | Colour | Description |
|-----|--------|-------------|
| 3 | Beige | Feed to starter |
| 5 | Grey | Starter relay |
| 6 | Red | Feed to fuses after Neiman switch |
| 8 | Salmon pink | Feed to coil |
| 100 | Red | Neiman ignition and starter switch |
| 101 | Blue | Neiman ignition and starter switch |
| 102 | Green | Neiman ignition and starter switch |
| 103 | Yellow | Neiman ignition and starter switch |

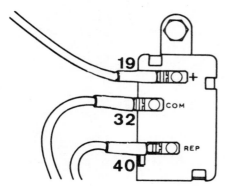

### 7 Flasher unit

| No. | Colour | Description |
|-----|--------|-------------|
| 19 | Grey, red sleeve | Feed to flasher switch |
| 32 | Salmon pink, clear sleeve | Feed to flasher unit |
| 40 | Black | Flasher pilot light |

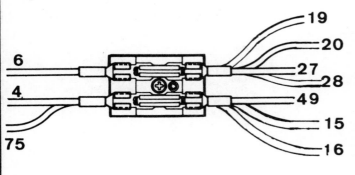

### 8 Fuses

| No. | Colour | Description |
|-----|--------|-------------|
| 4 | Salmon pink, blue sleeve | Feed to fuses |
| 6 | Red | Feed to fuses after ignition switch |
| 15 | Salmon pink, blue sleeve | Feed to windscreen wiper switch |
| 16 | Salmon pink, blue sleeve | Feed direct to windscreen wiper motor |
| 19 | Grey, red sleeve | Feed to flasher switch |
| 20 | Yellow, red sleeve | Feed to heater switch |
| 27 | Grey, red sleeve | Feed to instrument panel |
| 28 | Grey, red sleeve | Feed to brake light switch |
| 49 | White | Feed to roof panel light |
| 75 | Blue | Feed to parking light switch |

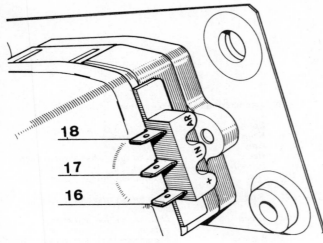

### 9 Windscreen wiper motor

| No. | Colour | Description |
|-----|--------|-------------|
| 16 | Salmon pink | Feed to w.w. motor direct |
| 17 | Green | Feed to w.w. motor |
| 18 | Grey | 'Arefix' windscreen wiper |

**MOTOR**

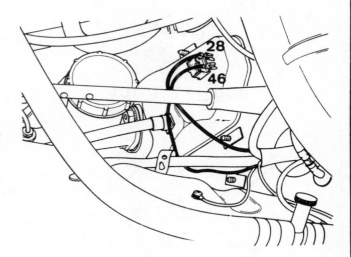

### 10 Brake light switch (R1180)

| No. | Colour | Description |
|-----|--------|-------------|
| 28 | Grey | Feed to brake light switch |
| 46 | Salmon pink | Feed to stop light |

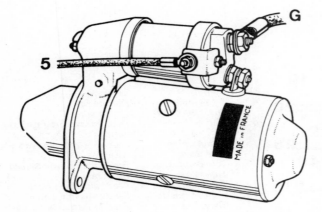

### 11 Starter

| No. | Colour | Description |
|-----|--------|-------------|
| 5 | Grey | Feed to starter relay |
| G | Grey | Main positive cable |

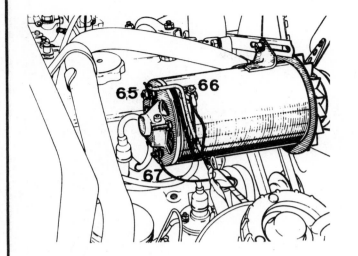

**12 Dynamo**

| No. | Colour | Description |
|-----|--------|-------------|
| 65 | Black | Dynamo + |
| 66 | Green | Dynamo field |
| 67 | Grey | Dynamo earth |

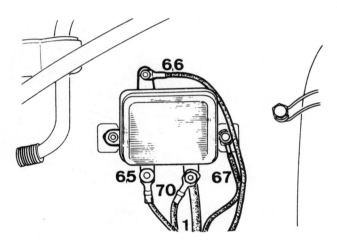

**13 Regulator**

| No. | Colour | Description |
|-----|--------|-------------|
| 1 | White | Main feed |
| 65 | Black | Dynamo + |
| 66 | Green | Dynamo field |
| 67 | Grey | Dynamo earth |
| 70 | White | Battery + |

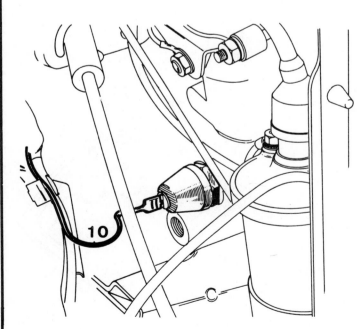

**14 Oil pressure sender switch**

| No. | Colour | Description |
|-----|--------|-------------|
| 10 | Green | Pressure sender switch |

**15 Coil**

| No. | Colour | Description |
|-----|--------|-------------|
| 8 | Salmon pink, black covered | Feed to coil |
| 100 | Black, red sleeve | Feed to contact points |

**16 Side lights and front flashers**

| No. | Colour | Description | No. | Colour | Description |
|-----|--------|-------------|-----|--------|-------------|
| 34 | White | Front side light LH side | 35 | White | Side light front RH side |
| 36 | Blue | Front flasher LH side | 37 | Red | Flasher front RH side |

**17 Rear lights and rear flasher**

| No. | Colour | Description | No. | Colour |
|-----|--------|-------------|-----|--------|
| 47 | Black | Stop light | 48 | Black |
| 55 | White | Rear light | 56 | White |
| 58 | Blue | Rear flasher | 59 | Red |

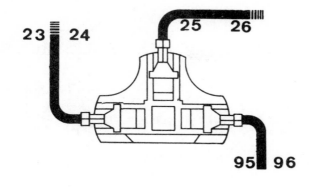

**18 Head lights**

| No. | Colour | Description |
|---|---|---|
| 23 | Green | Head light left-hand |
| 24 | Green | Head light right-hand |
| 25 | Salmon pink | Dipped beam left-hand |
| 26 | Salmon pink | Dipped beam right-hand |
| 95 | Grey | Earth left-hand |
| 96 | Grey | Earth right-hand |

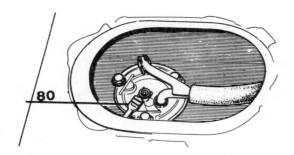

**19 Petrol gauge**

| No. | Colour | Description |
|---|---|---|
| 60 | White with protecting clips | Main feed to petrol gauge |
| 80 | White with protecting clips | Main feed to petrol gauge |

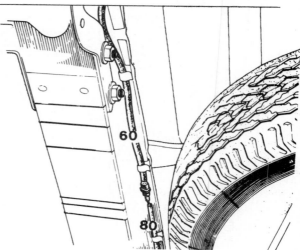

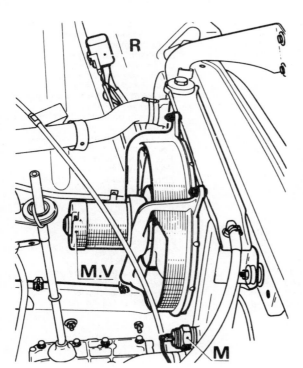

**20 Cooling fan motor and Mosta temperature switch on the radiator (R1181 models)**

R  Relay
MV  Cooling fan motor
M  'Mosta' temperature switch

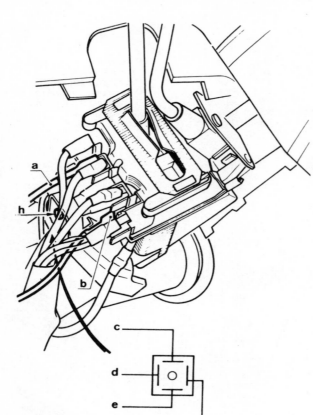

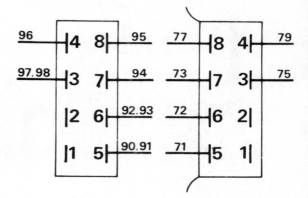

| 96 | |4  8| | 95 | | 77 | |8  4| | 79 |
| 97.98 | |3  7| | 94 | | 73 | |7  3| | 75 |
| | |2  6| | 92.93 | | 72 | |6  2| | |
| | |1  5| | 90.91 | | 71 | |5  1| | |

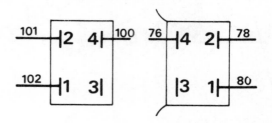

| 101 | |2  4| | 100 | | 76 | |4  2| | 78 |
| 102 | |1  3| | | | | |3  1| | 80 |

**21 Combination lighting-flasher switch and junction block coding**

| No. | Colour | Description |
|-----|--------|-------------|
| 71 | Blue | Feed to headlights |
| 72 | Red | Feed to 'dipped-beam' |
| 73 | White | Horns |
| 74 | Green | Feed to flasher change-over switch |
| 75 | White | Feed to front side lights |
| 76 | White | Feed to rear lights |
| 77 | Blue | Left-hand front flasher |
| 78 | Blue | Left-hand rear flasher |
| 79 | Red | Right-hand front flasher |
| 80 | Red | Right-hand rear flasher |
| a | Blue | Headlight main beam warning light |
| b | White | Instrument panel lighting |
| c | Blue | Feed to combination lighting flasher switch |
| d | Grey | Feed to cooling fan motor relay |
| e | White | Feed to licence plate |
| f | Pink | Feed to fuse (direct) |
| g | Beige | Feed to Neiman |
| h | White | Retaining wire |
| 90 | Green | Left-hand headlight |
| 91 | Green | Right-hand headlight |
| 92 | Pink | Left-hand dip beam |
| 93 | Pink | Right-hand dip beam |
| 94 | Grey | Horns |
| 95 | Blue | Left-hand front flasher |
| 96 | Red | Right-hand front flasher |
| 97 | White | Left-hand front side light |
| 98 | White | Right-hand front side light |
| 100 | Black | Feed to rear lights |
| 101 | Blue | Left-hand rear flasher |
| 102 | Red | Right-hand rear flasher |

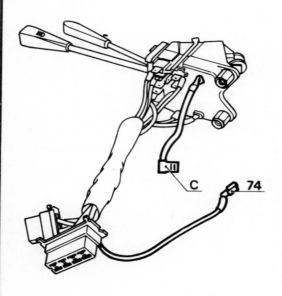

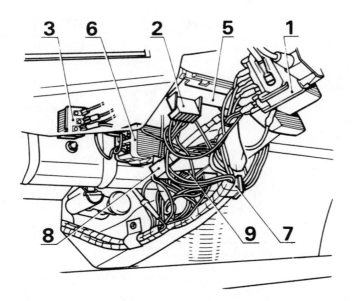

**22 Later type control layout**

1   *Combination lighting-flasher switch*
2   *Instrument panel junction block*
3   *Flasher unit*
5   *Instrument panel*
6   *Fuses*
7   *Neiman junction block*
8   *Combination lighting-flasher switch*
    *junction block and front harness*
9   *Combination lighting-flasher switch*
    *junction block and rear harness*

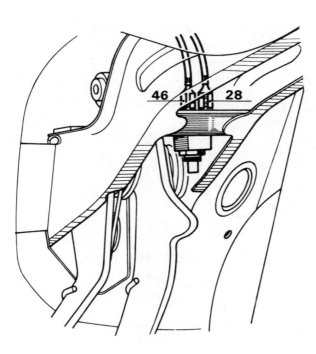

**23 Stop light switch (R1181)**

| No. | Colour | Description |
|-----|--------|-------------|
| 28 | *Grey* | *Feed to stop light switch* |
| 46 | *Pink* | *Feed to stop lights* |

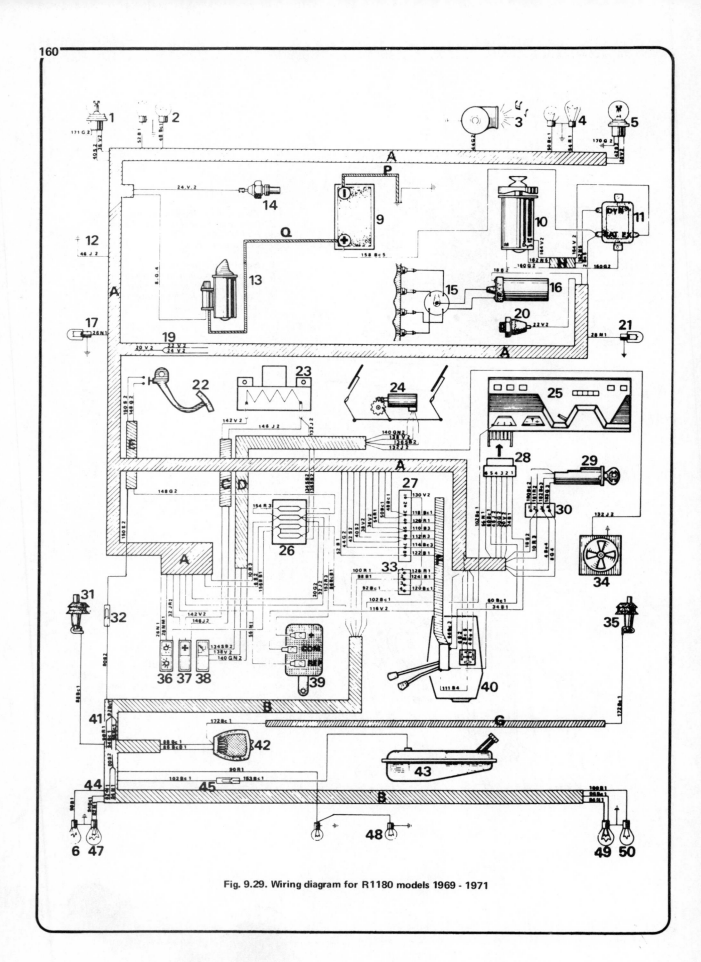

Fig. 9.29. Wiring diagram for R1180 models 1969 - 1971

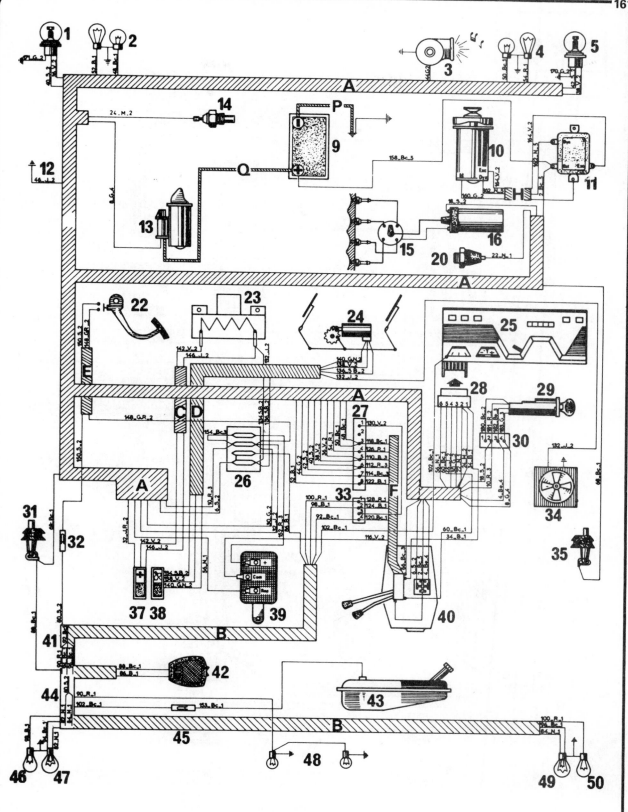

Fig. 9.30. Wiring diagram for R1180 models 1972 - 1973

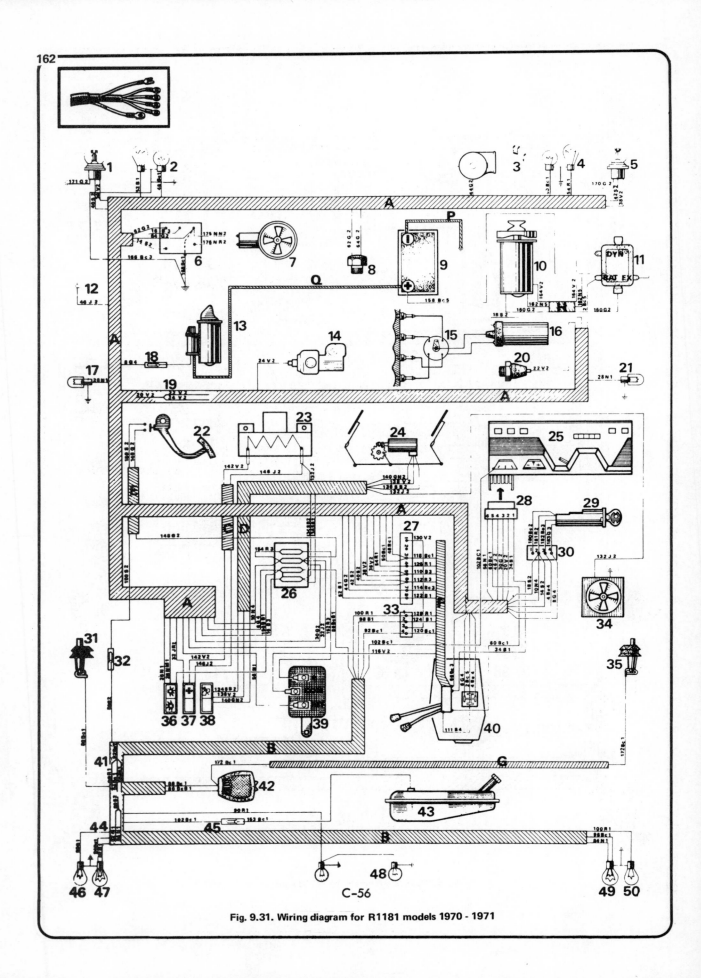

**Fig. 9.31. Wiring diagram for R1181 models 1970 - 1971**

C-56

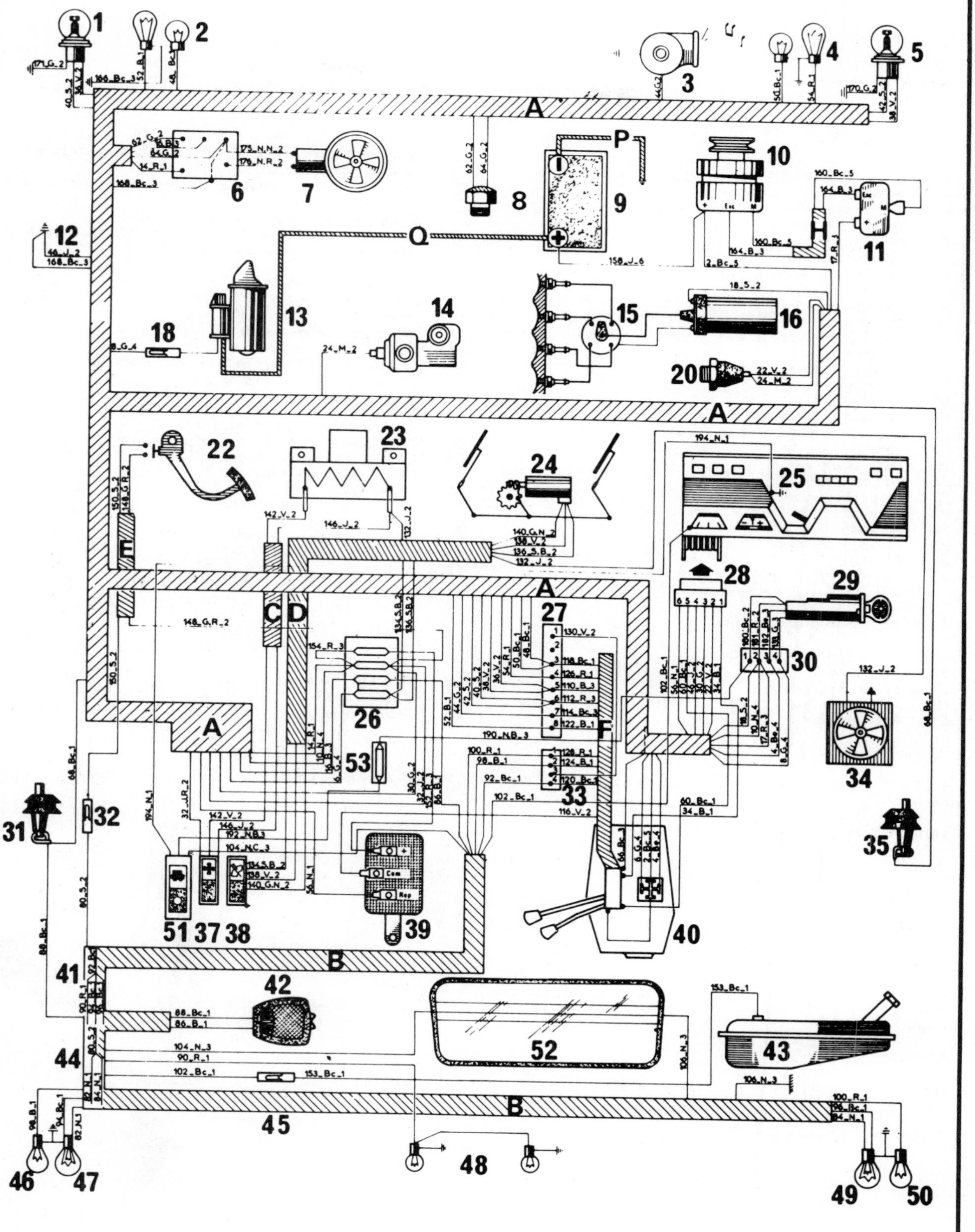

**Fig. 9.32. Wiring diagram for R1181 models 1972 - 1973**

## FIGS. 9.29 — 9.32 KEY TO ALL WIRING DIAGRAM LAYOUTS

Numerical list of components

| | | | |
|---|---|---|---|
| 1 | LH headlight | 28 | Junction block for front harness and instrument panel |
| 2 | LH front sidelight and direction indicator | 29 | Ignition-starter switch |
| 3 | Horn | 30 | Junction block for front harness and ignition-starter switch |
| 4 | RH front sidelight and direction indicator | 31 | LH door pillar switch |
| 5 | RH headlight | 32 | Spade plug and socket on stop lights wire |
| 6 | Cooling fan motor relay (R1181) | 33 | Junction block for rear harness and combination lighting-direction indicator switch |
| 7 | Cooling fan motor (R1181) | | |
| 8 | Coolant temperature switch on radiator (R1181) | 34 | Heater fan |
| 9 | Battery | 35 | RH door pillar switch |
| 10 | Dynamo or alternator | 36 | Parking lights switch |
| 11 | Regulator | 37 | Heating-ventilating switch |
| 12 | Front gusset earth (ground) | 38 | Windscreen wiper switch |
| 13 | Starter | 39 | Flasher unit |
| 14 | Coolant temperature switch | 40 | Combination lighting-direction indicator switch |
| 15 | Distributor | 41 | Wire junction on rear lights |
| 16 | Ignition coil | 42 | Interior light |
| 17 | LH parking light | 43 | Fuel tank |
| 18 | Spade plug and socket on starter wire (R1181) | 44 | Wire junction on stoplight wires |
| 19 | Wire junction on oil and water warning light | 45 | Spade plug and socket for fuel gauge wire |
| 20 | Oil pressure switch | 46 | LH rear direction indicator |
| 21 | RH parking light | 47 | LH rear light and stoplight |
| 22 | Stoplight switch | 48 | Licence plate light |
| 23 | Supplementary heater fan resistance | 49 | RH rear light and stoplight |
| 24 | Windscreen wiper | 50 | RH rear direction indicator |
| 25 | Instrument panel | 51 | Rear screen demister switch (R1181) |
| 26 | Fusebox | 52 | Heated rear screen (R1181) |
| 27 | Junction block for front harness and combination lighting-direction indicator switch | 53 | Heated rear screen fuse (R1181) |

Wiring harness identification

| | | | |
|---|---|---|---|
| A: | Front harness | F: | Combination lighting - direction indicator switch cable |
| B: | Rear harness | G: | Interior light |
| C: | Heater motor cable | H: | Dynamo or alternator cable |
| D: | Windscreen wiper cable | P: | Negative lead |
| E: | Stop light cable | Q: | Positive lead |

Wire identification

Each wire is identified by a number followed by letter(s) indicating the wire and sleeve colours, if fitted, and a number indicating the diameter.

Wire and sleeve colours

| Beige | White | Blue | Clear | Grey | Yellow | Black | Pink |
|---|---|---|---|---|---|---|---|
| Be | Bc | B | C | G | J | N | S |
| | | Red | Green | Maroon | | | |
| | | R | V | M | | | |

Wire diameters

| No. | 1 | 2 | 3 | 4 | 5 | 6 |
|---|---|---|---|---|---|---|
| mm | 9/10 | 12/10 | 16/10 | 20/10 | 25/10 | 30/10 |
| Gauge | 19 | 16 | 14 | 12 | 10 | 9 |

Example:

| No. | Wire colour | Sleeve colour | Diameter |
|---|---|---|---|
| 10 | Bc | B | 1 |

This is a No. 10 white wire with a blue sleeve, 9/10 mm diameter (19 gauge).

# Chapter 10 Suspension and steering

## Contents

## Specifications

**Front suspension**

Type ... ... ... ... ... ... ... ... ...   Independent, torsion bars with single lower arms and wishbone upper arms and anti-roll bar

**Rear suspension**

Type ... ... ... ... ... ... ... ... ...   Independent, single lever arms pivoting. Torsion bars. Anti-roll bar on R1181 model

**Shock absorbers**

Type ... ... ... ... ... ... ... ... ...   Telescopic double acting front and rear
Front - vertical
Rear - horizontal

**Steering**

| | |
|---|---|
| Type ... ... ... ... ... ... ... ... ... | Rack and pinion |
| Steering geometry and measurements | |
| Castor angle (normal) ... ... ... ... ... ... | $10^o$ to $11^o$ |
| Camber angle ... ... ... ... ... ... ... | $0^o$ to $1^o$ |
| Toe-out (unladen) ... ... ... ... ... ... | 0 to 5 mm (0 to 13/64 in.) |
| King pin angle (laden) ... ... ... ... ... ... | $14^o$ 40' |
| Track on level ground ... ... ... ... ... | 1.280 m (50 7/16 in.) |
| Wheelbase - Right ... ... ... ... ... ... | 8ft 7/16 in (2.45 m) |
| - Left ... ... ... ... ... ... | 7ft 10½ in (2.40 m) |
| Front track ... ... ... ... ... ... ... | 4 ft 2 3/8 in (1.28 m) |
| Rear track ... ... ... ... ... ... ... | 4 ft 1 3/16 in (1.25 m) |
| Turning circle - between kerbs ... ... ... ... | 32 ½ ft |
| Steering wheel turns, lock to lock ... ... ... ... | 4.5 |

| Torque wrench settings | lbf ft | kgf m |
|---|---|---|
| *Front suspension and steering* | | |
| Suspension upper balljoint ... ... ... ... ... ... | 25 | 3.5 |
| Suspension lower balljoint ... ... ... ... ... ... | 35 | 4.8 |
| Track rod end balljoint ... ... ... ... ... ... | 25 | 3.5 |
| Flexible coupling bolts ... ... ... ... ... ... | 10 | 1.4 |
| Steering wheel nut ... ... ... ... ... ... | 35 | 4.8 |
| Stub axle nut ... ... ... ... ... ... ... | 85 | 11.8 |
| Roadwheel nuts ... ... ... ... ... ... | 35 | 4.8 |
| Shock absorber upper mounting nuts ... ... ... ... | 28 | 3.9 |
| Shock absorber lower mounting bolts ... ... ... ... | 40 | 5.5 |
| Steering rack bolts ... ... ... ... ... ... | 25 | 3.5 |
| Upper wishbone pivot bolts ... ... ... ... ... ... | 35 | 4.8 |
| Lower wishbone pivot bolts ... ... ... ... ... ... | 30 | 4.1 |
| Steering arm bolts ... ... ... ... ... ... | 25 | 3.5 |
| Anti-roll bar nuts ... ... ... ... ... ... | 30 | 4.1 |
| Steering shaft universal joint bolt ... ... ... ... | 25 | 3.5 |

*Rear suspension*

| | | | | | | | |
|---|---|---|---|---|---|---|---|
| Shock absorber mounting nuts | ... | ... | ... | ... | ... | 28 | 3.9 |
| Shock absorber mounting pivot bolt | | ... | ... | ... | ... | 40 | 5.5 |
| Brake backplate nuts | ... | ... | ... | ... | ... | 30 | 4.1 |
| Torsion bar anchor cam nut | ... | ... | ... | ... | ... | 55 | 7.6 |
| Arm bearing retainer nuts | ... | ... | ... | ... | ... | 20 | 2.8 |

## 1  General description

The Renault 6 is fitted with independent front and rear suspension by means of torsion bars and telescopic hydraulic shock absorbers. Double wishbone suspension, with the double acting shock absorber with buit-in bump stops fixed vertically, is utilised with torsion bars, one each side, running along the floor of the car. Single arms are used at the rear, with horizontal double acting shock absorbers, and torsion bars run across the car. Bump stops are built into the suspension arms. The wheelbase is greater on one side of the car than the other because if the transverse torsion bars at the rear. Anti-roll bars are always fitted to the front suspension and on R1181 models to the rear. Underbody height is adjustable.

A rack and pinion steering unit is fitted, with self-centring action on some models.

Much of any necessary repair amd maintenance work is easily undertaken on the suspension and steering by the home mechanic although some special tools, which may possibly be home made, will be necessary. Before starting any such work be absolutely sure that you have the knowledge and facilities for finishing it and have the correct replacement parts for your model. There have been detailed changes during the production run from model to model, particularly on the steering. Asking the local Renault garage to come out and replace a torsion bar which you have removed and find you cannot replace will be very expensive!

Potential tasks are described in an order which indicates their ease and to an extent their likelihood.

## 2  Suspension and steering - testing

1   Because of the construction of these vehicles the suspension cannot be viewed in isolation from the steering and vice vera. The safety of a car depends more on the steering and suspension than anything else and this is the reason why the compulsory tests made for vehicles over three years old pay attention to the condition of all these components.

2   Any parts which are weak or broken must be renewed immediately. Take great care to check the following. The first list are those parts which will wear with use and the second list is of special check points.

**Check for wear:**
a)  Upper and lower ball joints.
b)  Upper and lower wishbone and rear suspension arm inner bushes.
c)  Shock absorbers and/or their mounting bushes.
d)  Steering arm ball joints and inner bushes.

All these points may be tested with a tyre lever or screwdriver to see whether there is any movement between them and a fixed component.

**Check:**
e)  Torsion bar sleeves for perishing.
f)  Steering rack mounting bolts for looseness.
g)  Steering rack to column coupling.
h)  Steering wheel to column.
i)  Steering column bush.

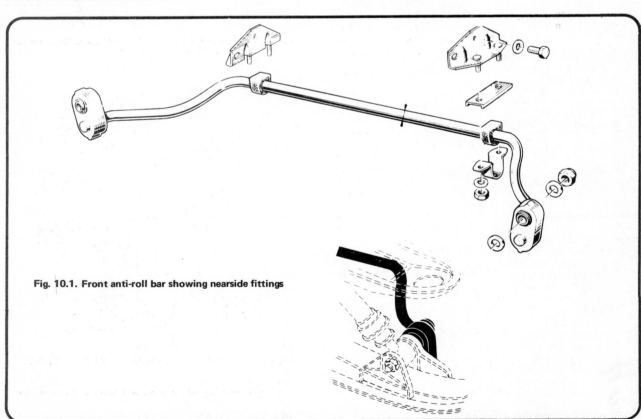

Fig. 10.1. Front anti-roll bar showing nearside fittings

j) Front and rear hub bearings (see Chapter 7).

k) Anti-roll bar bushes.

There should be no play nor failure in any single part of any of the forementioned components. It is dangerous to use a vehicle in a doubtful condition of this kind.

### 3  Front anti-roll bar and bushes - removal and replacement

1  It is easiest if the vehicle is over a pit when removing the anti-roll bar to replace the bushes or to replace other suspension parts, although it matters little. Make sure the vehicle is properly secure on stands (if available) or on the ground with the handbrake on. It is not always necessary to remove the front wheels.

2  Remove the four bolts or nuts, and washers, which locate the anti-roll bar at its centre section under the car, and pull off the two clamps.

Remove the two rubber bushes and their seats. That is all that need be done to renew these bushes. Fit new bushes, seats and refix the clamps.

3  To remove the bar from the vehicle completely undo the nut which holds the two-way bush to the pin which fixes the bottom end of the shock absorber to the lower wishbone. Pull off this two-way bush from each side and remove the bar. Inspect this bush at each insert and renew if doubtful.

4  Replacement is a direct reversal of its removal. It is not possible to refit the two-way bushes incorrectly. Never drive the vehicle without the anti-roll bar fitted, located in solid, unworn bushes.

5  The two centre mounting brackets are bolted to the chassis rails. They each have a special seating bracket onto which the flat side of the rubber bush sits.

### 4  Rear anti-roll bar (R1181) - removal and replacement

1  Rear anti-roll bar removal is much simpler than the front as it does not have any rubber bushing points. It is easily unbolted at its each end from the suspension arm. Two nuts locate it to each arm. It is not necessary to jack up the car - it is better to crawl under the rear and remove it lying on your back. Refitting is a reversal of its removal.

2  It is not possible to fit rear anti-roll bars to R1180 vehicles unless the proper rear suspension arms are fitted.

### 5  Front shock absorber - removal and replacement

1  Front shock absorbers need to be inspected for leaking and proper functioning more frequently on this vehicle than on most others because of the design of the suspension. Because of the built-in softness and the great length of suspension travel they operate under particularly hard conditions. If the car wallows and simply does not 'absorb' the 'shock' as it should, try to compare a suspect vehicle with a new one, by bouncing each corner by hand. If the shock absorber leaks fluid it should be renewed immediately. Try to replace front units in pairs, and only with the correct specified type.

2  Jack up the front of the car, remove the front wheels, having placed the car on stands, and removed the anti-roll bar as described in Section 3.

3  Place a scissor or screw jack under the relevant lower suspension arm and jack up the arm until a firmness is felt, with the car still solid on the stands. This counterbalances the torsion bar effect and allows the shock abosrber to be withdraw down through the upper wishbone.

4  Remove the shock absorber nut at the top. Do this from under the wing using a ring spanner and a pair of mole grips to hold the stud still. This part is not very easy as you are working in a restricted space, especially adjacent to the silencer. Wait for it to cool!

5  Remove the bottom shock absorber mounting pin. Compress the shock absorber by hand until it is at its shortest length and remove down and outwards. Retrieve all the washers and bushes.

6  Replacement is an exact reversal of removal but check that the top rubber bushes and their cups are correctly positioned and that the bottom pin is smeared with grease. No repair to a shock absorber is possible; it must be renewed complete as must the old rubber bushes. Tighten all fixing nuts well, to 28 lb ft torque.

### 6  Rear shock absorber - removal and replacement

1  The principle of checking the condition of the rear shock absorbers as frequently as the fronts is valid, although they do not generally take such abuse. They do need a little more care in removing and replacing.

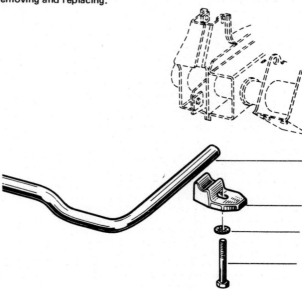

**Fig. 10.2. Rear anti-roll bar (R1181). The bar is fixed only at each end on the suspension arm**

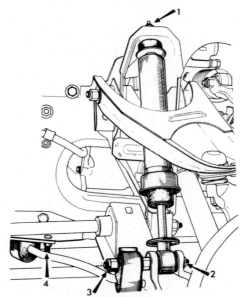

**FIG. 10.3. FRONT  SHOCK ABSORBER FITTINGS**

*1  Top mounting*
*2  Rear bottom nut for shock absorbers and anti-roll bar*
*3  Front, and anti-roll/shock absorber mounting*
*4  Centre anti-roll bar mounting*

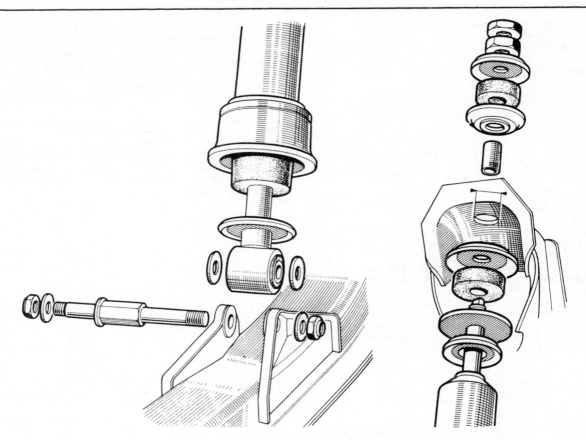

**Fig. 10.4. Top and bottom front shock absorber mounting fittings. It is necessary to put all fittings in the order shown**

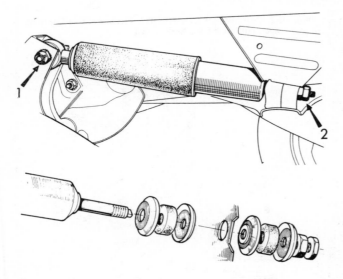

**FIG. 10.5. REAR SHOCK ABSORBER MOUNTINGS**

1   Front mounting
2   Rear mounting
*(Inset: Rear fitting order for the bushes)*

2   Jack up one side of the vehicle at a time and remove the wheel. Undo the two nuts on the rear or lower attachment point and remove, and then the nut which is visible at the top or front attachment pin. Remove this pin, which may have to be tapped through.

3   Using a scissor, trolley or screw jack, raise the suspension arm, free the shock absorber and remove it.

4   Replacement is an exact reversal of the removal sequence, but do not forget to smear the front attachment pin with grease before refitting and check that the bush cups are correctly fitted. Finally try to tighten the pin to 40 lb ft with the lower edge of the suspension arm parallel to the ground - the equivalent to a 'half-laden' position.

### 7   Tie bars and bushes - removal and replacement

1   Front suspension tie-bars are fitted between the lower wishbone and the chassis. They are adjustable for length and have a movable bush at the chassis fixing. It is possible to replace this tie-bar and each bush without dismantling any other part of the suspension. However, if these bars are removed or partially dismantled the vehicle must be checked by your local Renault (only) garage for correct castor and wheel alignment.

2   Disconnect the through bolt between the outer end of the tie-bar and the lower front wishbone. Remove the bolt between the yoke, at the other end of the tie-bar and the bush. The tie-bar can now be removed. It may help to loosen the adjusting nut next to the yoke to free the through bolts slightly.

3   Replacement is obviously a reversal of its removal. Because two types of tie-rod have been fitted, depending on the castor angle (R1180 - 13° R1181 9° to 11°) it is essential the correct part is refitted. Try to replace the yoke and arm as one new, matched unit. Always have the steering/suspension re-aligned if once removed.

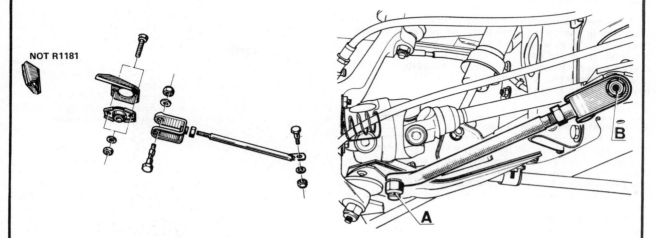

**NOT R1181**

**Fig. 10.6. Front suspension tie-bar components. See Figure 10.7**

**FIG. 10.7. TIE BAR IN POSITION — OFFSIDE**

A  *Bottom wishbone mounting*
B  *Chassis rail end with eye bush*

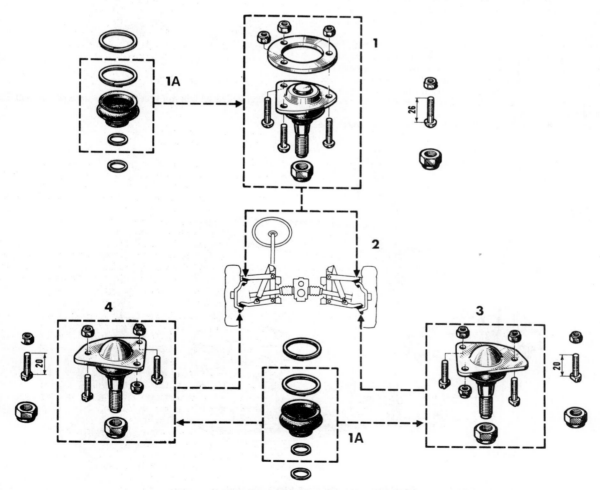

**FIG. 10.8. FRONT SUSPENSION BALL JOINT FITMENT**

1  *Top ball joints are interchangeable*
1a  *Ball joint gaiter kit*
2  *Cross section profile of ball joint fitment*

3  *Nearside lower handed ball joint*
4  *Offside lower handed ball joint*
*(Figures on setscrews indicate length in millimetres)*

4   To remove the bush on the chassis, remove first the tie-rod. Then remove the two nuts and bolts and pull away the bush. Replace the bush in an opposite procedure. It is sensible to use new securing nuts and bolts.

Special note: Never use the car without these tie-rods fitted and in perfect condition. It is potentially dangerous and certainly costly on tyre wear not so to do.

### 8   Ball joints - removal and replacement

1   The four suspension ball joints, two on each side of the front suspension, at the outer end of each wishbone, are sealed for life. Their only possible maintenance is to replace the rubber cover. They therefore need replacing rather than servicing.

2   For either top or bottom ball joint replacement jack up that side of the vehicle and place on a stand.

3   Fit the drive shaft inner Bendix-Weiss or Spider joint retaining tool, having driven out the roll pin where fitted. This is not essential but will safeguard the possibility of the drive shaft being stretched and the joint coming apart as the ball joint is removed from the suspension stub axle carrier.

4   Remove the relevant front wheel.

5   With a patent ball joint remover or two wedges, having undone the nylon nut, dislodge the balljoint from the suspension stub axle carrier. Tie up the suspension stub axle carrier so that it does not rest on the hydraulic brake pipe whether the top or bottom joint is being removed.

6   The original ball joints are rivetted onto the wishbone. These rivets will have to be drilled out. Clean up the rivet heads with a wire brush and file a good flat onto their heads. Use an electric drill if possible. Be patient and very careful. It is not a 'rush' job. Do not attempt to drill from below and try not to drill into the wishbone itself. If done carefully it is not necessary to remove the wishbones from the vehicle.

7   When purchasing new ball joints make sure that the

CORRECT fixing setscrews and nuts, to replace the rivets are also supplied. This is important. Also only the top ball joints are interchangeable, the bottoms can only be fixed in one way, on one side.

8   Replace the new ball joint into its correct seating and place the setscrews from below up through the ball joint and then wishbone. Tighten the nyloc nuts firmly.

9   Replace all the parts in an opposite procedure to their removal. Be sure that the ball joints are finally tight onto the stub axle carrier when the car is resting on all four wheels.

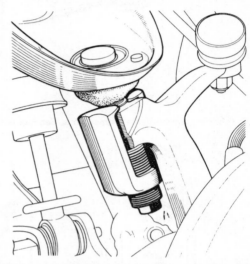

Fig. 10.9. Universal ball joint 'remover' in place on top ball joint

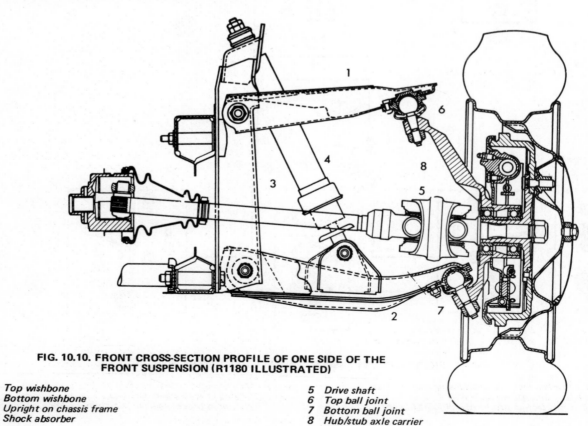

**FIG. 10.10. FRONT CROSS-SECTION PROFILE OF ONE SIDE OF THE
FRONT SUSPENSION (R1180 ILLUSTRATED)**

*1   Top wishbone*
*2   Bottom wishbone*
*3   Upright on chassis frame*
*4   Shock absorber*

*5   Drive shaft*
*6   Top ball joint*
*7   Bottom ball joint*
*8   Hub/stub axle carrier*

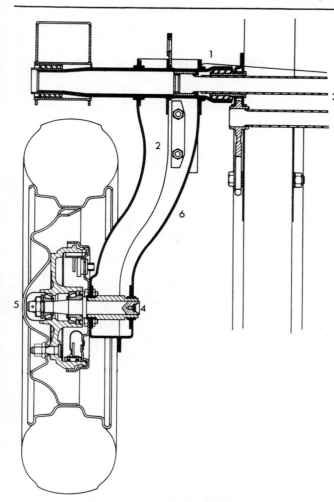

**FIG. 10.11. REAR SUSPENSION CROSS-SECTION (R1181 ILLUSTRATED)**

*1  Suspension arm pivot*
*2  Anti-roll bar mounting (R1181 only)*
*3  Torsion bar*
*4  Stub axle*
*5  Hub*
*6  Suspension arm*

10 Removal and replacement of just the ball joints' rubber bellows is only an effective repair for a new leaking joint. This will not help a worn one. It is undertaken, if new rubber bellows are in fact available for the vehicle, as in this Section (8) from paragraphs 1 to 5 inclusive. Then remove the old bellows and clean the ball joint. Make sure the plastic sleeves are intact.
11 Pack the new bellows with Castrol LM Grease, fit onto the ball joint and press up the outer plastic sleeve. The bellows retaining clip should then be fitted. It may be pinched with a piece of string to allow the clip to go on.
12 Replace the ball joint into the suspension upright, bolt up and replace as in paragraph 9.

### 9  Upper wishbone and bushes - removal and replacement

1  Proceed as in Section 8, paragraphs 1 to 5 inclusive, removing the top ball joint.
2  Undo the hinge pin and remove it. It may need a gentle tapping through with a soft metal drift.
3  Remove the wishbone and retain the special pin, nut and washers.

4  Upper wishbones are not interchangeable from side to side and again it is essential that the correct type is fitted.
5  The removal of the inner brushes is not a practical do-it-yourself task. Take the wishbone to the local Renault garage and have them remove the old and press in the new. Order the new bushes beforehand. It may under some circumstances be more economic to replace the whole wishbone if the bushes and the ball joint are worn - new wishbones are supplied with both already fitted.
6  Replacement of the upper wishbone is a straight reversal of the removal procedure.
7  Have the steering/suspension alignment checked upon the replacement of new inner wishbone bushes.

### 10  Lower suspension arm and bushes - removal and replacement

The suspension arm or lower wishbone is attached directly by itself to the front torsion bar. Although a simple suspension system, such is the need for special tools to work on the system it is not possible for the home mechanic to work on this part. It is not possible to make suitable tools at home and their purchase price from the Renault garage does not make a once-only use viable. It is better under nearly all circumstances to gain a quotation from the Renault garage for any work needed in this area. It does not normally take a great deal of time to remove the suspension with the correct tools. It is dangerous to dismantle any part of the suspension connected to the torsion bars without the correct equipment. Read on to the next Section and Sections 12 and 13 which cover the removal of the torsion bars on the two types of vehicle, and then Section 9 for bush replacement.

### 11  Rear suspension arm and bushes - removal and replacement

1  Rear suspension arm removal is a very simple operation once the rear torsion bar has been removed. However as has been explained in Sections 13 and 14, 'Rear Torsion Bar Removal', this is not a task able to be tackled by the do-it-yourself mechanic although it is briefly explained. For this reason little can be said here except to say once the relevant torsion bar is removed and the flexible brake pipe disconnected the rear suspension arm can be removed by undoing and withdrawing the three locating bolts. (Do not forget the rear anti-roll bar on the R1181). The suspension arm will then pull away from the chassis. Replacement is obviously a direct reversal procedure.
2  Once the arm is removed from the vehicle the bushes can be removed and replaced but only with the help of a press. It is not safe to use any other method.
3  Under most prevailing circumstances it is much safer and more economic to allow an official Renault garage do this work for you. It may also be cheaper if a replacement arm, complete with bushes is fitted. Fortunately these bushes often outlast the rest of the vehicle. If, however, a non-franchise garage tackles this repair make sure it fits the correct suspension arm and bushes as several non-interchangeable types have been used.

### 12  Front torsion bar - removal and replacement

1  Because of what has already been said about the need for special tools to undertake the proper dismantling of the front suspension in Section 10 no special details will be given in this Section except to reiterate the necessity to go to the local Renault garage with any problem relating directly to the torsion bars. However there is included a basic procedure of dismantling and reassembly following.
2  Removal of a front torsion bar would only normally be necessary if it had broken or the suspension had been bent or in extreme cases of excess weakness, sagging. It is essential to use a pit or hydraulic lift to remove torsion bars on these vehicles.
3  Jack up the front of the car leaving both sides of the front suspension hanging free. Remove the relevant road wheel.
4  Remove the anchor housing protective cover (see Fig. 10.12) and loosen setscrews from inside the car.

## FIG. 10.12. FRONT SUSPENSION TORSION BARS

1  Torsion bar       4  Adjuster lever
2  Rubber sleeve     5  Adjuster cam
3  End cap           6  End cap gasket

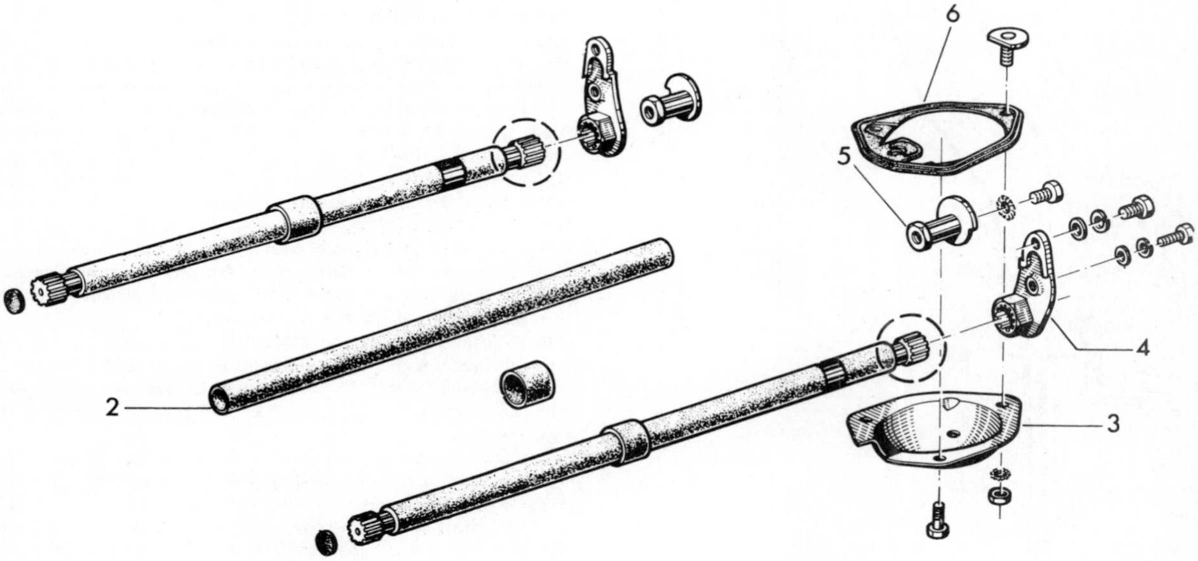

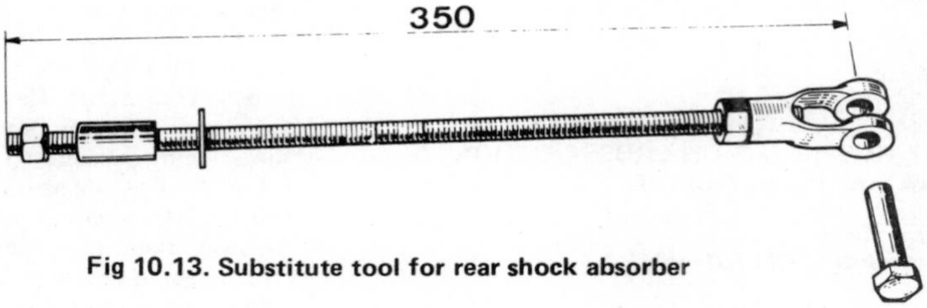

**Fig 10.13. Substitute tool for rear shock absorber**

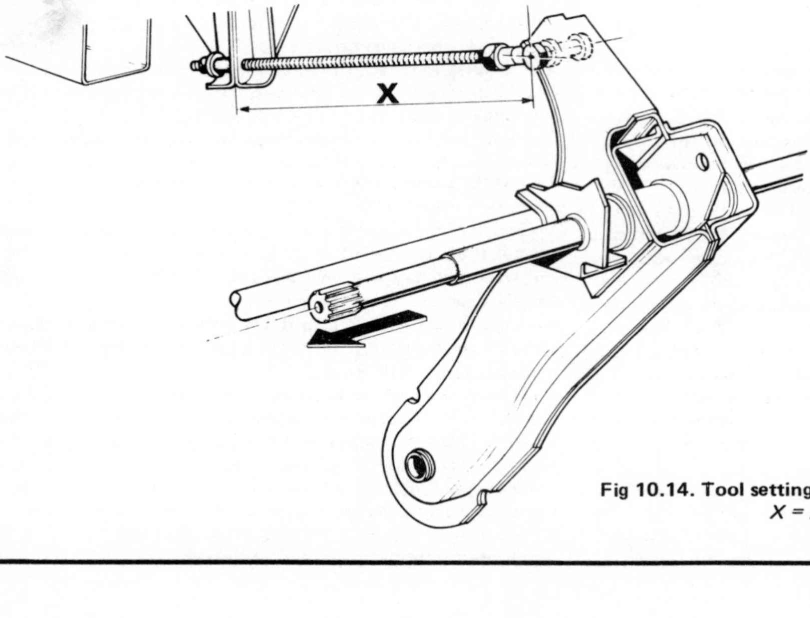

350

X

**Fig 10.14. Tool setting for installation of rear torsion bar**
X = 280 mm (11 in)

## FIG. 10.15. REAR SUSPENSION TORSION BARS

1  Torsion bar          3  Adjuster lever
2  Rubber sleeve        4  Adjuster cam

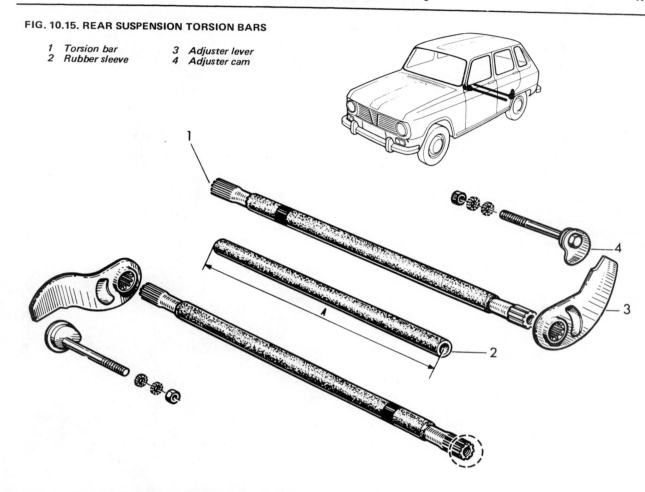

5   Zero the cam by turning it towards the outside of the vehicle using an appropriate box spanner.

6   Screw an 8 mm bolt into the cam end. Using a special spanner and a long tubular lever (about 3 feet in length) counterbalance the effect of the torsion bar.

7   A second person should now unscrew and remove the bolts.

8   The person inside the vehicle should now move the cam, with the 8 mm bolt fitted earlier towards the front to free it from the anchor lever.

9   With the torsion bar now free remove the lower suspension pivot pin nut and with a bronze drift drive out the torsion bar.

10  Push the anchorage lever towards the front of the vehicle and slide the torsion bar in the direction of the rear of the vehicle in order to disconnect it from the lower suspension arm and anti-roll bar. (The lower suspension arm is now obviously removed, having fitted drive shaft coupling retainers and removed the lower outer ball joint).

11  Lower the front end of the torsion bar and pull it forwards and out of the car. Remove the anchor lever.

12  Replacement of the torsion bar is a direct reversal of the removal sequence but make sure all the parts are correctly located before attempting the next stage.

13  Smear each end of the torsion bar with molybdenum disulphide grease and position the anchor lever correctly.

14  Fit the anchor lever in such a way that from the edge of the hole on the anchor lever to the edge of the anchor lever bracket measures 40 mm.

15  Use a torque wrench to replace the tubular bar to obtain a torque reading of 204 lb ft.

16  Road test the vehicle and then adjust the suspension height as detailed in Section 14.

Special Note: The replacement of the lower suspension arm is

easily done with the torsion bar removed.

## 13 Rear torsion bar - removal and replacement

1   Place the rear of the vehicle on stands over a pit or on a hydraulic ramp with both road wheels clear. Remove the relevant wheel. (On the right hand side it is necessary to remove the brake limiter valve protective cover).

2   Set the adjusting cam to zero.

3   Remove the shock absorber as described in Section 6.

4   Replace the shock absorber with a special tool eyebolt and nuts and tighten the nut until the anchor lever lifts off the cam..

5   The torsion bar can now be removed from the vehicle.

6   To replace the torsion bar first tighten the special tool which has replaced the shock absorber until the length of X is 280 mm (11 in). When this has been done slide the torsion bar through the bearing, having smeared the splines with molybdenum disulphide grease.

7   Position the anchor lever so that its cam is at zero adjustment.

8   When the lever is in this position slide the torsion bar into it. If this position is correctly aligned then the torsion bar should slide freely into the suspension arm and lever splines. It may however be necessary to try the torsion bar several times to achieve this. Leave 10 mm of the spline bare in order to be able to check the torque setting at the point where the anchor lever lifts off the cam.

10  Use the special tool to grip the torsion bar and with a torque wrench fitted check that the anchor lever lifts off the cam at 55 lb ft. For testing left hand torsion bars fit a clamp to stop the bar from moving.

### 14 Vehicle ride height adjustment

1   Ride height adjustment is necessary whenever any part of the suspension has been removed and replaced and possibly when heavy loads are to be carried for a large mileage. Read Sections 12 or 13.
2   Ride height is altered by turning the adjusting cam in a clockwise direction. Measurement is taken at the front and rear hubs to a level ground surface.
3   See Fig. 10.16 for the direction of settings. The difference between left and right hand sides should not exceed 10 mm for setting operations. Difference between H1 and H2 56 mm (2 7/32 in). Difference between H4 and H5 123 mm (4 7/8 in).

### 15 Torsion bar rubber sleeve - removal and replacement

All torsion bars are fitted with a rubber sleeve which may perish with the passing of time. Also sometimes rubber bushes are fitted over these sleeves to hold off the torsion bar from the underside of the chassis and absorb vibration. It is not usually necessary to replace these sleeves unless a torsion bar breaks or the vibration is unbearable. Once the torsion bar is removed from the car cut off the old sleeve and grease the torsion bar with a grease suitable for rubber components. Slide on the new rubber.

### 16 Steering rack - removal and replacement

1   Different steering racks are fitted to the R 1180 and R 1181 as are different columns. However, there is little practical difference when it comes to removal and replacement.
2   To remove just the steering rack, unhook the handbrake return spring and then remove the flexible coupling bolts connecting the steering column to the rack.
3   Uncouple the steering arms from the rack by undoing the

16.3 Undoing these bolts is not easy if dirty

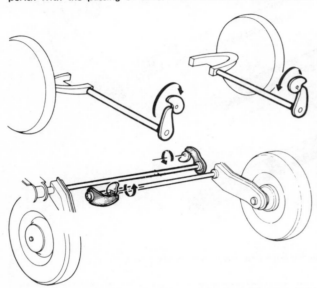

Fig. 10.16. Direction of movement for height adjustment

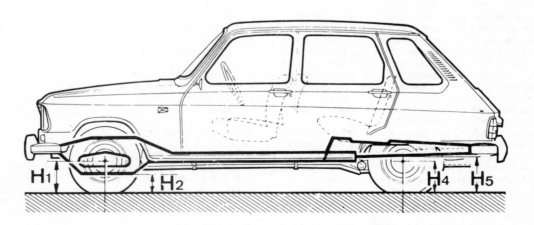

Fig 10.17. Vehicle ride height checking diagram (empty but with full fuel tank)
*H1 and H4 = Hub centres*
*H2 and H5 = Under side of chassis side members*

16.4 A steering rack shim. Do not omit

two through bolts.

4   Unscrew and remove the bolts which hold the radiator to the steering rack and the bolts which hold the rack to the bodyframe. The steering rack will now lift up and around and out. Retain and record any shims which may be fitted. See the next Section.

5   It is not possible under any circumstances to repair a steering rack. It must always be replaced. No maintenance is necessary.

6   Replacement is again a straight reversal of the removal sequence. Replace the shims, if fitted, in the correct order to avoid resetting. Should resetting be necessary you must have this done by your local Renault (only) garage. It is wise to replace the flexible coupling and the front wheel track must always be re-adjusted if the rack is ever removed or replaced. Check the tightness of the rack-to-chassis bolts, to 25 lb ft.

## 17 Steering arms - removal and replacement

1   When replacing a steering rack it is advisable to look at the condition of the bushes at the ends of the adjustable arms. If these are worn have the short removable arm renewed. At the same time check the condition of the steering arm and ball joint. No maintenance is available for this joint except the replacement of the rubber dust cover. If it is worn renew the whole steering arm. Make sure that the replacement part is for the correct side and is of the right specification, as these arms have been modified. They are not interchangeable from side to side.

2   To remove the steering arm remove the through bolt connecting it to the rack and then with a ball joint remover or two wedges release the ball joint from the stub axle carrier.

3   Replacement is a reversal sequence. Have the front wheel track checked once reassembled.

## 18 Steering wheel and column - removal and replacement

1   Essentially the two methods used for right hand drive versions of the R1180 are the same; a one piece steering shaft and a two piece. Most of the removal and replacement sequence is the same.

2   To remove the steering wheel unclip the centre boss covering by removing the two set screws from underneath the spokes of the wheel.

3   Undo the centre shaft nut. Sometimes a few careful taps with a punch will start it.

4   Now try to jar the steering wheel off. Renault recommend a special puller but it should be possible to tap it off. Wrap the spokes with rag and use a wooden mallet, not a steel hammer. Note the position of the splines for correct refitment. Use a dot punch if necessary.

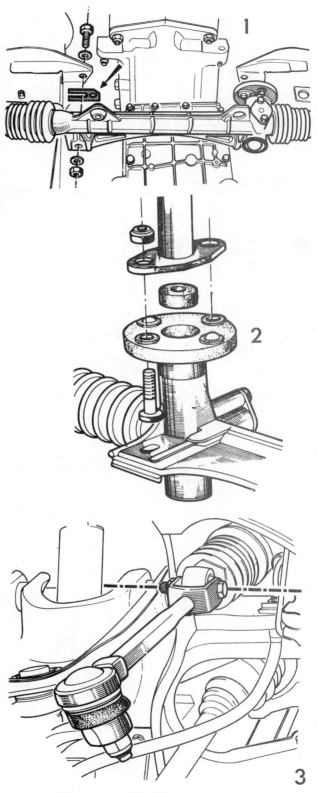

**FIG. 10.18. STEERING RACK FITTINGS**

1   *Rack fixing on chassis rails. Note the shims*
2   *Steering column flexible coupling*
3   *Steering arm bush fitting*

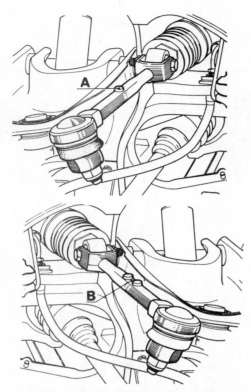

**FIG. 10.19. STEERING ARM RECOGNITION**

A   *One boss in the centre    -   RIGHT*
B   *Two bosses in the centre   -   LEFT*

5   Disconnect the battery, remove the bottom cover of the facia panel. Disconnect the junction blocks and remove the lighting/flasher/horn switch.

6   Remove the brake and clutch pedals. See Chapter 8.

7   Remove the two steering column bracket screws but be careful to retain the shims. Then remove the seven nuts which fix the bottom column support plate.

8   Undo the brake master cylinder fixing nuts, and the clutch outer cable location at the bulkhead under the bonnet.

9   It is now possible to pull the column off the centre steering shaft. Obviously all that is now necessary to remove the shaft itself is to undo the lower connection on the steering rack. The split column can be separated once out of the car. When removing the shaft(s) be careful of all the wiring and pipes when extracting it. It is not necessary to remove the column to extract the shaft on the split type but it is on the one piece.

10   Reassembly is a reverse sequence. Make sure all is aligned and that the column grommet is intact.

11   There is only one replaceable bush in the one piece column set-up and that is the top one held in by a circlip. Remove the circlip with circlip pliers and drive out the old bush. Tap in a new bush having lubricated the tube and refit the circlip.

12   On the two piece column the top bush is renewed in the same way whilst the bottom bush simply omits the circlip. The universal joint connecting the two shafts together is repairable; once dismantled the position of the bushes is obvious. Grease the new bushes.

13   When re-connecting the two halves together it is important that the universal joint is tightened, each half of the joint, in the horizontal plane, check clutch free play and brake pedal push rod clearance after refitting the column.

## 19 Steering lock

1   The steering lock is an integral part of the ignition switch, and one must be removed with the other. It is possible to separate them and to purchase parts separately.

2   To remove disconnect the battery.

3   Remove the protective panel below the facia panel.

4   Remove the steering wheel.

5   Disconnect the junction block to the ignition switch. Insert the ignition key.

6   Undo the visible securing screws and then press down on the retaining ring at the top side of the barrel and push from below and behind the switch. The switch/lock should come away.

7   To separate the switch from the lock remove the ignition key and undo the two securing screws half way down the barrel. Slide out the switch to the bottom.

8   Renewal and replacement are in the reverse sequence.

## 20 Steering and suspension alignment

Such is the complexity of steering and suspension adjustment and its relative importance to the total correct functioning of the vehicle it is advised that any adjustment of this type be made by the local Renault garage which will be equipped with the necessary optical and measuring jigs. If any major suspension or steering part is removed and/or replaced it is absolutely necessary to have the vehicle checked. The following measurements may be necessary depending on what has been removed. See the Specifications for their tolerances. To some extent you will be in the hands of the Renault garage as to what they will actually measure, but each component mentioned in the Specifications when removed will place the vehicle in need of one or more measurement checking. Tell the garage to make the relevant check and to report on any adjustment found to be necessary.

a)   The camber angle (which cannot in fact be altered).

b)   The castor angle.

c)   The steering box setting.

d)   The front axle toe-out.

e)   The position of the wheels in relation to the steering centre point.

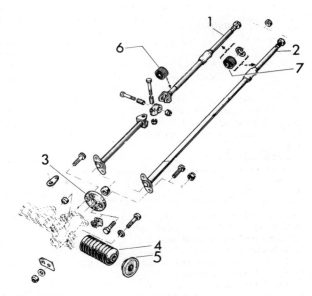

**FIG. 10.20. STEERING COLUMNS**

| | | | |
|---|---|---|---|
| 1 | Split column | 4 | Rack gaiter |
| 2 | One piece column | 5 | Gaiter clip plate |
| 3 | Flexible coupling | 6 | Column bush |
| | | 7 | Top column bush |

## 21 Fault diagnosis

Before diagnosing faults from the following chart, check that any irregularities are not caused by:—

1 Binding brakes
2 Incorrect 'mix' of tyres
3 Incorrect tyre pressures
4 Misalignment of the body frame or rear suspension

| Symptom | Reason/s | Remedy |
|---|---|---|
| Steering wheel can be moved considerably before any sign of movement of the wheels is apparent | Wear in the steering linkage, gear and column coupling | Check movement in all joints and steering gear and renew as required. |
| Vehicle difficult to steer in a consistent straight line - wandering | As above<br>Wheel alignment incorrect (indicated by excessive or uneven tyre wear) | As above<br>Check wheel alignment. |
| | Front wheel hub bearings loose or worn | Renew as necessary. |
| | Worn ball joints, or suspension arms | Renew as necessary. |
| Steering stiff and heavy | Incorrect wheel alignment (indicated by excessive or uneven tyre wear) | Check wheel alignment. |
| | Excessive wear or seizure in one or more of the joints in the steering linkage or suspension arm ball joints | Renew as necessary. |
| | Excessive wear in the steering unit | Renew. |
| Wheel wobble and vibration | Road wheels out of balance | Balance wheels. |
| | Road wheels buckled | Check for damage. |
| | Wheel alignment incorrect | Check wheel alignment. |
| | Wear in the steering linkage, suspension arm ball joints or suspension arm inner bushes | Check and renew as necessary. |
| Excessive pitching and rolling on corners and during braking | Defective shock absorbers and/or broken torsion bar, anti-roll bar broken away | Check and renew as necessary. |

# Chapter 11 Bodywork and chassis

## Contents

## 1 General description

The Renault 6 has a separate body and chassis. The body is bolted to the chassis, a box type with welded-in floor pan, at specific securing points (see Fig. 11.3). The engine, transmission and suspension are bolted to the chassis. The front wings, bonnet, front panel, doors and tailgate are all affixed to the basic body shell, which is a strong welded structure, and are all separately removable being either bolted or hinged to it. The body shell and the chassis are therefore not structurally reliant on each other and the wings and most other body panels are in no way stressed. Such is the quality of the total composite structure both as a vehicle unit, and separately, that the life of the chassis and body is as long as, if not longer than, a more modern combined monocoque chassis/body.

There are two body shells, the R1180 and R1181, basically the same, but different in 'cosmetic' detail bolted to one chassis pan design but again not identical. The bodyshells are available with a factory built roll-top sunroof as an option, but are always four door plus a rear tailgate. The interior floor is flat. All models are factory undersealed.

## 2 Maintenance - body exterior

1 The general condition of a car's bodywork is the one thing that significantly affects its value. Maintenance is easy but needs to be regular and particular. Neglect - particularly after minor damage - can quickly lead to further deterioration and costly repair bills. It is important also to keep watch on those parts of the bodywork not immediately visible, for example the underside, inside all the wheel arches and the lower part of the engine compartment.

2 The basic maintenance routine for the bodywork is washing - preferably with a lot of water from a hose. This will remove all the loose solids which may have stuck to the car. It is important to flush these off in such a way as to prevent grit from scratching the finish. The wheel arches and underbody need washing in the same way, to remove any accumulated mud which will retain moisture and tend to encourage rust. The Renault 6 collects mud in the inner side of the rear bumper bar and at the inner edge of the tailgate. This is thrown up by the rear wheels. Wash this out too. Take the spare wheel out from below the rear floor and wash it in the same way. It collects mud.

Paradoxically enough, the best time to clean the underbody and wheel arches is in wet weather when the mud is thoroughly wet and soft. In very wet weather the underbody is usually cleaned of large accumulations automatically and this is a good time for inspection.

If you have the energy jack up the car, remove all the road wheels and clean their inner sides. The wheel offset keeps mud captive for a long time and could unbalance the wheel! Do NOT hose excessive quantities of water at the windows, heater vents etc.

3 Periodically have the whole of the underside steam cleaned, engine compartment as well so that a thorough inspection can be carried out to see what minor repairs and renovations are necessary. Steam cleaning is available at some garages and is necessary for removal of the accumulation of oily grime which sometimes collects thickly in areas near the engine and gearbox. If steam facilities are not available there are one or two grease solvents available which can be brush applied. The dirt can then be simply hosed off. Any signs of rust on the underside panels and chassis members must be attended to immediately. Thorough wire brushing followed by treatment with an anti-rust compound, primer and underbody sealer will prevent continued deterioration. If not dealt with the car could eventually become structurally unsound and therefore unsafe.

4 After washing the paintwork wipe it off with a chamois leather to give a clear unspotted finish. A coat of clear wax polish will give added protection against chemical pollutants in the air and will survive several subsequent washings. If the paintwork sheen has dulled or oxidised use a cleaner/polisher combination to restore the brilliance of the shine. This requires a little effort but is usually because regular washing has been neglected! Always check that door and drain holes and pipes are completely clear so that water can drain out. Brightwork should be treated the same way as paintwork. Windscreens and windows can be kept clear of the smeary film which often appears if a little ammonia is added to the water. If glasswork is scratched a good rub with a proprietary metal polish will often clean it. Never use any form of wax or other paint/chromium polish on glass.

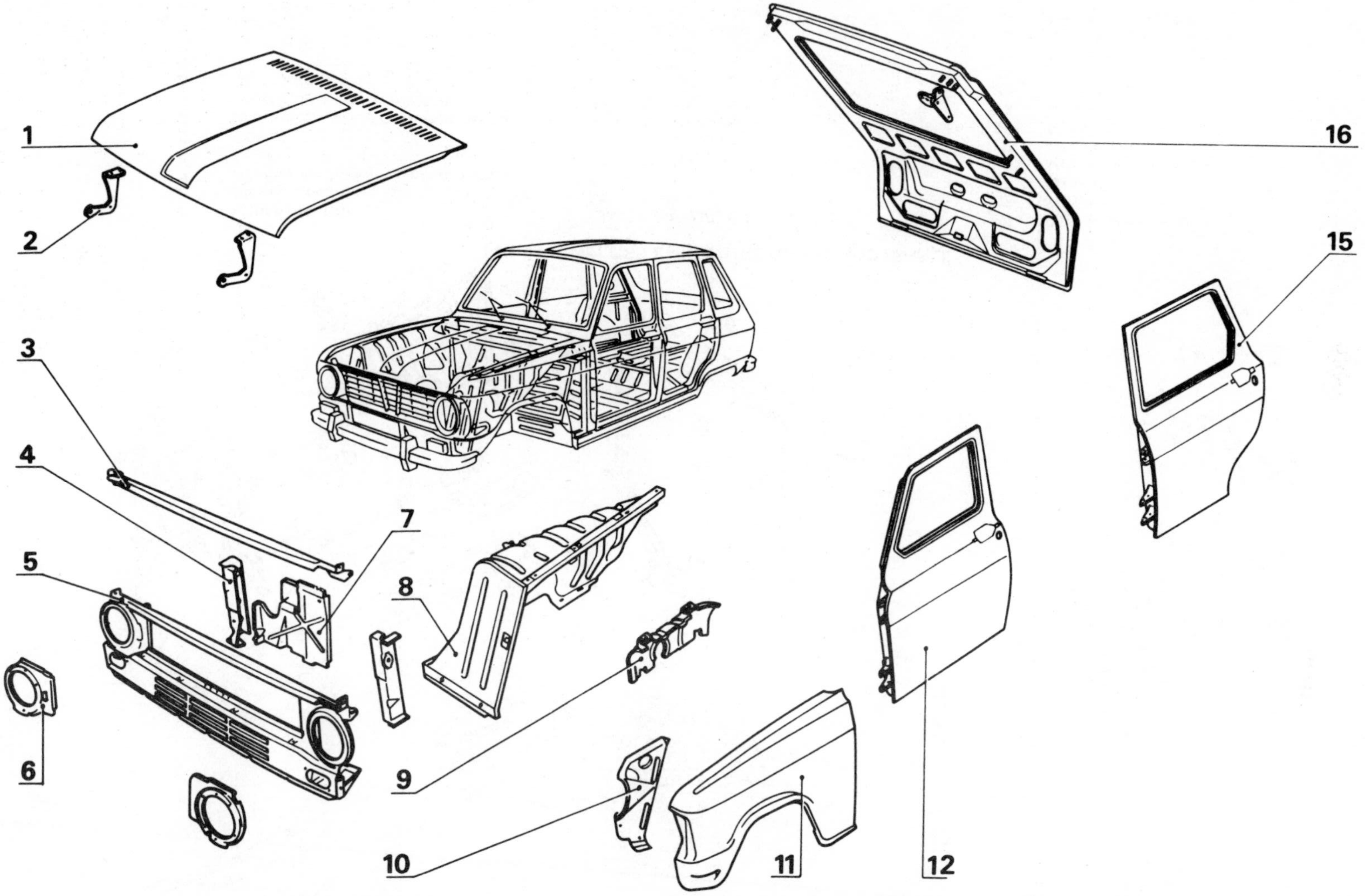

**FIG. 11.1. REMOVABLE BODY PANELS AND DOORS**

| 1 | Bonnet | 6 | Protective flange | 11 | Front wing |
| 2 | Swan's neck hinge | 7 | Screen panel | 12 | Front door |
| 3 | Front end panel top cross member | 8 | Cowl side | 15 | Rear door |
| 4 | Swan's neck hinge bracket | 9 | Heat shield | 16 | Tailgate |
| 5 | Front end panel | 10 | Front wing flange | | |

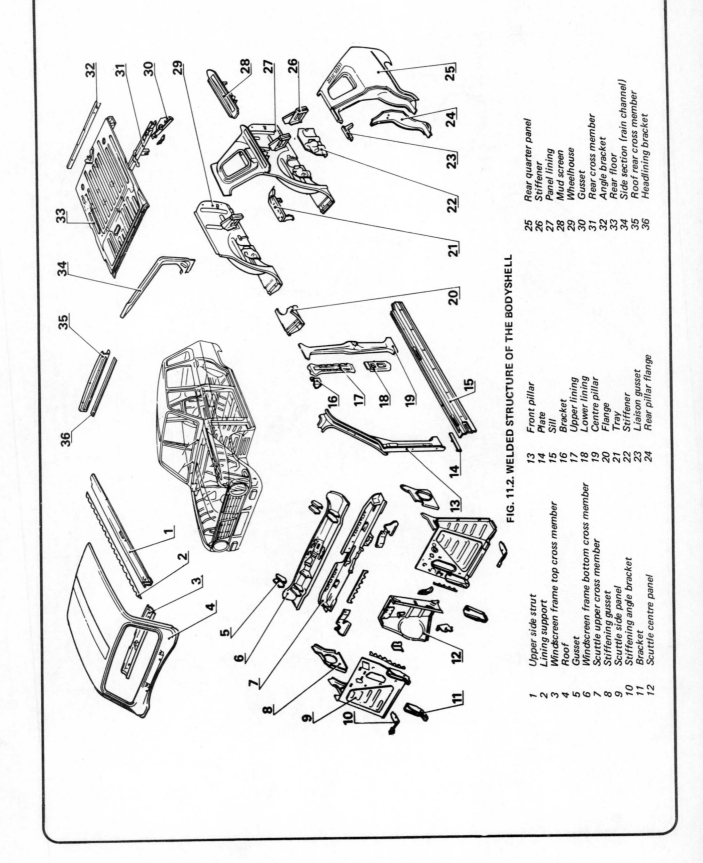

**FIG. 11.2. WELDED STRUCTURE OF THE BODYSHELL**

1 Upper side strut
2 Lining support
3 Windscreen frame top cross member
4 Roof
5 Gusset
6 Windscreen frame bottom cross member
7 Scuttle upper cross member
8 Stiffening gusset
9 Scuttle side panel
10 Stiffening angle bracket
11 Bracket
12 Scuttle centre panel

13 Front pillar
14 Plate
15 Sill
16 Bracket
17 Upper lining
18 Lower lining
19 Centre pillar
20 Flange
21 Tray
22 Stiffener
23 Liaison gusset
24 Rear pillar flange

25 Rear quarter panel
26 Stiffener
27 Panel lining
28 Mud screen
29 Wheelhouse
30 Gusset
31 Rear cross member
32 Angle bracket
33 Rear floor
34 Side section (rain channel)
35 Roof rear cross member
36 Headlining bracket

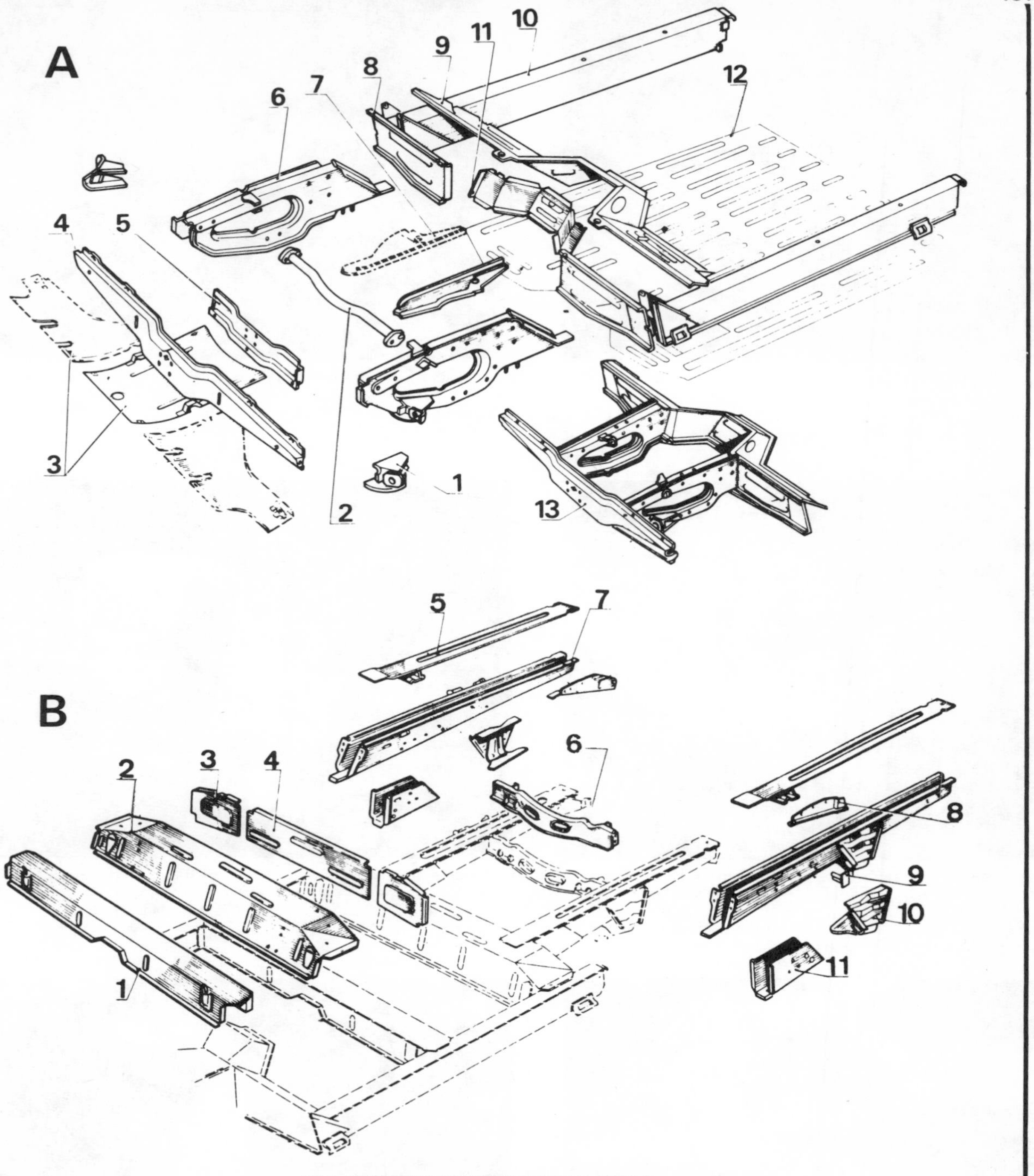

**FIG. 11.3. CHASSIS COMPONENT PARTS**

A    Front half
1   Tie-rod bracket
2   Tubular cross member
3   Engine undertrays
4   Front cross member
5   Front cross member lining
6   Front side member
7   Box gusset
8   Front side face
9   Toe board
10   Centre side member
11   Front centre panel
12   Floor panel
13   Front unit (special repair)

B    Rear half
1   Centre cross member
2   Rear cross member
3   Rear side face
4   Rear centre face
5   Side member closure panel
6   Fuel tank cross member
7   Rear side member
8   Shock absorber mounting stiffener
9   Torsion bar cam hinge plate
10   Shock absorber bracket
11   Side member stiffener

This sequence of photographs deals with the repair of the dent and scratch (above rear lamp) shown in this photo. The procedure will be similar for the repair of a hole. It should be noted that the procedures given here are simplified - more explicit instructions will be found in the text

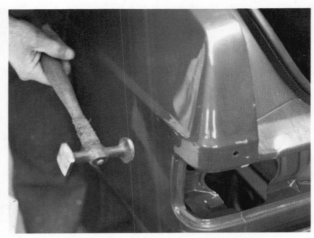

In the case of a dent the first job - after removing surrounding trim - is to hammer out the dent where access is possible. This will minimise filling. Here, the large dent having been hammered out, the damaged area is being made slightly concave

Now all paint must be removed from the damaged area, by rubbing with coarse abrasive paper. Alternatively, a wire brush or abrasive pad can be used in a power drill. Where the repair area meets good paintwork, the edge pf the paintwork should be 'feathered', using a finer grade of abrasive paper

In the case of a hole caused by rusting, all damaged sheet-metal should be cut away before proceeding to this stage. Here, the damaged area is being treated with rust remover and inhibitor before being filled

Mix the body filler according to its manufacturer's instructions. In the case of corrosion damage, it will be necessary to block off any large holes before filling - this can be done with zinc gauze or aluminium tape. Make sure the area is absolutely clean before ...

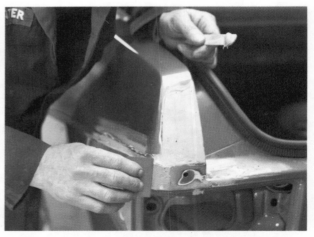

... applying the filler. Filler should be applied with a flexible applicator, as shown, for best results: the wooden spatula being used for confined areas. Apply thin layers of filler at 20-minute intervals, until the surface of the filler is slightly proud of the surrounding bodywork

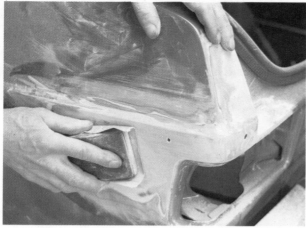

Initial shaping can be done with a Surform plane or Dreadnought file. Then, using progressively finer grades of wet-and-dry paper, wrapped around a sanding block, and copious amounts of clean water, rub-down the filler until really smooth and flat. Again, feather the edges of adjoining paintwork

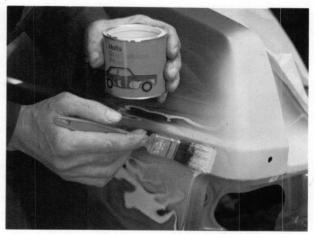

The whole repair area can now be sprayed or brush-painted with primer. If spraying, ensure adjoining areas are protected from over-spray. Note that at least one-inch of the surrounding sound paintwork should be coated with primer. Primer has a 'thick' consistency, so will fill small imperfections

Again, using plenty of water, rub down the primer with a fine grade of wet-and-dry paper (400 grade is probably best) until it is really smooth and well blended into the surrounding paintwork. Any remaining imperfections can now be filled by carefully applied knifing stopper paste

When the stopper has hardened, rub-down the repair area again before applying the final coat of primer. Before rubbing-down this last coat of primer, ensure the repair area is blemish-free - use more stopper if necessary. To ensure that the surface of the primer is really smooth use some finishing compound

The top coat can now be applied. When working out of doors, pick a dry, warm and wind-free day. Ensure surrounding areas are protected from over-spray. Agitate the aerosol thoroughly, then spray the centre of the repair area, working outwards with a circular motion. Apply the paint as several thin coats.

After a period of about two-weeks, which the paint needs to harden fully, the surface of the repaired area can be 'cut' with a mild cutting compound prior to wax polishing. When carrying out bodywork repairs, remember that the quality of the finished job is proportional to the time and effort expended

## 3  Maintenance - interior

The flooring cover should be brushed or vacuum cleaned regularly to keep it free of grit. (This is a 'rubber' cover) If badly stained, remove it from the car for scrubbing or sponging and make quite sure that it is dry before replacement. Seat and interior trim panels can be kept clean with a wipe over with a damp cloth. If they do become stained (which can be more apparent on light coloured upholstery) use a little liquid detergent and a soft nailbrush to scour the grime out of the grain of the material. Do not forget to keep the headlining clean in the same way as the upholstery. When using liquid cleaners inside the car do not over-wet the surface being cleaned. Excessive damp could get into the upholstery seams and padded interior, causing stains, offensive odours or even rot. If the inside of the car gets wet accidentally it is worthwhile taking some trouble to dry it out properly. Do NOT leave oil or electric heaters inside the car for this purpose. If, when removing mats for cleaning, there are signs of damp underneath, all the interior of the car floor should be uncovered and the point of water entry found. It may only be a missing grommet, but it could be a rusted through floor panel and this demands immediate attention as described in the previous Section. More often than not both sides of the panel will require treatment. On cars fitted with the factory sunroof avoid touching the interior canvas. Keep it clean and rectify all tears immediately. Consult your local Renault agent as to the most suitable type of repair depending on the material used. Keep the stays and fixings very lightly but frequently oiled, particularly at the front of the roof, and periodically release and roll back the roof so that it does not become too stiff and weak.

## 4  Minor body damage — repair

*The photo sequence on pages 182 and 183 illustrates the operations detailed in the following sub-sections.*

### Repair of minor scratches in the car's bodywork

If the scratch is very superficial, and does not penetrate to the metal of the bodywork, repair is very simple. Lightly rub the area of the scratch with a paintwork renovator, or a very fine cutting paste, to remove loose paint from the scratch and to clear the surrounding bodywork of wax polish. Rinse the area with clean water.

Apply touch-up paint to the scratch using a thin paint brush; continue to apply thin layers of paint until the surface of the paint in the scratch is level with the surrounding paintwork. Allow the new paint at least two weeks to harden; then blend it into the surrounding paintwork by rubbing the paintwork in the scratch area, with a paintwork renovator or a very fine cutting paste. Finally, apply wax polish.

An alternative to painting over the scratch is to use a paint patch. Use the same preparation for the affected area, then simply pick a patch of a suitable size to cover the scratch completely. Hold the patch against the scratch and burnish its backing paper; the patch will adhere to the paintwork, freeing itself from the backing paper at the same time. Polish the affected area to blend the patch into the surrounding paintwork.

Where the scratch has penetrated right through to the metal of the bodywork, causing the metal to rust, a different repair technique is required. Remove any loose rust from the bottom of the scratch with a penknife, then apply rust inhibiting paint to prevent the formation of rust in the future. Using a rubber or nylon applicator fill the scratch with bodystopper paste. If required, this paste can be mixed with cellulose thinners to provide a very thin paste which is ideal for filling narrow scratches. Before the stopper-paste in the scratch hardens, wrap a piece of smooth cotton rag around the top of a finger. Dip the finger in cellulose thinners and then quickly sweep it across the surface of the stopper-paste in the scratch; this will ensure that

the surface of the stopper-paste is slightly hollowed. The scratch can now be painted over as described earlier in this Section.

### Repair of dents in the car's bodywork

When deep denting of the car's bodywork has taken place, the first task is to pull the dent out, until the affected bodywork almost attains its original shape. There is little point in trying to restore the original shape completely, as the metal in the damaged area will have stretched on impact and cannot be reshaped fully to its original contour. It is better to bring the level of the dent up to a point which is about 1/8 in (3 mm) below the level of the surrounding bodywork. In cases where the dent is very shallow anyway, it is not worth trying to pull it out at all. If the underside of the dent is accessible, it can be hammered out gently from behind, using a mallet with a wooden or plastic head. Whilst doing this, hold a suitable block of wood firmly against the outside of the dent. This block will absorb the impact from the hammer blows and thus prevent a large area of the bodywork from being 'belled-out'.

Should the dent be in a section of the bodywork which has double skin or some other factor making it inaccessible from behind, a different technique is called for. Drill several small holes through the metal inside the dent area - particularly in the deeper sections. Then screw long self-tapping screws into the holes just sufficiently for them to gain a good purchase in the metal. Now the dent can be pulled out by pulling on the protruding heads of the screws with a pair of pliers.

The next stage of the repair is the removal of the paint from the damaged area, and from an inch or so of the surrounding 'sound' bodywork. This is accomplished most easily by using a wire brush or abrasive pad on a power drill, although it can be done just as effectively by hand using sheets of abrasive paper. To complete the preparation for filling, score the surface of the bare metal with a screwdriver or the tang of a file, or alternatively, drill small holes in the affected area. This will provide a really good 'key' for the filler paste.

To complete the repair see the Section on filling and respraying.

### Repair of rust holes or gashes in the car's bodywork

Remove all paint from the affected area and from an inch or so of the surrounding 'sound' bodywork, using an abrasive pad or a wire brush on a power drill. If these are not available a few sheets of abrasive paper will do the job just as effectively. With the paint removed you will be able to gauge the severity of the corrosion and therefore decide whether to renew the whole panel (if this is possible) or to repair the affected area. New body panels are not as expensive as most people think and it is often quicker and more satisfactory to fit a new panel than to attempt to repair large areas of corrosion.

Remove all fittings from the affected area except those which will act as a guide to the original shape of the damaged bodywork (eg headlamp shells etc). Then, using tin snips or a hacksaw blade, remove all loose metal and any other metal badly affected by corrosion. Hammer the edges of the hole inwards in order to create a slight depression for the filler paste.

Wire brush the affected area to remove powdery rust from the surface of the remaining metal. Paint the affected area with rust inhibiting paint; if the back of the rusted area is accessible treat this also.

Before filling can take place it will be necessary to block the hole in some way. This can be achieved by the use of one of the following materials: Zinc gauze, Aluminum tape or Polyurethane foam.

Zinc gauze is probably the best material to use for a large hole. Cut a piece to the approximate size and shape of the hole to be filled, then position it in the hole so that its edges are below the level of the surrounding bodywork. It can be retained in position by several blobs of filler paste around its periphery.

Aluminum tape should be used for small or very narrow holes. Pull a piece off the roll and trim it to the approximate size and shape required, then pull off the backing paper (if used) and stick the tape over the hole; it can be overlapped if the thickness of one piece is insufficient. Burnish down the edges of the tape with the handle of a screwdriver or similar, to ensure that the tape is securely attached to the metal underneath.

Polyurethane foam is best used where the hole is situated in a section of bodywork of complex shape, backed by a small box section (eg where the sill panel meets the rear wheel arch - most cars). The usual mixing procedure for this foam is as follows: Put equal amounts of fliud from each of the two cans provided in the kit into one container. Stir until the mixture begins to thicken, then quickly pour this mixture into the hole, and hold a piece of cardboard over the larger apertures. Almost immediately the polyurethane will begin to expand, gushing out of any small holes left unblocked. When the foam hardens it can be cut back to just below the level of the surrounding bodywork with a hacksaw blade.

### Bodywork repairs — filling and re-spraying

Before using this Section, see the Sections on dent, deep scratch, rust hole and gash repairs.

Many types of bodyfiller are available, but generally speaking those proprietary kits which contain a tin of filler paste and a tube of resin hardener are best for this type of repair. A wide, flexible plastic or nylon applicator will be found invaluable for imparting a smooth and well contoured finish to the surface of the filler.

Mix up a little filler on a clean piece of card or board — use the hardener sparingly (follow the maker's instructions on the pack) otherwise the filler will set very rapidly.

Using the applicator, apply the filler paste to the prepared area; draw the applicator across the surface of the filler to achieve the correct contour and to level the filler surface. As soon as a contour that approximates the correct one is achieved, stop working the paste — if you carry on too long the paste will become sticky and begin to 'pick-up' on the applicator. Continue to add thin layers of filler paste at twenty-minute intervals until the level of the filler is just 'proud' of the surrounding bodywork.

Once the filler has hardened, excess can be removed using a metal plane or file. From then on, progressively finer grades of abrasive paper should be used, starting with a 40 grade production paper and finishing with 400 grade 'wet-or-dry' paper. Always wrap the abrasive paper around a flat rubber, cork or wooden block — otherwise the surface of the filler will not be completely flat. During the smoothing of the filler surface the 'wet-or-dry' paper should be periodically rinsed in water. This will ensure that a very smooth finish is imparted to the filler at the final stage.

At this stage the 'dent' should be surrounded by a ring of bare metal, which in turn should be encircled by the finely 'feathered' edge of the good paintwork. Rinse the repair area with clean water, until all of the dust produced by the rubbing-down operation has gone.

Spray the whole repair area with a light coat of primer -- this will show up any imperfections in the surface of the filler. Repair these imperfections with fresh filler paste or bodystopper, and once more smooth the surface with abrasive paper. If body-stopper is used, it can be mixed with cellulose thinners to form a .eally thin paste which is ideal for filling small holes. Repeat this spray and repair procedure until you are satisfied that the surface of the filler, and the feathered edge of the paintwork are perfect. Clean the repair area with clean water and allow to dry fully.

The repair area is now ready for spraying. Paint spraying must be carried out in a warm, dry, windless and dust free atmosphere. This condition can be created artificially if you have access to a large indoor working area, but if you are forced to work in the open, you will have to pick your day very carefully. If you are working indoors, dousing the floor in the work area with water will 'lay' the dust which would otherwise be in the atmosphere. If the repair area is confined to one body panel, mask off the surrounding panels; this will help minimise the effects of a slight mis-match in paint colours. Bodywork fittings (eg chrome strips, door handles etc) will also need to be masked off. Use genuine masking tape and several thicknesses of newspaper for the masking operations.

Before commencing to spray, agitate the aerosol can thoroughly, then spray a test area (an old tin, or similar) until the technique is mastered. Cover the repair area with a thick coat of primer; the thickness should be built up using several thin layers of paint rather than one thick one. Using 400 grade 'wet-or-dry' paper, rub down the surface of the primer until it is really smooth. While doing this, the work area should be thoroughly doused with water, and the 'wet-or-dry' paper periodically rinsed in water. Allow to dry before spraying on more paint.

Spray on the top coat, again building up the thickness by using several thin layers of paint. Start spraying in the centre of the repair area and then, using a circular motion, work outwards until the whole repair area and about 2 inches of the surrounding original paintwork is covered. Remove all masking material 10 to 15 minutes after spraying on the final coat of paint.

Allow the new paint at least two weeks to harden fully, then, using a paintwork renovator or a very fine cutting paste, blend the edges of the new paint into the existing paintwork. Finally, apply wax polish.

### 5 Major body damage — repair

Where serious damage has occurred or large areas need due to neglect, it means certainly that completely new sections or panels will need welding in and this is best left to professionals. If the damage is due to impact it will also be necessary to completely check the alignment of the bodyshell structure. Due to the principle of construction the strength and shape of the whole can be affected by damage to a part. In such instances the services of a Renault agent with specialist checking jigs are essential. If a frame is left misaligned it is first of all dangerous as the vehicle will not handle properly and secondly uneven stresses will be imposed on the steering, engine and transmission, causing abnormal wear or complete failure. Tyre wear may also be excessive.

### 6 Doors - tracing and silencing rattles

Having established that a rattle does come from the door(s) check first that it is not loose on its hinges and that the latch is holding it firmly closed. The hinges can be checked by rocking the door up and down when open to detect any play. If the hinges are worn at the pin the hinge pin and possibly the 'inner' hinge will need renewal. When the door is closed the panel should be flush. If not then the hinges or latch striker plate need adjustment. The door hinges are welded to the door and bolted to the pillars. The hinge pins can be tapped out once the circlips are removed. To adjust the setting of the door catch first slacken the screws holding the striker plate to the door pillar just enough so that it can be moved but will hold its position. Then close the door, with the latch button pressed, and then release the latch. This is so that the striker plate position is not drastically disturbed on closing the door. Then set the door position by moving it without touching the catch, so that the panel is flush with the bodywork and the other door. This will set the striker plate in the proper place. Then carefully release the catch so as not to disturb the striker plate, open the door and tighten the screws. Rattles within the door will be due to loose fixtures or something haveing been dropped inside them. Tailgate or rear door fixings are adjusted in a similar method. Do make sure that all sealing rubbers are effective and that the prop stay is not itself loose.

### 7 Bolt-on panels - removal and replacement

1 The front wings and front panel are simply bolted to the body and chassis and can be quickly and economically removed and replaced: the front inner wings inside them are too. Before replacing any panel make sure that a sealer, such as Glastican Dum Dum type putty is available.

2  To remove a front wing it helps first to remove the parcel shelf (on the relevent side) inside the car. Using a 10 mm ring spanner undo and remove all the bolts, in fact spire screws, and their washers. Do not dislodge the wing at this stage. It is not necessary and is possibly disadvantageous to remove the bonnet, unless the inner wing is to be removed too and the front bumper too. Remove the securing nut and bolt which locates the front bottom corner of the wing to the front crossmember on which the bonnet hinges and check that the two screws which are visible outside the car at the lower edge of the wing just in front of the leading edge of the door (they are setscrews) are removed.

3  Ease the lower sill running strip (below the doors) out of its fixings and then disconnect and remove the side flasher repeater lamp (if fitted).

4  From the top running edge pull the wing away from the inner wing and scuttle. It may have to be tapped and levered slightly if well established. Also remove the wing bead (Section 13).

5  To replace the wing, whether old or new, clean all the mating edges completely with a penknife and reapply a long length of the slightly stiff sealer which has been rolled out by hand as you would a piece of plasticine. Check also that all the spire screws and their locating clips are in good usable condition. Some screws have different threads. Place the wing over the sealing strip and press down by hand so that the sealer just begins to compress and ooze out.

6  Locate all the screws and washers before tightening any fully home. Tighten them all, finally locating the nut and bolt, carefully checking periodically that the profile appears correct.

7  Painting of a new wing can be done either on or off the car, The refitting process should not damage it.

8  Replace the flasher repeater and sill running strip, and the inner parcel shelf. It may be necessary to drill the appropriate holes for the flasher and trim.

9  Special note: It is worth undersealing new wings before they are placed on the car - it is much easier. Also while the wing is off it is profitable to clean the wheel arch and check for chipped underseal. Replace there and then if necessary.

10 To replace the front panel which goes across the front of the two wings and is hidden by the grille and headlamp surrounds is an equally simple task. First remove the gearbox undertray, the grille and headlamps, the sidelights and their wiring harness, the horn, the car jack (R1180) and earth strap and the bonnet. The whole panel is then screwed by 10 screws along its lower side and the upright sides. Do not remove the bumper nor the front wings. For R1181 models you will have to remove the radiator, its mountings and the cooling fan as described in Chapter 1, before removing anything else.

11 Replacement is a direct reversal procedure. It is important that replacement position is correct and firm for much depends on this panel for its safe fixing. It acts as a cross brace for the front wings and carries the bonnet hinges.

12 The removal and replacement of the inner wings is equally as simple although there may be variations in type of fastening used. For inner wings under the bonnet, always remove the bonnet the outer wings and the front panel, and any other obvious parts which will obstruct its removal such as the exhaust pipe between the silencer and manifold, or wheelbrace. As the inner wings determine the outer contour of the wing be especially careful when tightening the fixings. Do these in conjunction finally with the bonnet and outer wing to ensure the gaps are all correct.

---

### 8  Bonnet and catch - removal and replacement

1  The bonnet hinges on two swan necked hinges at the front. Removal and replacement require the services of an assistant otherwise damage is bound to result.

2  The bonnet can be removed at two points: hinge on bonnet with 4 bolts and washers or at the front top cross-brace, hinge pin to fixing, with two large bolts. If a new bonnet is to be fitted undo the 4 bolts, if not, save yourself the need to adjust its

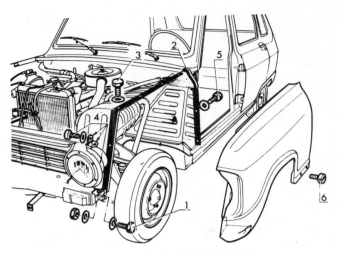

**FIG. 11.4. FRONT WING FITTING**

1  *Lower front through bolt*
2  *Rubber foam seal*
3  *Spire screws*
4  *Front screw fixings*
5  *Rear screw fixings*
6  *Bottom rear special screws*

**Fig. 11.5. Early type (pre 1974 model) front grille fixings**

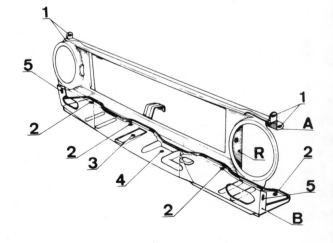

**Fig. 11.6. Front cross member fixings**

position and undo the two large hinge pin bolts.

3   Its position is adjusted by loosening the 4 fixing bolts.

4   Replacement is the reverse sequence to removal. Do not forget the rubber buffers.

5   The bonnet catch and cable control is best described by the diagram (Fig. 11.8). If left alone they seldom give trouble. Cable and catch spring replacement are obvious. Do not adjust the bonnet fitting by playing with this catch.

### 9   Door and window winder - removal and replacement

1   Door removal is no easy task. Its not their actual removal which is difficult but they are difficult to adjust accurately and an assistant is necessary.

2   The front and rear doors are best removed by unbolting the hinge on the door pillar. If the doors are to be renewed the hinge pin can be punched out once the door is removed. Punching the hinge pin out is not easy on the car. (See Section 6).

3   To remove a front door unclip the interior trim from inside the front pillar and unbolt the three fixings from each hinge. The rear doors, hinging in the centre can be released in the same way once the pillar trim is unscrewed and removed. The R1181 is fitted with door check straps, the R1180 having integral hinge/check straps.

4   Replacement is obviously a direct reverse sequence of the removal. Adjust the final swing of the doors before replacing the trim to the pillar.

5   It is possible to remove the window winder mechanism but not the glass without removing the door lock and catch mechanism. Lock and catch mechanism is given in Section 12.

6   Remove the door trim slowly and carefully. Its expensive to replace if ruined. Pull back the plastic covering on the window winder handle, push back the locking tab of the fixing nut and remove the nut and then the handle. Remove the door pull (2 Phillips screws).

7   Insert a piece of wood (make sure the window is fully closed) approximately 1 inch by 1½ inches between the doorframe and the trim and twist it to spring out the trim panel clips. Do not use a screwdriver around the edges. Unseal the doorframe and see the window winder mechanism.

8   Remove the three fixing screws and then wind down the window so that only 5.7/8" of glass still appears in the window-frame. Disconnect the winder mechanism from the lower glass frame and pull out the mechanism in a downward direction towards the trailing edge of the door.

9   To remove the window glass, first remove the door catch mechanism. See Section 12. Remove the seal between it and the doorframe using a screwdriver and then lift out the glass through its frame (inner side) by pivoting it at the bottom. Then remove the outer seal held by six clips.

10   All replacement sequences are the exact reversal of the removal sequences.

### 10   Tailgate - removal and replacement

1   To remove the tailgate an assistant is essential otherwise the panel could fall on your head. Its removal is similar to that of the bonnet. Again remove the four bolts which fix the hinges to the bodyframe rather than the hinges to the tailgate. Do not forget to disconnect the wiring to the number plate lights and to the heated rear window (R1181). Treat the panel very carefully.

2   It is necessary to disconnect the tailgate catch/counter balance. This is a simple operation but watch that the spring does not fly if it is under tension.

3   Replacement is a reverse of the removal sequence. Adjustment of the fit of the tailgate is undertaken at the three bolts on each hinge on the tailgate. Any final catch adjustment should be undertaken at the catch.

4   Once again look closely at the catch and experiment with the fit of the tailgate by moving the catch on the tailgate. Leave the striker peg on the bodywork. (See Fig. 11.11). Use shims under the catch only if all else fails.

### 11   Windscreen and glass - preparation and replacement

1   The windscreen is curved and all the other glass fitted to the Renault 6 is flat. Various types of fitting, rubber surround and trim have been fitted through its production life and it is essential that an exactly similar fitting is used.

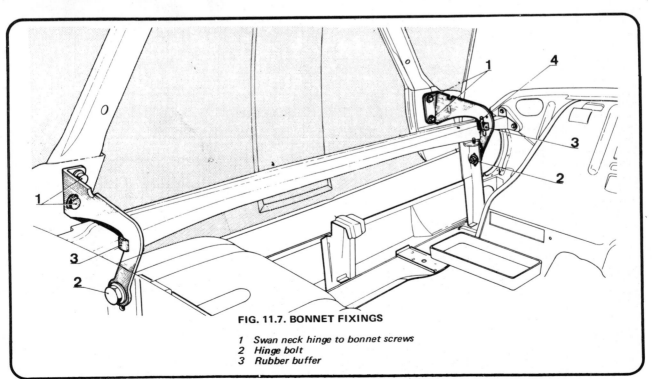

**FIG. 11.7. BONNET FIXINGS**

1   *Swan neck hinge to bonnet screws*
2   *Hinge bolt*
3   *Rubber buffer*

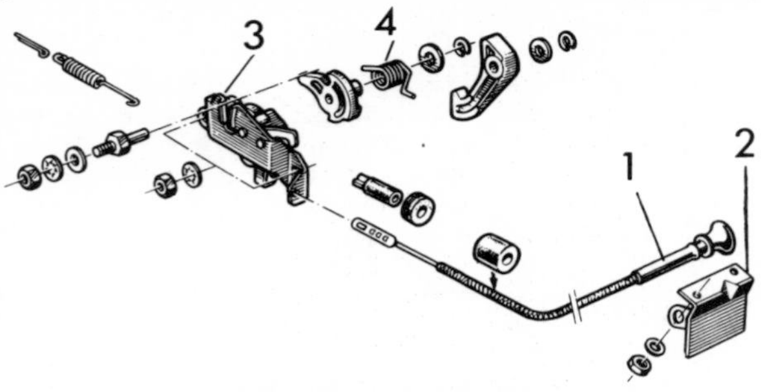

**FIG. 11.8. BONNET RELEASE AND CATCH COMPONENTS**

1  Pull, and cable
2  Pull bracket
3  Lock/catch
4  Return spring

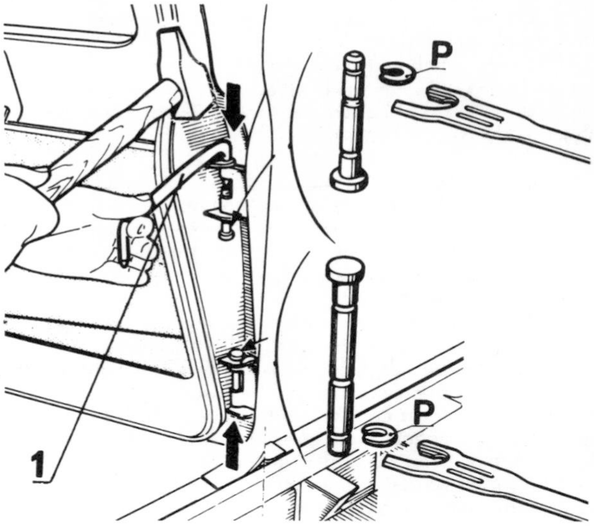

**FIG. 11.9. DOOR HINGE PIN REMOVAL**

1  Special right-angle punch
P  Special circlip

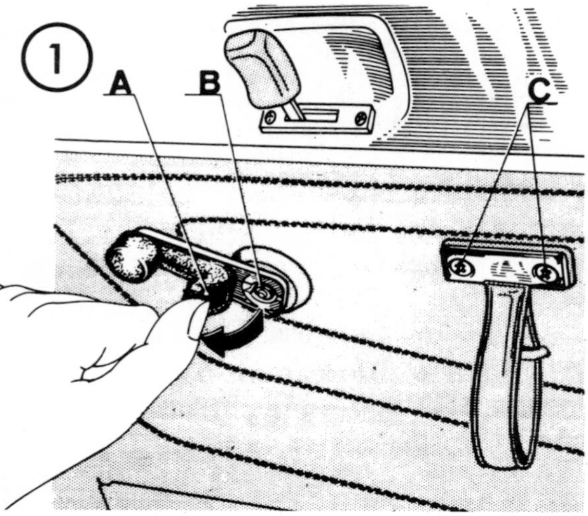

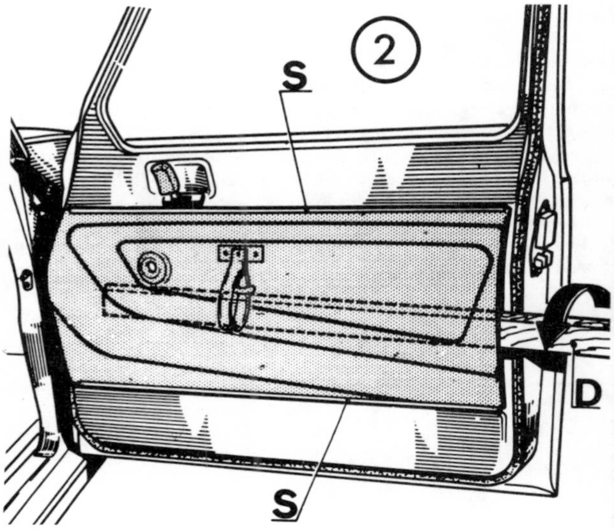

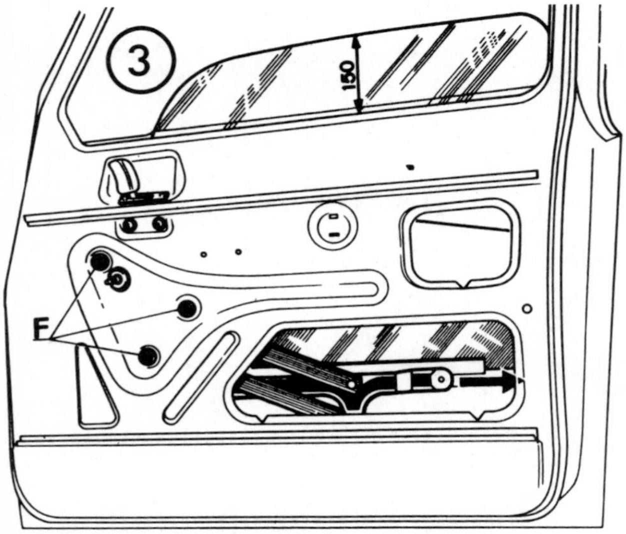

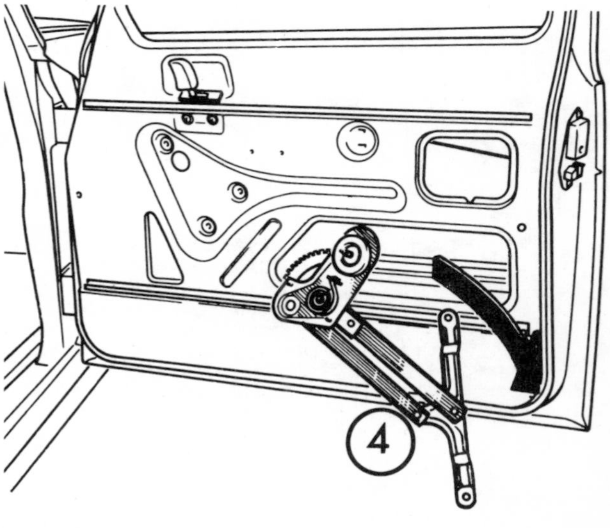

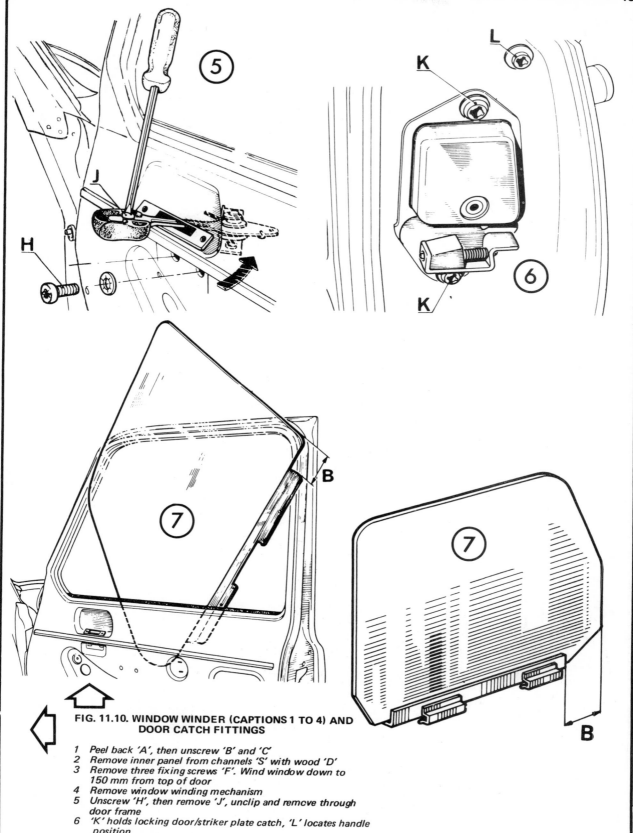

FIG. 11.10. WINDOW WINDER (CAPTIONS 1 TO 4) AND
DOOR CATCH FITTINGS

1  Peel back 'A', then unscrew 'B' and 'C'
2  Remove inner panel from channels 'S' with wood 'D'
3  Remove three fixing screws 'F'. Wind window down to
   150 mm from top of door
4  Remove window winding mechanism
5  Unscrew 'H', then remove 'J', unclip and remove through
   door frame
6  'K' holds locking door/striker plate catch, 'L' locates handle
   position
7  'B' indicate position of window glass on channel.
   B  =  87 mm (3 7/16 in.)
   (Left  -  front door,   Right  -  rear door)

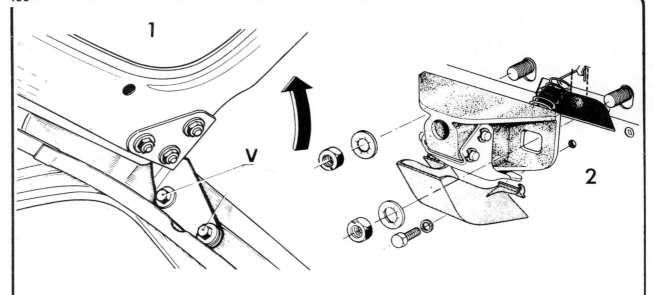

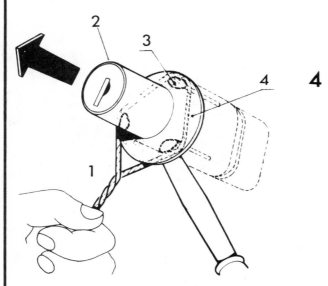

**FIG. 11.11. TAILGATE FIXINGS**

1  Hinge mechanism - 'V' shows the two side screws
2  Lock/catch mechanism components on tailgate
3  Catch stud
4  Tailgate lock removal

   1  Use string to 'pull in' clips
   2  Lock barrel
   3  Clips
   4  Base of lock barrel

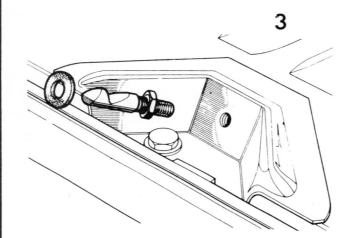

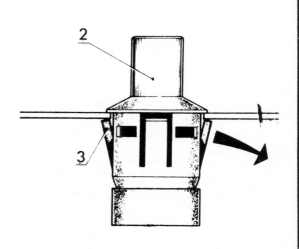

2  To replace a front or rear screen or any non-opening window glass clean out the window surround and remove the rubber seal. Check that it is in good condition - not stretched, perished or cracked. However, do make sure that your fitting the glass is necessary - many windscreen replacement companies fit free. On windscreen fitting, if the previous glass has been broken plug the gap between the facia panel and window as well as closing the ventilator flap, to avoid splinters entering.

Special Note: Refitment of the heated rear window (R1181) takes special care. If you are in any doubt, don't! Leave it to one with this experience.

3  Fit the rubber seal around the glass (see Fig. 11.12 for sealer placement) and lay on a good flat working surface. Insert a piece of string 3 to 4 mm in diameter into the slot of the seal. Pass it totally around the seal and exit it with about 5 inches overlap and 8 inches hanging near a bottom corner.

4  Position the glass and seal into the window from outside with the string inside hanging, with the help of an assistant.

5  Centralise and press on the outside of the glass where the ends of the string cross.

6  From the inside of the car pull each string alternately, lifting the lip over the edge of the bodyframe all the way round.

7  At the same time, have an assistant hold and press the glass in gently from the outside. Eventually the string will come out from the centre top edge of the rubber and the glass will be fully in position.

8  The bright trim will now have to be fitted into the surround. Unless the special tool is available, a great deal of patience will be required to engage it under the lips of the rubber using a small screwdriver or blunt blade.

### 13 Trim - removal and replacement

1  The trim fitted both internally and externally is of very simple and utilitarian construction. Its removal is obvious in each case. If a screw is not visible then it is either a push-on fit or is slid on. Check each part - but never force anything Door trim is covered in Section 9 dealing with the window winder.

2  The front grille, apart from the model identification markings, is the only major piece of external trim. The headlamp surrounds are dealt with in Chapter 9.

3  The grille is removed by unscrewing the four top self tapping screws and the four lower retaining bar self tapping screws. Be gentle it is constructed of moulded plastic and aluminum and is relatively expensive to replace. The grille is removed by pulling out and down.

4  The grille itself can be dismantled by levering out the down members and unscrewing the badge.

### 14 Bumper bar - removal and replacement

1  Both front and rear bumper bars together with their over-riders are simple and obvious to remove and replace. See Fig. 11.13 for the components involved.

2  On post 1973 models the side/flasher lights are fixed in the front bumper. Don't remove the electrical connection - undo the two Phillips screws and remove the complete flasher/side light and allow it to hang!

3  Late model bumpers have rubber strip inserts.

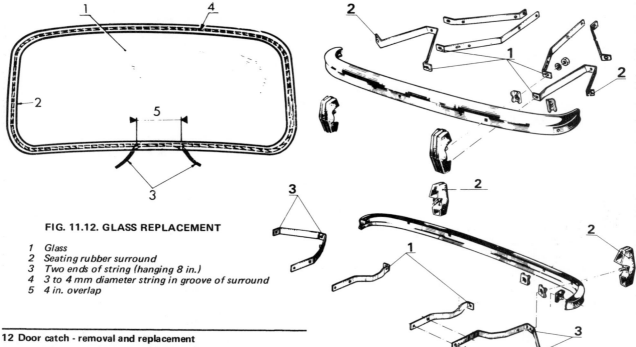

### FIG. 11.12. GLASS REPLACEMENT

1  Glass
2  Seating rubber surround
3  Two ends of string (hanging 8 in.)
4  3 to 4 mm diameter string in groove of surround
5  4 in. overlap

### FIG. 11.13. BUMPERS (PRE 1974 MODELS)

Top  -  Front
   1  Centre bracing supports
   2  Outer bracing supports
Lower  -  Rear
   1  Centre bracing supports
   2  Over-riders
   3  Outer bracing supports
*(Post 1973 models have very similar fixings, although the bumpers are different)*

### 12 Door catch - removal and replacement

1  Front and rear door catches, whether locking with a key or internally, fitted with a childproof override or not, are all basically the same. Replacement of the catch, lock or mechanism is a simple though fiddly procedure.

2  Always remove the door trim, see Section 9 and have a Phillips screwdriver ready. See Fig. 11.10, captions 1 to 4 inclusive for details.

Note: It will always be necessary to re-adjust the door catches if ever dismantled, to avoid door malfunction and slamming. See Section 6.

3  Tailgate lock is shown in Fig. 11.11.

**15 Facia panel and parcel trays - removal and replacement**

1   Never remove the facia panel unnecessarily. It is not difficult but very tiring removing and replacing it. Remove the fresh air grille and grille control knobs which are a push-on fit. Then remove the lower cover on the lighting/indicator/horn switch fixed by five recessed Phillips screws.
2   Disconnect the battery. Prise out with a screwdriver the three-panel switches, note the wing connections and pull them off.
3   Disconnect the instrument panel connections from behind noting 'which wires go where'. Unscrew the speedometer drive cable.
4   Disconnect the choke cable at the carburettor and pull it all the way out. Remove the ashtray and the heater control panel noting the connections.
5   Remove the steering wheel. See Chapter 10.
6   Disconnect the gear change control rod under the bonnet and pull it out into the car's interior - early R1180 models only.
7   Once the Neiman steering lock rubber ring cover is removed the facia panel and instrument panel complete can be removed by unscrewing the following fixing points: at earth end of the facia panel, lower edge; under the fresh air grille and inside the glove box.
8   Replacement is a reverse sequence of the removal.
9   The front parcel tray is fixed under the facia panel at five points on the right and four on the left. It is secured at three points in its centre. All are Phillips screws.
10 The rear parcel shelf is an integral part of the rear seat and is unlikely ever to need replacement. It too is an obvious fitment. the brushes, and bearing end plates as total units, but if anything else needs overhauling it is better to exchange or renew the motor as a whole.

**16 Heater body, ducting and motor - removal and replacement**

1   Disconnect the battery under the bonnet using the quick release contact and then remove the facia panel as described in Section 15.

2   Disconnect the electrical feed wire and the support bracket to the gearchange rod.
3   Remove the heater body, panel and connections. The heater body is fixed on three studs. You will have to unseal the ducting tube outlets.
4   Once the heater body is away from the car its two casing halves can be separated (4 screws) and the motor and fan removed from one half (3 nuts).
5   The fan is then easily removed from the motor.
6   Assembly is straightforward but make sure that the motor sits properly in the casing on its rubber blocks and that the air ducting hose is properly resealed to the heater body.
7   Air ducting is connected in sections. Removal and replacement is straightforward provided sufficient care is taken with resealing. Use tape around the joints if necessary.

**17 Heater motor repair**

1   The heater motors fitted are extremely hardy and reliable if not subjected to great misuse. It is economically viable to replace
2   To replace the brushes (make sure the correct replacement is to hand), unhook the spring which retains them together unsolder the brush carrier and remove it. Solder in the new brush carrier and place into position. Rehook the spring. You must remove the motor from the cover to do this.
3   To replace the bearing end plates remove the circlip and washer at the opposite end to the fan. Remove the two long fixing screws (they are not the same length, remember) and draw out the armature. Replace the bearing end plates as necessary and reassemble. Note the spacer washer.
4   A heater motor supplementary resistance is fitted into the wiring circuiting. Again if malfunction is suspected an auto electrician will have to check this out.

**18 Heater radiators - removal and replacement**

1   Heat is transmitted in the medium of hot air from two radiators, one in front of each front seat, heated by the engine coolant. These radiators are connected in series and are situated under the facia panel and are only accessible from under the

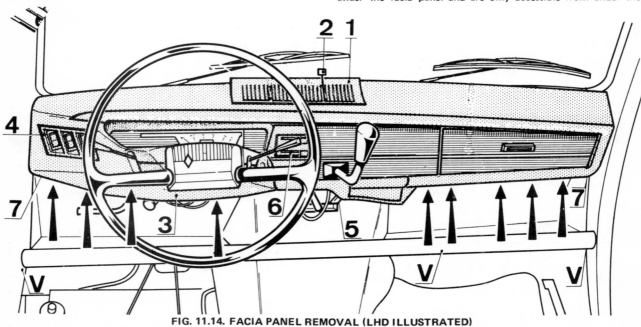

**FIG. 11.14. FACIA PANEL REMOVAL (LHD ILLUSTRATED)**

1   Fresh air grille (top screws)
2   Grille levers (knobs pull off)
3   Lower steering column panel (screws)
4   Switch panel (pulls out)
5   Lower panel brace
6   Heater control panel (screws)
7   End screws
V   Parcel shelf fixing points

*Arrows indicate positions of screws*

bonnet. Obviously all that has been said about coolant hoses, clips and the bleeding of the system in Chapter 2 applies here.

2  Remove the engine air filter and the bonnet catch mechanism. Push the wiring harness running across the bulkhead down out of the way. Disconnect the gearchange rod and push the lever through into the interior.

3  Unfix the black padding which goes across the bulkhead to expose the hoses, connections and two radiators.

4  To remove a radiator, disconnect the relevant hoses. Have some rag ready to absorb the flow of coolant.

5  Unscrew the three cold air trap securing screws and then the two radiator screws and pull out the radiator. Repeat for the

other radiator if necessary.

6  Special note: Although they appear to be the same R1180 and R1181 radiators are different, because of the different flow direction of the coolant and because coolant flows in at the bottom and out at the top of each radiator they are not interchangeable.

7  When replacing the radiators make sure all is fitted correctly. The heater will not work if it is not! Always reseal all ducting and use new hose clips. You must bleed the cooling system each time a disconnection takes place. See Chapter 2.

8  The heater control tap is removed from under the bonnet once the hose connections are unfastened. Remove the heater

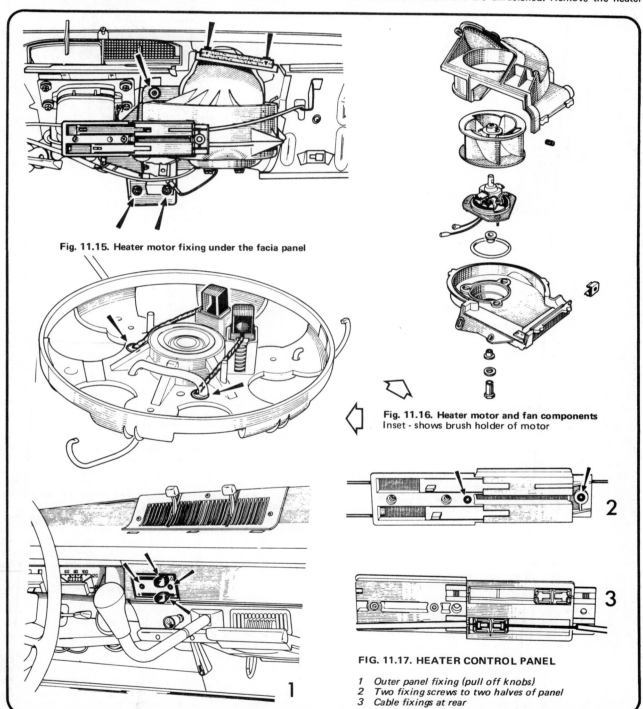

Fig. 11.15. Heater motor fixing under the facia panel

Fig. 11.16. Heater motor and fan components
Inset - shows brush holder of motor

FIG. 11.17. HEATER CONTROL PANEL

1   Outer panel fixing (pull off knobs)
2   Two fixing screws to two halves of panel
3   Cable fixings at rear

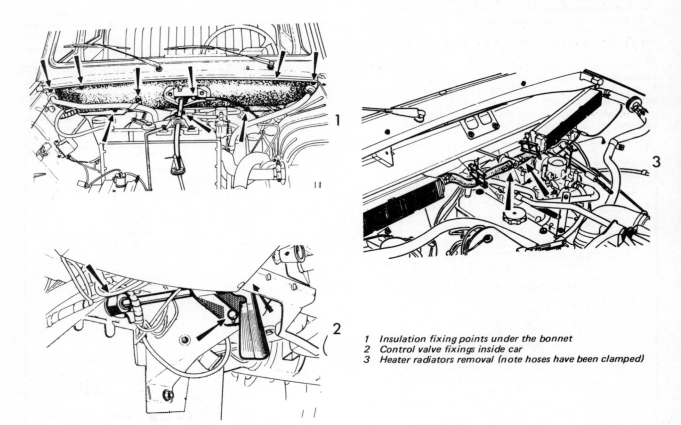

1  Insulation fixing points under the bonnet
2  Control valve fixings inside car
3  Heater radiators removal (note hoses have been clamped)

FIG. 11.18. HEATER RADIATORS AND CONTROL VALVE

control rod bracket, the tap securing nut and then lower it to unscrew the fixing knob screw. Unscrew the bracket nut and push it through once the knob is removed.

### 19 Spare wheel cradle

1  The spare wheel cradle is a simple U shaped wire cradle slung under the rear of the vehicle which holds the spare wheel flat up against the underside of the rear floor. The cradle is released by loosening the bolt inside the vehicle in the centre of the rear doorway with the wheel brace. There are two positions on the locking mechanism. It is a good idea to lubricate the bolt thread periodically so that it does not rust solid.

2  It is necessary to remove the cradle before removing the fuel tank. Its outer ends are looped over two studs on the chassis; remove the two nuts and remove. Replacement is an opposite movement.

### 20 Fuel tank - removal and replacement

1  Fuel tank removal is a simple operation. The Renault 6 is quite prone to the fuel tank rusting internally and tank renewal is often necessary, particularly on older models.

2  Remove the spare wheel cradle. Remove the rubber pipe which connects the body filler orifice and the downpipe, inside the offside rear wing arch. It is easiest if that rear wheel has been removed, and the vehicle is jacked as high as possible at that corner. Prop the chassis. Remove and discard the hose clips from this hose. Disconnect the tank breather pipe and its clip from the filler orifice.

3  Undo the four bolts which locate the rear crossmember to

the chassis. This crossmember is also bolted to the fuel tank but it is not necessary to undo these two bolts yet. Remove the bolts. The R1181 does not have the rear cross-member. The fuel tank is mounted on two brackets welded to the chassis. Also you may find it helpful to remove the rear anti-roll bar, on this model. On early R1181s fitted with the electric fuel pump, remove the pumps protective shield and disconnect it. You may have to juggle the tank filter around it.

4  Inside the vehicle (under the rear seat) practically in its centre is the head of the last tank securing bolt. This head should be held with a spanner, either suitably wedged or by an assistant. Undo its nut under the vehicle with a tubular spanner. It is located at the fore edge of the tank, on its outer lip. Once removed the tank can come out. It will not fall out because it is resting on the rear torsion bars.

5  Pull the tank rearwards, then gently downwards, watching the downpipe. As soon as you can see and touch the top of the tank pull off the petrol feed pipe and the electrical sender unit connection. DO NOT STRETCH THESE. Now juggle the tank out. If it still has petrol in it, be careful not to lose any from the downpipe.

6  Remove the rear crossmember from the tank. Hold on to the rubber cushioning pads.

7  Generally speaking it is not possible to repair a fuel tank. Under most circumstances it is cheaper simply to renew. Certainly do not repair with fibreglass and do not put any heat near the tank.

8  Replacement is a direct reversal of removal but make sure both the fuel feed pipe and sender unit connections are home. Be careful not to rest the tank on the join between the downpipe and the tank. Always use new worm drive hose clips for the rubber hose. See Chapter 3, for details of the sender unit.

# Chapter 12 Supplement: Revisions and information on later models

## Contents

## 1 Introduction

This Chapter details the principal modifications that have been made to the Renault 6 range since 1975. The various items in this Chapter should be read in conjunction with the corresponding Chapter on that subject.

In many instances, old and modified parts are not interchangeable and it is therefore of the utmost importance to quote the car and engine numbers when ordering new parts.

## 2 Jacking

Use the jack supplied with the vehicle for roadside wheel changing only. Fit the jack into the attachments provided under each side body sill. If a trolley or other jack is used for repair and maintenance work, position this just behind the side sill directly under the centre pillar. Always use a block of wood to spread the load.

The front of the vehicle can be raised by placing a baulk of timber under both side members directly beneath the tubular cross support and then use a jack.

Do not jack-up any other part of the vehicle or distortion may occur.

Before jacking-up by any method, make sure that the doors and the tailgate are fully closed to avoid the body flexing during lifting.

Always supplement the jacks with axle-stands before crawling under the vehicle.

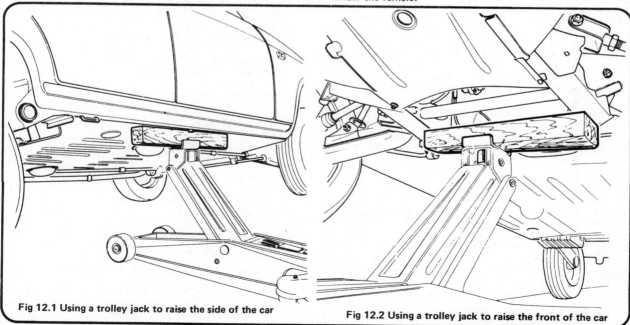

**Fig 12.1 Using a trolley jack to raise the side of the car**

**Fig 12.2 Using a trolley jack to raise the front of the car**

## 3  Specifications

*Fuel system — carburettors*

### Carter 32 RBS (Mark 4599S - 610002-1)

| | |
|---|---|
| Float level            ...    ...    ...    ...    ...    ...    ...    ... | 10 mm (0.394 in) |
| Pump stroke            ...    ...    ...    ...    ...    ...    ...    ... | 5.3 mm (0.209 in) |
| Initial throttle opening ...   ...    ...    ...    ...    ...    ...    ... | 0.80 mm (0.032 in) |
| Choke tube             ...    ...    ...    ...    ...    ...    ...    ... | 24 |
| Idle speed             ...    ...    ...    ...    ...    ...    ...    ... | 625 to 675 rpm |

### Carter 32 RBS (Mark 610004 - 610004-1)

| | |
|---|---|
| Float level            ...    ...    ...    ...    ...    ...    ...    ... | 10 mm (0.394 in) |
| Pump stroke            ...    ...    ...    ...    ...    ...    ...    ... | 3 mm (0.118 in) |
| Initial throttle opening ...   ...    ...    ...    ...    ...    ...    ... | 0.85 mm (0.34 in) |
| Choke tube             ...    ...    ...    ...    ...    ...    ...    ... | 24 |
| Idle speed             ...    ...    ...    ...    ...    ...    ...    ... | 625 to 675 rpm |

### Zenith 32 IF (Mark V10.201)

| | |
|---|---|
| Choke tube             ...    ...    ...    ...    ...    ...    ...    ... | 23 |
| Idle speed jet         ...    ...    ...    ...    ...    ...    ...    ... | 39 |
| Initial throttle opening ...   ...    ...    ...    ...    ...    ...    ... | 0.70 to 0.80 mm (0.028 to 0.032 in) |
| Main jet  ...    ...    ...    ...    ...    ...    ...    ...    ... | 125 |
| Needle valve           ...    ...    ...    ...    ...    ...    ...    ... | 1.25 mm (0.049 in) |
| Air compensating jet   ...    ...    ...    ...    ...    ...    ... | 120 x 140 |
| Idle speed             ...    ...    ...    ...    ...    ...    ...    ... | 625 to 675 rpm |

### Zenith 32 IF (Mark V10.203)

| | |
|---|---|
| Choke tube             ...    ...    ...    ...    ...    ...    ...    ... | 24 |
| Idle speed jet         ...    ...    ...    ...    ...    ...    ...    ... | 39 |
| Initial throttle opening ...   ...    ...    ...    ...    ...    ...    ... | 0.80 mm (0.032 in) |
| Main jet  ...    ...    ...    ...    ...    ...    ...    ...    ... | 124 |
| Needle valve           ...    ...    ...    ...    ...    ...    ...    ... | 1.25 mm (0.049 in) |
| Air compensating jet   ...    ...    ...    ...    ...    ...    ... | 130 x 115 |
| Enrichener             ...    ...    ...    ...    ...    ...    ...    ... | 70 |
| Idle speed             ...    ...    ...    ...    ...    ...    ...    ... | 625 to 675 rpm |

### Solex type 32 E1SA

| | Mk 512 | Mk 560 | Mk 570 |
|---|---|---|---|
| Choke tube            ...    ...    ...    ...    ...    ...    ... | 23 | 23 | 22 |
| Main jet  ...    ...    ...    ...    ...    ...    ...    ... | 120 | 120 | 117.5 |
| Air compensator jet  ...    ...    ...    ...    ...    ... | 125 NA | 125 NA | 150 N4 |
| Idle speed jet       ...    ...    ...    ...    ...    ...    ... | 47 | 45 | 45 |
| Accelerator pump jet ...    ...    ...    ...    ...    ... | 40 | 40 | 40 |
| Needle valve         ...    ...    ...    ...    ...    ...    ... | 1.5 mm | 1.5 mm | 1.5 mm |
| Econostat            ...    ...    ...    ...    ...    ...    ... | — | — | 50 |
| Initial throttle opening ... ...    ...    ...    ...    ... | 90 mm (0.035 in) | 90 mm (0.035 in) | 60 mm (0.024 in) |
| Idle speed           ...    ...    ...    ...    ...    ...    ... | | 725 to 775 rpm | |

*Ignition system*

### Distributor (static ignition setting)

| | Distributor No | Static setting (degrees) | Equivalent marking on crankshaft |
|---|---|---|---|
| 800 series engine | SEV 27914 27915 27916 27917 | 5 to 7º BTDC | 10.2 to 12.8 mm BTDC (23/64 to ¾ in BTDC) |
| | SEV 4000 2002 4002 9002 | 1º BTDC to 1º ATDC | 2 mm BTDC to 2 mm ATDC (5/64 in BTDC to 5/64 in ATDC) |
| | Ducellier 4226, 4227 | 5 to 7º BTDC | 10.2 to 12.8 mm BTDC (23/64 to ¾ in BTDC) |
| | Ducellier 4274, 4275 | 1º BTDC to 1º ATDC | 2 mm BTDC to 2 mm ATDC (5/64 in BTDC to 5/64 in ATDC) |
| 688 series engine | SEV 4030 3502, 4032 9502, 4030 3702 4032 9702 | 1º BTDC to 1º ATDC | 2 mm BTDC to 2 mm ATDC (5/64 in BTDC to 5/64 in ATDC) |

| Ducellier 4336, | | |
|---|---|---|
| 4337, | 1º BTDC to | 2 mm BTDC to 2 mm ATDC |
| 4326, | 1º ATDC | (5/64 in BTDC to 5/64 in ATDC) |
| 4327, | | |
| 4406, | | |
| 4410 | | |

**Dwell angle (all foregoing distributors)**    ...    ...    ...    54 to 60º

**Spark plug recommendations**
800 series engine    ...    ...    ...    ...    ...    ...    ...    AC 43FS, Autolite AE32, Champion L87Y,
SEV Marchal 35/36, Eyquem 705S or
Marcelli CW5NT

688 series engine    ...    ...    ...    ...    ...    ...    ...    AC 42FS, Champion L87Y or Eyquem 705S

**Electrode gap (all plugs)**    ...    ...    ...    ...    ...    ...    0.024 in (0.6 mm)

---

### 4 Engine

*Oil filter cartridge — renewal*

1 It is most important that the engine oil filter cartridge be changed at the specified intervals (9000 miles or annually - whichever comes first). A more frequent change should be made in adverse working conditions such as stop/start city driving or dusty country road use.

2 The cartridge type filter is easily changed by unscrewing the old cartridge, but have a container handy underneath to catch the spillage. It may be necessary to use a strap wrench to assist in unscrewing the old filter cartridge if it has been overtightened. Discard the old filter on removal.

3 Wipe clean the mating face on the cylinder block and fit the new seal carefully into position and lubricate it with clean engine oil to prevent it from being distorted when the new cartridge is tightened.

4 Locate and hand tighten the new cartridge filter. Run the engine up to its normal operating temperature and check for leaks around the filter and check it for tightness.

*Camshaft pulley — 1100 cc engines*

5 From March of 1976 the camshaft pulley wheel fitted was manufactured in cast steel in place of the original sheet steel pressing type. The new pulley is fitted to the camshaft direct and not via a cast hub as before. To facilitate this modification the camshaft end boss has been lengthened on the oilseal bearing flange.

6 If fitting a late type pulley to the original type camshaft, a distance piece will be required to lengthen the flange boss of the camshaft to suit.

7 The securing bolts are also of different lengths so check with your Renault dealer about the necessary requirements if changing the pulley.

8 When assembled make sure that the pulleys are in line with each other.

---

### 5 Cooling system

*Water pump drivebelt tension — 1100 cc engines*

1 On Type 688 engines from March 1977, the water pump

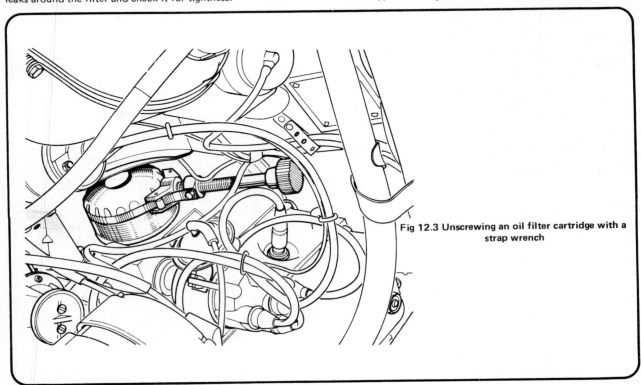

Fig 12.3 Unscrewing an oil filter cartridge with a strap wrench

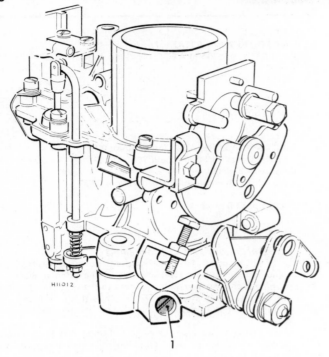

Fig 12.4 Zenith carburettor
1 Fuel mixture screw

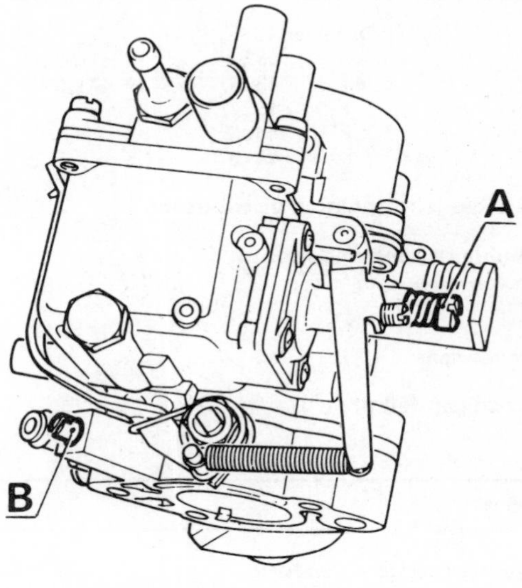

**Fig 12.5 Solex 32 E1SA carburettor**
*A Air screw (speed)*
*B Fuel/mixture screw*

**Fig 12.6 Solex 32 PD1S**
*1 Fuel/mixture screw*
*2 Throttle speed screw*

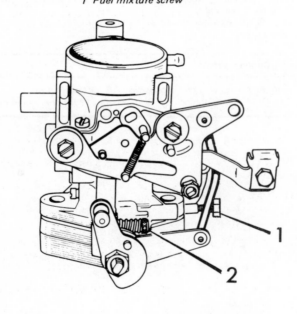

Fig 12.7 Carter 32 RBS (Marks 610004 and 610004–1)
carburettor

1 Throttle fast idle screw
2 Locknut
L Link rod
R Cam to screw alignment mark
T Choke flap intermediate cold
   position hole

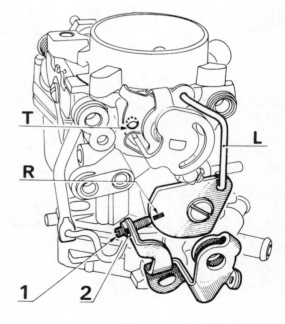

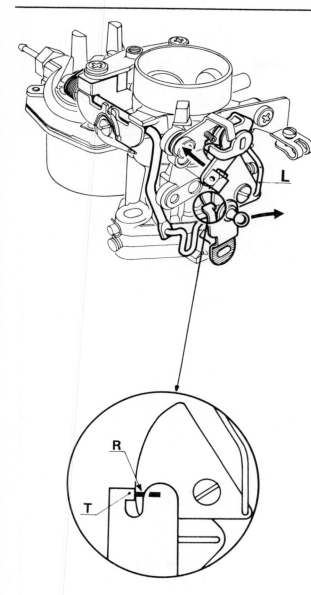

**Fig 12.8 Carter 32RBS (Marks 45995 and 610002—1) carburettor**

*L Link rod*

*R and T Alignment marks*

drivebelt tension should be measured at the midway point between the water pump pulley and the tensioner pulley.

2 For normal maintenance checks the free play allowance should be 0.08 to 0.13 in (2.0 mm to 3.3 mm) whilst a new belt free play should be 0.06 to 0.09 in (1.5 to 2.3 mm).

## 6 Fuel system

### Carburettors — general

1 On later models, the type of carburettor fitted is varied according to the engine and date of production (see the Specification at the beginning of this Chapter).

2 Always refer to the reference number on the identification plate under the fixing screws of the float chamber.

### Idle speed adjustment — Zenith and Carter carburettors

3 Always have the engine at the normal operating temperature before carring out any adjustment.

4 On many versions of these carburettors, the fuel (mixture) screw is sealed, in which case only the throttle speed screw should be adjusted to bring the idle speed within the specified range.

5 If the fuel (mixture) screw is not sealed or due to major overhaul or renewal of internal components it is essential to break the seal, then adjust in the following way.

6 Turn the fuel (mixture) screw in or out until the idle speed is at its highest point and then adjust the idle speed to that specified by means of the throttle speed screw. Again turn the fuel (mixture) screw until the idle speed is at its highest point. Repeat these operations until no further increase can be achieved.

7 Turn the fuel (mixture) screw in until the idle speed just starts to drop. Do not touch the fuel (mixture) screw any more but adjust the throttle speed screw to bring the idle speed up to that specified.

8 It is recommended that to ensure that the engine meets current anti-pollutant regulations, all adjustments to the idle and mixture settings are carried out using an exhaust gas analyser and a tachometer.

9 If a seal was broken off the fuel screw a new one should be fitted on completion.

### Idle speed adjustment — Solex 32 E1SA carburettor

10 The fuel screw is normally sealed on these carburettors and any alteration to the idle speed should be made by turning the air screw in or out as necessary. Do not disturb any other adjuster screw settings (throttle speed or fast idle).

11 If due to overhaul or renewal of components, the seal on the fuel screw must be broken, adjustments must be carried out as described in paragraphs 6 to 9 of this Section except that the air screw will be used to alter the idle speed.

### Idle speed adjustment — Solex 32 PD1S carburettor

12 The idling adjustment is carried out in a similar way to that described for the Zenith and Carter carburettors.

### Carter 32 RBS carburettor (Mark 610004 and 610004-1) — fast idle adjustment

13 Check that the throttle lever adjustment screw is in alignment with the marked 'R' on the operating cam, and if not, adjust by bending the connection rod (L) between the choke flap swivel and the cam just enough to align the adjustment screw.

14 The initial throttle opening must now be checked using a gauge rod of the specified thickness, use Renault special tool number MS 532 if available.

15 To adjust the opening, unscrew the locknut and turn the adjustment screw accordingly. When set at the correct opening retighten the locknut.

### Carter 32 RBS carburettor (Mark 4599S and 610002-1) — fast idle adjustment

16 Two adjustments are necessary to adjust the throttle opening. Refer to Fig. 12.8.

17 With the choke opened fully and the throttle shut, check that

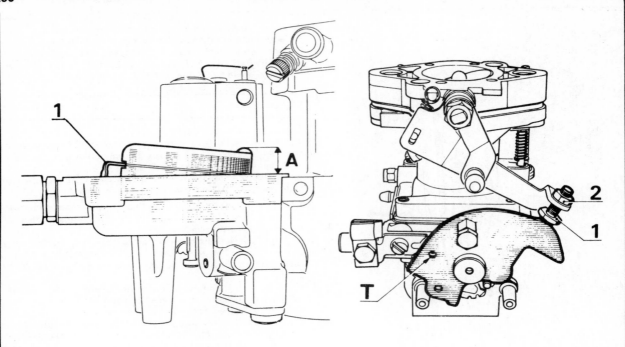

**Fig 12.9 Float level checking diagram**
*1 Tongue*
*A Float measuring point*

**Fig 12.10 Zenith carburettor fast idle components**
*1 Fast idle screw*
*2 Locknut*
*T Choke flap intermediate detent*

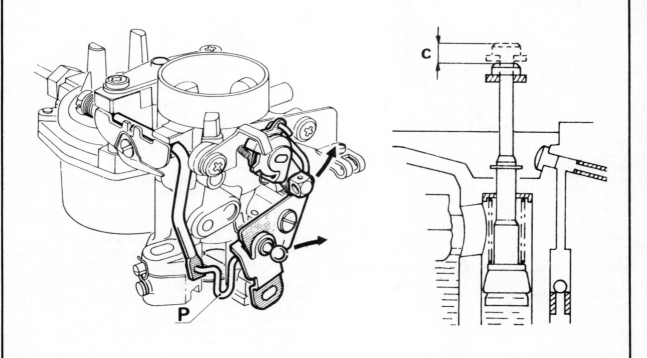

**Fig 12.11 Accelerator pump details (Carter carburettor)**

*C Piston stroke   P Adjustable link rod*

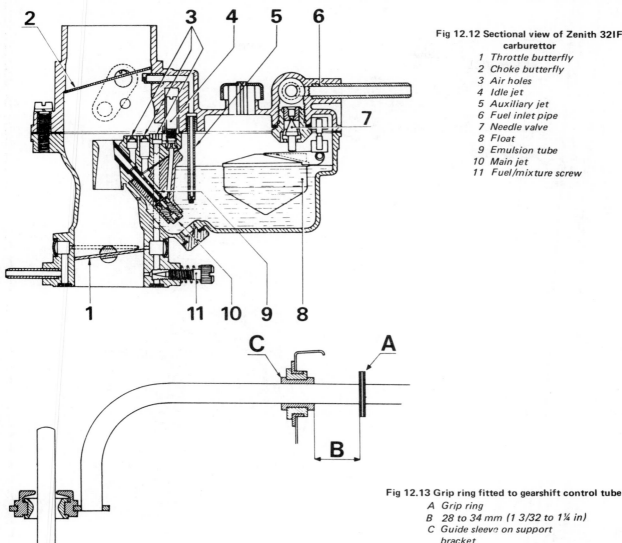

**Fig 12.12 Sectional view of Zenith 32IF
carburettor**

1 Throttle butterfly
2 Choke butterfly
3 Air holes
4 Idle jet
5 Auxiliary jet
6 Fuel inlet pipe
7 Needle valve
8 Float
9 Emulsion tube
10 Main jet
11 Fuel/mixture screw

**Fig 12.13 Grip ring fitted to gearshift control tube**

A Grip ring
B 28 to 34 mm (1 3/32 to 1¼ in)
C Guide sleeve on support
bracket

the lines marked on the cam (R) and the throttle lever (T) are in alignment as shown in the inset. Should adjustment be necessary this can be made via the connection link (L) between the choke flap and cam.

18 Fully close the choke flap and then push the throttle lever up against the cam. Now check the initial throttle opening using a gauge rod of the specified thickness or if available, Renault special tool number MS 532. To adjust the opening bend the heel of the throttle lever (T) accordingly.

*Float level – checking and adjusting*

19 Remove the carburettor and float chamber.
20 Invert the carburettor and holding it level measure the clearance between the cover joint face and the uppermost point of the pip on the float. Should adjustment be necessary, bend the float tongue accordingly but do not apply any pressure to the needle valve.

*Accelerator pump (Carter carburettor) – adjustment*

21 Refer to Fig. 12.11 and fully open the choke flap.
22 Now measure the distance of piston travel between the fully open and idle positions. If the distance is not as specified, bend the accelerator pump to throttle lever connecting rod to adjust to the recommended amount.

*Zenith 32IF carburettor – fast idle adjustment*

23 Set the choke flap cam at the medium cold position. To do this refer to Fig. 12.10 and align the detent ball and hole (T) then with the throttle lever in the closed position, insert a gauge rod of the specified amount (Renault tool number MS 532) between the inner carburettor body and the butterfly as shown, on the progression hole side of the aperture.
24 To adjust, loosen the locknut and turn the adjusting screw accordingly to obtain the correct clearance; tighten the locknut.

---

**7 Ignition system**

*Dwell angle – checking and adjusting*

1 A more precise method of adjusting the distributor contact breaker points gap is to measure the dwell angle rather than use feeler blades.
2 The dwell angle is the number of degrees through which the distributor cam turns during the period between the instants of closure and opening of the contact breaker points.
3 The angle can only be checked using a dwell meter connected in accordance with the maker's instructions.
4 The correct dwell angle is between 54 and 60°.
5 If the angle is too large, increase the points gap. If it is too small, reduce the gap.

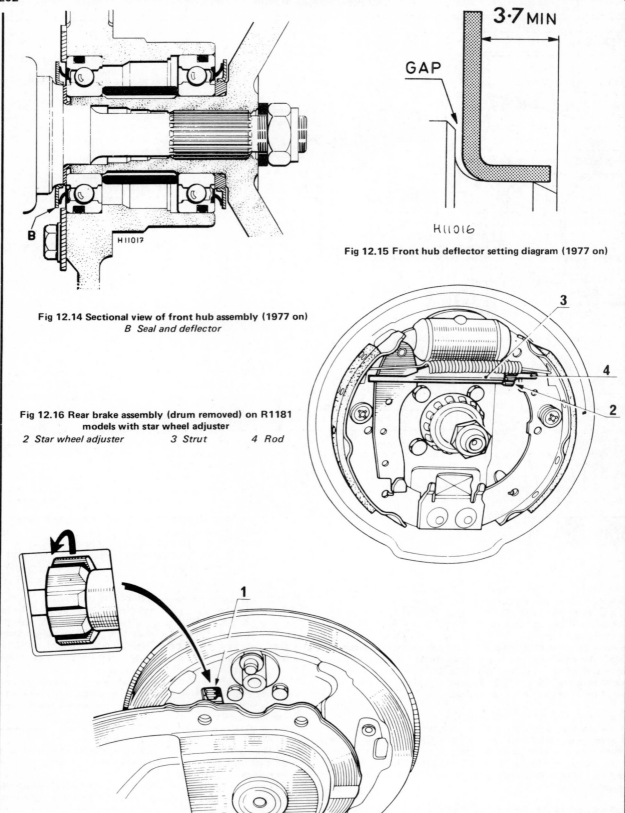

H11017

**Fig 12.14 Sectional view of front hub assembly (1977 on)**
*B Seal and deflector*

3·7 MIN

GAP

H11016

**Fig 12.15 Front hub deflector setting diagram (1977 on)**

**Fig 12.16 Rear brake assembly (drum removed) on R1181
models with star wheel adjuster**
*2 Star wheel adjuster    3 Strut    4 Rod*

**Fig 12.17 Rear brake adjuster star wheel
seen through the backplate aperture**
*1 Adjuster star wheel*

## 8 Transmission

### Gearshift control tube

1   Late model R1181 models are now fitted with a 'Grip Ring' on the gearshift control tube. This limits the travel of the control tube when selecting 3rd gear.
2   After any dismantling has been carried out it is important that the ring is set in accordance with Fig. 12.13.

## 9 Suspension and steering

### Front stub axle assembly

1   From the end of 1977 the front hub unit was fitted with a modified stub axle assembly. The following items are all new parts and are not individually interchangeable with their earlier counterparts, but only as an assembly. The principal modification has been the bearing seal and deflector but all of the following items have been modified: driveshaft deflector, bearing spacer, bearing thrust washer (and deflector), bearing closure plate, bearings (inner and outer) with lip seal and the stub axle carrier.
2   The bearings are replaced in the same manner described in Chapter 7, Section 5 but note, when fitting a new assembly in place of the old type, the deflector must be changed and be positioned as shown in Fig. 12.15, allowing a gap of 0.145 in (3.7 mm) between it and the anti-squeak washer face.

## 10 Braking system

### Rear brake adjustment — (R1181 models)

1   From March 1977 a revised brake adjustment arrangement is fitted to the rear of all R1181 models, and is shown in Figs 12.17 and 12.16.
2   To adjust the brakes, first check the front wheels and release the handbrake.
3   Raise the rear wheels clear of the ground.
4   Remove the plastic cap from the backplate to gain access to the toothed adjuster wheel.

5   Using a screwdriver turn the adjuster wheel whilst slowly turning the roadwheel.
6   On most models the adjuster wheel is prised downwards to take up the adjustment, but on some earlier models fitted with this type of adjuster it may be found necessary to prise the adjuster wheel upwards to achieve this.
7   If the adjuster is hard to turn get an assistant to pump the brake pedal a few times and then release it.
8   Continue turning the adjuster wheel until the brake shoes have been adjusted sufficiently to prevent the roadwheel from being turned.
9   Now turn the adjuster wheel in the opposite direction until the roadwheel can be rotated without undue binding or resistance.
10   Apply the footbrake pedal and recheck the adjustment.
11   Repeat the operation for the other rear brake.

### Rear brake drum and shoes (R1181 with star wheel adjuster) — removal and refitting

12   On later models (1977 on) all brake backplates incorporate an inspection aperture through which the lining wear can be inspected. If renewal is required or if an inspection aperture is not included on your particular model, carry out the following operations.
13   Chock the front wheels and jack-up the rear of the car. Remember to support the car with either axle-stands or strong wooden packing blocks. Never rely on the jack as the sole method of support.
14   Remove the roadwheel and release the handbrake.
15   Remove the adjuster wheel blanking cap from the backplate and turn the adjuster wheel in the correct direction to back the brake shoes off. (Refer to the previous sub-section for details).
16   Now remove the brake drum/hub assembly as described in Chapter 8.
17   If the brake shoes are to be removed proceed by removing the upper shoe return spring which links the front (leading) and rear (trailing) brake shoes together. Renault use a special spring removal tool for this operation, however, a screwdriver and a pair of pliers are just as effective.
18   Carefully release the handbrake cable from the operating link.
19   Release the shoe steady spring and cup. Use pliers or a suitable socket and extension bar to compress the shoe steady spring.

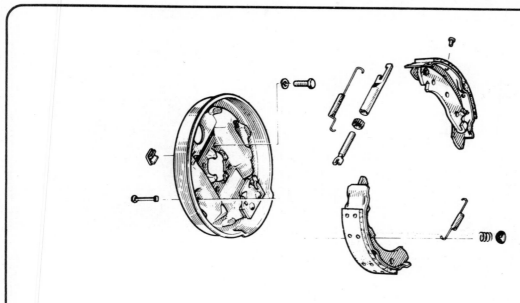

Fig 12.18 Exploded view of rear brake (star wheel adjuster type)

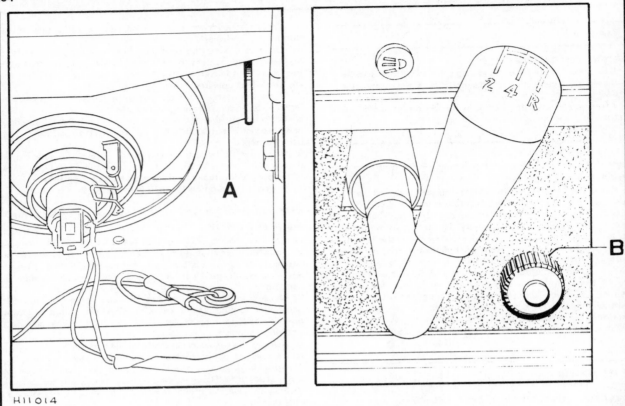

H11014

**Fig 12.19 Alternative headlamp adjustment controls for load**
*A  Interior type lever     B  Dashboard mounted knob*

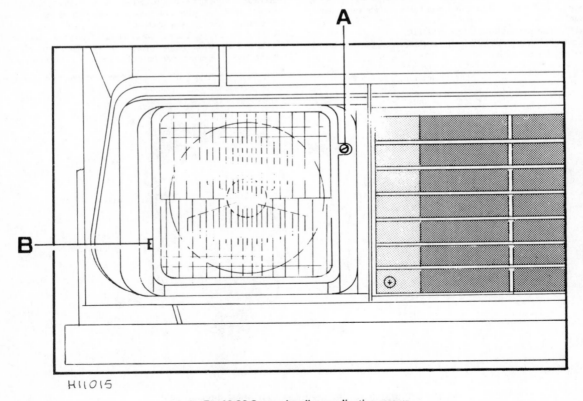

H11015

**Fig 12.20 Square headlamp adjusting screws**
*A  Horizontal movement    B  Vertical movement*

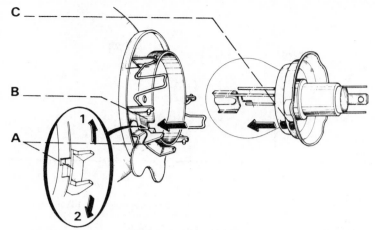

**Fig 12.21 Adjustable bulb holder for conversion from left-hand drive to right-hand drive road conditions**
*1 RHD setting    2 LHD setting*
*A Swivelling lever    B Bulb holder alignment slot*
*C Bulb holder projection*

With the spring in the compressed state from behind the backplate rotate the steady pin through 90° to release it from the steady spring cup.

20 Repeat this operation for the other shoe steady spring.

21 Remove the lower shoe return spring and remove the brake shoes.

22 Renault use a special tool to restrain the wheel cylinder pistons which tend to move outwards under the influence of a spring fitted between them. A strong rubber band will serve the same purpose. Remember that the brake pedal must not be pressed down with the shoes and drum removed.

23 Before refitting the brake shoes dismantle the adjuster mechanism and examine it for wear and operation. The threaded link can be cleaned with a wire brush and lightly lubricated. Remember to screw the adjuster wheel back to the position which would fully release the adjustment of the brake shoes.

24 Refitting the brake shoes is the reverse of the dismantling procedure but ensure that the brake shoes are refitted the correct way round, ie. with the longer lining towards the front and the shorter lining towards the rear.

25 Refit the drum/hub assembly as described in Chapter 8 making reference to Chapter 7 for adjustment.

26 Adjust the brake shoes as described previously.

27 Remember to refit the blanking caps to the adjuster holes in the backplate.

### Brake lining inspection — 1977 on

28 In addition to the rear brakes on R1181 models the front and rear brakes on R1180 models also incorporate an inspection aperture covered with a plastic plug to enable shoe lining wear to be inspected without the need to remove the drum.

---

### 11 Electrical system

---

### Headlights — bulb replacement and adjustment

1 Late models are now fitted with 'square' type headlights and surrounds. The bulb replacement procedure remains the same as given in Chapter 9, Section 20.

2 To adjust the beam alignment the vehicle must be unladen and the adjusting levers on the inside panel (adjacent to the headlight shell) must be set in the lowered position (unladen). On some models this last adjustment can be operated via a knob on the dashboard - turn the knob to the right in this instance.

3 Refer to Fig. 12.20 and turn screw 'A' to adjust the horizontal plane setting and turn screw 'B' to adjust the vertical plane of the beam.

4 Without the use of optical equipment it is difficult to accurately align the beam adjustment and therefore the settings should be periodically checked by your Renault dealer or local garage who will have the necessary equipment for this task.

### Headlight bulb setting

5 Some models may be fitted with a bulb holder which will enable the bulb setting to be adjusted for right or left-hand drive conditions as required, see Fig. 12.21.

6 Access to the bulb holder is the same as the instructions for bulb replacement but on removing the bulb from its holder, rotate the lever mechanism to the right when driving on the left or to the left for driving on the right. Refit the bulbs and operate the lights to check that they are functioning correctly before driving.

### Driver-operated headlight beam adjuster

7 Some models are now fitted with a hydraulically operated headlight beam adjustment which can be operated from the driving seat.

8 Should the mechanism malfunction, there is no way of repairing the hydraulic tube circuit and it must therefore be renewed as a unit. This can be easily disconnected from the dashboard switch at one end and the headlight unit at the other, and the new unit fitted.

# Index

**Printed by
Haynes Publishing Group
Sparkford Yeovil Somerset
England**